METALLURGY AND METALLURGICAL ENGINEERING SERIES

ROBERT F. MEHL, PH.D., D.Sc., *Consulting Editor*

THE PHYSICS OF METALS

*The quality of the materials used in the manufacture
of this book is governed by continued postwar shortages.*

METALLURGY AND METALLURGICAL ENGINEERING SERIES

Barrett—STRUCTURE OF METALS

Brick and Phillips—STRUCTURE AND PROPERTIES OF ALLOYS

Briggs—THE METALLURGY OF STEEL CASTINGS

Butts—METALLURGICAL PROBLEMS
Second Edition

Eckel and Raudebaugh—LABORATORY MANUAL IN METALLOGRAPHY

Kehl—THE PRINCIPLES OF METALLOGRAPHIC LABORATORY PRACTICE
Second Edition

Seitz—THE PHYSICS OF METALS

THE PHYSICS

of

METALS

BY

FREDERICK SEITZ

Professor of Physics and Department Head
Carnegie Institute of Technology

First Edition
Sixth Impression

McGRAW-HILL BOOK COMPANY, Inc.

NEW YORK AND LONDON

1943

To the Metals Research Laboratory of the Carnegie Institute of Technology as a modest tribute to the outstanding contribution it is making to American metallurgical science

PREFACE

This book has arisen out of an evening lecture course entitled The Physics of Metals given during the last four years, first at the University of Pennsylvania and then at the Carnegie Institute of Technology. Since the audience consisted of metallurgists with a limited knowledge of physics and of physicists with a limited knowledge of metallurgy, the lectures were intentionally made both nonmathematical and elementary. This feature has been carried over into the book as a glance at the pages will indicate.

The point of view taken in the book and in the lectures is almost entirely that of an atomic physicist. This point of view is quite natural when one is planning lectures on the properties of matter for graduate students in physics; however, it was not obvious to the author that the plan adopted would seem either natural or interesting to metallurgical students or to metallurgists who have been engaged in practical work for a number of years. The response from metallurgists proved most gratifying, however, indicating that there is a large group which possesses deep-seated curiosity concerning the ultimate nature of metals and related substances. It is this fact that ultimately led the writer to submit the manuscript for publication after the suggestion was made to him by Professors Mehl and Barrett of the Metals Research Laboratory.

The author is grateful to Professor G. P. Harnwell for his support in developing certain phases of applied physics at the University of Pennsylvania. The lecture course on which this book is based was part of that development. He also wishes to express his profound gratitude to his colleagues, Professors Mehl, Barrett, Rhines, Gensamer, and Derge, of the Metals Research Laboratory, for innumerable suggestions for the improvement of the book. Finally, he thanks his wife, Elizabeth Marshall Seitz, for critical readings of the several versions of the manuscript.

PITTSBURGH, PA.,   FREDERICK SEITZ.
  June, 1943.

CONTENTS

CHAPTER VI

The Plastic Properties of Single Crystals

CHAPTER VII

The Plastic Properties of Polycrystalline Media

CHAPTER VIII

The Plastic Properties of Alloys

CHAPTER IX

Creep and Secondary Plastic Effects

CHAPTER X

Internal Friction

CHAPTER XI

Rupture and Fatigue

CHAPTER XII

Diffusion in Metals

CHAPTER XIII

The Solubility of Gases in Metals

CHAPTER XIV

The Properties of Iron-Carbon Alloys

CHAPTER XV

Introduction to the Concepts of Modern Physics

CHAPTER XVI

The Development of the Electron Theory of Metals

CHAPTER XVII

The Band Theory of Solids

CHAPTER XVIII

The Cohesion of Solids

CHAPTER XIX

Alloys

CHAPTER XX

The Magnetic Properties of Metals

CHAPTER XXI

The Electrical Conductivity of Metals

THE PHYSICS OF METALS

CHAPTER I

ATOMIC ARRANGEMENTS IN METALS

1. The Atom.[1]—All material substances are composed of atoms. This fact was first suggested by observation of the simple combining proportions of the elements in many compounds; however, it has since been proved conclusively by a large amount of research, which we shall make no attempt to describe in this book. Suffice it to say that we now have a very complete picture of those parts of atoms which are essential for understanding their chemical properties.

Briefly, it is known that every atom consists of a small positively charged nucleus about which are swarming negatively charged particles called *electrons*. The chemical nature of an atom is determined uniquely by the charge on the nucleus, which is always an integer multiple of a fundamental unit e equal to $1.6 \cdot 10^{-19}$ coulomb.[2] This integer, which is called the *atomic number*, generally increases with the atomic weight of the element, being equal to unity for the lightest element, hydrogen, and 92 for the heaviest element, uranium. The values for the other elements in the periodic system are given in the chart on the back cover of the book. The electrons moving about the nucleus are identical and have charge $-e$. In the normal state

[1] General references for this chapter are as follows: W. H. BRAGG, *X-Rays and Crystal Structure* (Harcourt, Brace and Company, New York, 1924), *The Crystalline State* (George Bell & Sons, Ltd., London, 1933); *Strukturbericht* (Akademische Verlagsgesellschaft m.b.H., Leipzig, 1931–1937); R. W. G. WYCKOFF, *The Structure of Crystals* (Chemical Catalog Company, Inc., New York, 1931); W. HUME-ROTHERY, *The Structure of Metals and Alloys* (The Macmillan Company, New York, 1936); C. S. BARRETT, *Structure of Metals* (McGraw-Hill Book Company, Inc., New York, 1943).

[2] A coulomb is the amount of electricity that flows by a point in a circuit in one second when the current is one ampere.

of the atom they are equal in number to the atomic number of the atom. Thus the atom is electrically neutral in its normal condition. Experimental work has shown that the greater part of the mass of an atom resides in the nucleus. In fact, the ratio of the mass associated with the nucleus to that associated with the electrons is usually greater than 2,000.

The exact nature of the motion of the electrons about the nucleus can be described only in mathematical language more formidable than is necessary for our purpose. In an approximate, though adequate, way it can be said that the electrons revolve about the nucleus in orbits resembling somewhat the orbits of the planets about the sun (Fig. 1). In the simplest case, namely, hydrogen, there is a single electron moving in a single orbit, whereas in the most complicated atom, namely, uranium, there are 92 electrons moving in about half that number of *different* orbits. Some of these orbits lie very close to the nucleus, whereas others are considerably farther away, much as the orbits of the planets about the sun. Experimental determinations of the size of these orbits show that the average diameter of the various orbits in an atom is about the same for all atoms, namely, about 10^{-8} cm. From the standpoint of the chemistry of atoms, this may be regarded as the average atomic size. This distance is found to be about 100,000 times larger than the diameter of the nucleus of an atom, which shows that the analogy between the atom and the solar system is a good one. It should be added that the diameter of the electron is somewhat larger than that of the nucleus but is still many thousand times smaller than that of the orbits in which the electrons move. This fact has given rise to the comment that an atom is mainly composed of empty space!

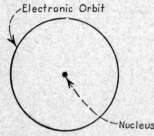

FIG. 1.—Schematic picture of an atom. The electronic orbits cannot be drawn in a precise manner.

At the present time it is believed that an electron is a fundamental particle in the sense that it cannot be broken into fragments. The nucleus, however, is not a fundamental particle. Extensive research during the past ten years has shown that all nuclei are composed of two fundamental particles, namely, *protons* and *neutrons*. The first of these is simply the singly charged nucleus of atomic hydrogen, whereas the second is an uncharged particle having almost exactly the same mass. Thus the masses of all nuclei are very nearly equal to integer multiples of the mass of the hydrogen atom. The total charge on the nucleus evidently is determined by the number of protons, so that this number is just the atomic number. It frequently happens that two nuclei have the same number of protons but different numbers of neutrons. In this event, they have different masses, but identical charges, and hence have equal numbers of orbital electrons. Such nuclei, which are called *isotopes*, have the same chemical properties. Many pure elements such as chlorine are mixtures of isotopic atoms and, for this reason, possess an atomic weight that is not an integer multiple of that of hydrogen.

In performing the experiments that led to the discovery of the ultimate constituents of atoms, the investigators disrupted the nuclei by bombardment with other atoms, traveling at a high rate of speed. The frequent result of such disruption is to change the number of protons in the atom and hence to change its chemical species. Thus transmutation of the elements is an accomplished fact of modern physics. It seems unlikely, however, that such transmutation will provide a practical source of rare metals in the near future.

The force holding an electron to its path about the nucleus is just the attraction between the positively and negatively charged bodies. The source of attractive force between the neutrons and protons in the nucleus is only imperfectly understood at present and represents one of the frontier problems of physics. Fortunately, the chemical properties of atoms are derived almost exclusively from the electrostatic forces, about which much is known.

The arrangement of atoms in gases is perfectly random—a fact intimately related to their high degree of deformability. On the other hand, the arrangement in crystalline solids is very orderly, as might be judged from the degree of symmetry their external form frequently presents. Investigation has shown that in all cases this arrangement may be described in terms of an assembly of parallelepipeds which form a three-dimensional lattice (Fig. 2), each parallelepiped, or *unit cell*, containing identical arrangements of atoms. The three edge lengths of this cell are called the *primitive translations* since the entire lattice may be constructed by translating a single unit cell through unending repetition of these three distances. It frequently is possible to choose the unit cell in many different ways, but there is always a unique way in which the cell possesses the smallest number of atoms. We shall call the cell chosen in this way the *basic cell*. Cells other

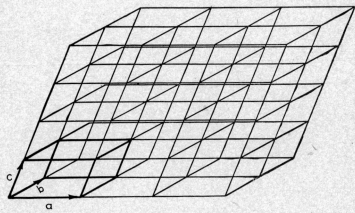

Fig. 2.—A three-dimensional lattice. It may be constructed by packing identical parallelepipeds side by side. In crystals, the arrangement of atoms in each parallelepiped, or cell, is identical. The three edge lengths *a*, *b* and *c* of the cell are called the primitive translations of the lattice. A unit cell is accentuated by heavy lines in the lower left-hand corner.

than the basic cell are often used in discussion, for they may possess geometrical advantages. In most monatomic metals there are only one or two atoms per unit cell so that their structures are characterized by simplicity. On the other hand, the basic cells of the phases of manganese and of the γ-brass type of structure contain large numbers of atoms.

Before discussing the observed structures of particular metals in detail, we shall outline the principal method used in determining these structures, namely, that of X-ray diffraction.

2. The Interaction between X Rays and Atoms.—It is now known with certainty that X rays are a form of electromagnetic radiation analogous to ordinary light. In both cases, the radiation consists of waves of oscillating electric and magnetic fields (Fig. 3). The essential difference between the two types of wave lies in the fact that ordinary light has a wave length of the order of 10^{-4} cm, whereas commonly used X rays have wave lengths near 10^{-8} cm.

The influence of an electromagnetic wave upon an atom is not difficult to understand. If we place an atom in an electric field, the positively charged nucleus experiences a force in the direction of the field, and the negatively charged electrons experience a force in the opposite direction. As a result of these forces the

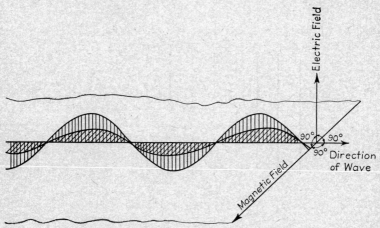

FIG. 3.—A simple electromagnetic wave. This consists of oscillating electric and magnetic fields whose directions of intensity are perpendicular both to one another and to the direction in which the wave is moving.

electronic orbits become somewhat eccentric, or, in more precise language, the atom becomes *polarized*. If the field is oscillating, as when an electromagnetic wave passes, the direction of displacement of the electronic orbits relative to the nucleus reverses in each cycle and the atom behaves like an electric oscillator having the same frequency as the wave. If the time required for one of the electrons to traverse its orbit once happens to be the same as the period of the wave, the electron will resonate to the radiation, gaining energy from it just as a fan blade resonates when the period of rotation approaches its natural vibrational frequency. In this case the electron may gain sufficient energy to jump to a larger orbit or may even be ejected from the atom. If the frequency of the wave is not a resonant frequency, however, the amount of orbital eccentricity will remain small.

It is a general theorem of electricity that if a positive and negative charge oscillate relative to one another they will send out an electromagnetic wave having the same frequency as the oscillation. The wave will have a spherical front centered about the oscillating electric dipole, similar to the sound waves from a ringing bell. For this reason the atoms in which an oscillating displacement of electrons relative to the nucleus has been induced by the electromagnetic wave will send out secondary waves having the same frequency as the incident wave (Fig. 4).

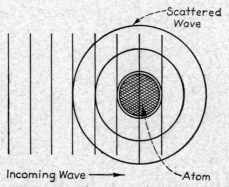

Fig. 4.—The scattering of an electromagnetic wave by an atom. Successive peaks of the incoming plane wave are indicated by the vertical lines, whereas successive peaks of the scattered spherical wave are indicated by the circles.

The phenomenon is sometimes characterized by saying that the atom *scatters* a part of the incident radiation. The effect is easy to observe in everyday life, for the blue color of cigarette smoke is a result of the scattering of blue light by the tiny smoke particles. In this case the light wave induces an oscillatory displacement of the charges in the particle, which proceeds to emit secondary waves of the same color. All wave lengths are scattered to some extent by the particles, but the effect increases so strongly in going from the red to the blue end of the color spectrum that the particles appear blue in white light.

Another illustration of the generation of electromagnetic waves by oscillating charges is a radio transmitter. In this device a current is made to surge back and forth in an antenna, and radio waves are produced as a result. These waves differ from light and X rays only by having much longer wave lengths.

An indication of the manner in which the lattice arrangement of atoms in a crystal alters the spherical character of the waves emitted by the individual atoms when they are excited by an electromagnetic wave is had from a consideration of the linear case shown in Fig. 5. In this case, the atoms are distributed at equal distances along a line and, for simplicity, the wave front of

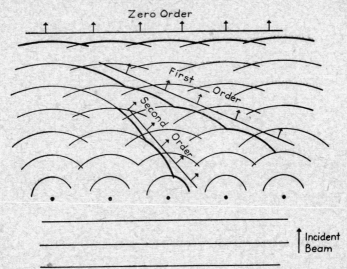

Fig. 5.—The scattering of a plane wave by a lattice. Each atom scatters spherical waves, but these combine as a result of constructive and destructive interference to form plane waves.

the incident radiation is taken to be parallel to the line, in the manner illustrated. Under these conditions, the entire group of atoms is in a trough or a crest of the oncoming wave at the same instant. Successive crests of the incident wave are illustrated by horizontal straight lines in the figure. The spheres corresponding to successive crests of the secondary waves emitted by the atoms are indicated by sets of concentric circles. Since each atom emits a crest (or a trough) at the same instant in the present case, the circles are the same sizes for all atoms at each instant. Through constructive and destructive interference, however, the spherical waves combine to form a number of concentric conical waves moving in various directions. The resultant waves are indicated by the heavy lines in the figure.

Thus the net effect of the scattering from the atoms is the production of a number of waves moving off in specific directions as shown. These waves are said to be produced by *diffraction*. A simple geometrical analysis of the situation shows that the angle α between the direction of one of these secondary waves and the direction of the incident wave satisfies the equation

$$n\lambda = d \sin \alpha. \tag{1}$$

Here n is an integer, λ is the wave length of the incident radiation, and d is the spacing between atoms in the line. One secondary wave is observed for each of the values of n for which Eq. (1) may be satisfied when λ and d are fixed. That only a finite number of such waves is to be expected may be seen as follows: The largest value that $\sin \alpha$ may take is 1, which occurs for $\alpha = 90$ deg. Thus the largest value of n for which the equation can be satisfied is the integer nearest to but smaller than the ratio d/λ. If this ratio is 2.5, the equation can be satisfied for $n = 0$, 1, or 2, but not for larger values. It is to be noted that if λ is larger than d, so that d/λ is less than unity, the value $n = 0$, corresponding to $\alpha = 0$ deg, is the only allowed value. In this case the diffracted wave joins the incident wave in Fig. 5. We see, then, that, in general, diffracted waves cannot be observed if the wave length is greater than the spacing between atoms. This fact explains why X rays rather than light or radio waves are used in the study of crystal structures—only the former type of electro-magnetic radiation has wave length sufficiently small to be diffracted by lattices with interatomic spacings as small as occur in actual solids.

The type of diffraction discussed above can actually be observed for ordinary light waves by using a machine-ruled grating in which the spacing of consecutive lines is somewhat larger than the wave lengths to be studied. Such gratings can be produced with as many as 30,000 lines per inch and are commonly prepared on either glass or metal surfaces. Since the angle α is different for different wave lengths, the gratings can be used to break a continuous spectrum into its component parts, thus serving the same purpose as a prism.

The gratings corresponding to actual crystals differ from the simple example, shown in Fig. 5, inasmuch as they are three dimensional rather than one dimensional. The principal consequence of the additional two dimensions is that there are two additional equations of the form (1) which must be satisfied before a given incident wave can be diffracted. As a result of these additional restrictions the given wave is diffracted only if it enters the crystal in one of a definite number of definite directions. This situation is to be contrasted with the simple one above in which any wave can be diffracted so long as its wave length is less than d.

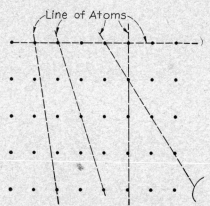

Fig. 6.—Two-dimensional lattice showing set of lines of atoms.

The conditions for diffraction in actual lattices have been conveniently systematized by Bragg by the use of the following type of construction: In any three-dimensional lattice there are a large number of systems of equally spaced parallel planes of atoms. This principle is illustrated schematically in Fig. 6 for a simple two-dimensional array of atoms. It will be seen that several sets of equally spaced parallel lines can be drawn in this case. Bragg has shown that any diffracted ray can be regarded as if it were reflected from one of these systems of planes, much as though it were reflected from a mirror parallel to the planes. However, the given wave can be reflected from the planes only if it satisfies the equation

$$n\lambda = 2d \sin \theta \qquad (2)$$

where d is the spacing between neighboring planes in the set, θ is the angle between the direction of the wave and the plane, λ is the wave length, and n is an integer. This equation evidently bears a strong resemblance to Eq. (1). For given λ we see that the equation can be satisfied only if θ takes particular values, which implies that the ray must strike the plane at a definite angle. Conversely, if a diffracted ray is observed for a given angle, it may be concluded that the crystal possesses a set of planes with a normal in that direction which bisects the direction

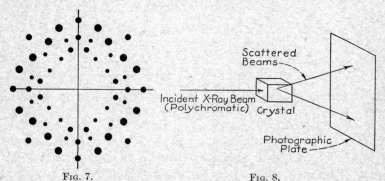

Fig. 7.   Fig. 8.

Fig. 7.—The X-ray diffraction pattern obtained by passing continuous X rays through rock salt parallel to the cubic axis. The diameters of the circles are proportional to the intensity of the spots.

Fig. 8.—The arrangement of specimen and plate employed in obtaining Fig. 7.

of the incident and diffracted rays and that the spacing of these planes is related to λ and θ by Eq. (2).

Equation (2) can usually be satisfied by one or more of the constituent wave lengths if the incident beam is continuous and contains a range of frequencies satisfying the relation $\lambda/d < 1$. Thus if a crystal is irradiated with a continuous beam of properly chosen radiation, a number of monochromatic rays will be diffracted. Figure 7 shows the type of pattern obtained in this way from a specimen of rock salt (NaCl). The arrangement of the crystal, X-ray film, and source is shown schematically in Fig. 8. This arrangement, which uses continuous radiation and a single crystal, is called the "Laue method" in honor of the discoverer of X-ray diffraction. Each spot in Fig. 7 corresponds to a ray produced by diffraction of one of the constituent wave lengths in the incident beam.

The basic problem of the X-ray crystallographer is not that of determining the diffracted rays from a crystal of known structure, but rather the converse one of working back to an unknown structure from measurements of the diffraction pattern. An indirect procedure is to guess a structure and then to justify the guess and to determine the lattice parameters by the use of Eq. (2). This clearly is possible only when the investigator has sufficient intuitive sense to propose a reasonable structure at the start; actually, most structures are determined in essentially this manner. In practice, the experienced crystallographer first determines the probable angles between the edges of the primitive cell by inspection of the external form of the crystal. Next, he determines the lengths of the three edges of a unit cell from measurements of the diffraction pattern. It is most common to use monochromatic radiation and to rotate the crystal so that the beam is reflected by a number of the sets of crystallographic planes. From this information the crystallographer is able to compute the size of the unit cell and the number of atoms in it. He then attempts to arrange these atoms in various ways that are in agreement with the symmetry of the crystal. There may be a unique reasonable arrangement if there are very few atoms in the unit cell; in this case, the problem is solved. It turns out that the relative intensities of the diffracted waves from different sets of planes are determined by the distribution of atoms in the unit cell so that the analyst may decide among several alternative distributions by measuring the relative intensities and comparing these with the values calculated by the use of diffraction theory. If the unit cell contains a large number of atoms, the labor involved in testing various possible distributions of atoms may be considerable. We shall not discuss the details of particular cases since that would carry us too far afield.

It frequently happens that a given material is available only in powder or other polycrystalline form. If the crystal size is sufficiently small and there is a sufficiently large number of grains, a few are oriented in such a way that a monochromatic beam may be reflected from each of the possible sets of planes. These refracted rays are radiated from the specimen in the form of circular cones whose axes lie along the line of the incident beam (Fig. 9). They are usually photographed either by means of a plane plate placed perpendicular to this axis, in which case the diffraction pattern consists of circles, or by means of a narrow film bent in the form of a semicircle and placed with its center of curvature at the position of the specimen.   In the second case

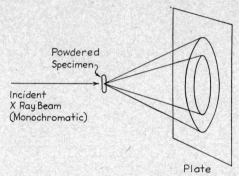

Fig. 9.—The diffracted rays from a powder or polycrystal.

the intercepts of the film with the cones are arcs of circles.   The information derived in this way is seldom sufficient to permit the determination of an essentially new structure, but it is frequently used to show whether two materials have the same or different structures.   In addition, the first arrangement, in which complete

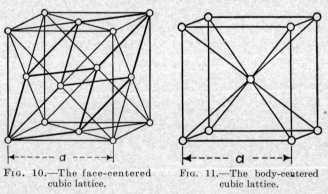

Fig. 10.—The face-centered cubic lattice.   Fig. 11.—The body-centered cubic lattice.

circles are photographed, is often used in metallurgical work to determine whether or not the orientation of grains in a specimen is random.   If it is random, as many grains diffract rays into one part of a given circle as into another, and the photographic darkening around the circle is uniform.   On the other hand, it is not uniform if the grains show a preferred orientation. We shall discuss this topic again later.

3. The Observed Crystal Structures.—We shall now discuss the results obtained by the methods of crystal-structure analysis. The most common structures of monatomic metals are three types shown in Figs. 10 to 12. The first of these is the face-centered cubic lattice, the second is the body-centered cubic lattice, and the third is the hexagonal close-packed lattice. Relative to a cubic unit cell, the first possesses four atoms and the second two atoms per cell. Actually, the cube is not the basic cell, for both lattices can be constructed from parallelepipeds containing one atom. The basic cell for the face-centered

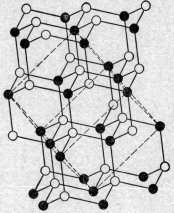

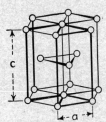

FIG. 12.—The hexagonal close-packed lattice.

FIG. 13.—The diamond lattice. Both black and white spheres represent carbon atoms in this case.

lattice is indicated in Fig. 10. The basic cell of the hexagonal lattice is the prism possessing an equilateral triangular base shown in Fig. 12. This cell contains two atoms. The hexagonal close-packed lattice derives its name from the fact that it is one of the possible arrangements of spheres possessing highest density. The face-centered cubic lattice also corresponds to closest packing.

Common metals possessing the three simple structures are listed in Table I.

Typical nonmetallic structures are shown in Figs. 13 and 14. The first of these is that of diamond. In this, each atom is surrounded by four neighboring atoms arranged at the apexes of a tetrahedron. This type of distribution, in which the number of

TABLE I.—METALS POSSESSING THE THREE SIMPLE METALLIC LATTICES

Face-centered cubic	Body-centered cubic	Hexagonal close-packed
Cu	Li	Be
Ag	Na	Mg
Au	K	Zn
Al	V	Cd
Th	Ta	Tl
Pb	α Cr	Ti
γ Fe	Mo	Zr
α Co	W	Hf
Ni	α Fe	Cr
Rh	δ Fe	Co
Pd		Ru
Ir		Os
Pt		

nearest neighbors of a given atom is equal to the valence number of the atom, is characteristic of *valence crystals*. Silicon, germanium, and gray tin possess the same lattice. Figure 14 represents

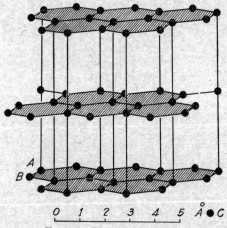

FIG. 14.—The graphite lattice.

the lattice of graphite, in which the carbon atoms are arranged in relatively widely separated planes. The lubricating properties of graphite are believed to be related to the fact that the planes of atoms slide past one another under the application of a comparatively low stress. Figure 15 shows the sodium chloride structure which is typical of an ionic crystal. It should be noted that each sodium ion is surrounded by six equidistant chlorine ions, and vice versa. This in-dicates that there is no unit other than the crystal itself which may be regarded as a chemical molecule. Each type of atom is arranged in a face-centered cubic lattice similar to that occurring in copper. The structure of cesium chloride, also typical of an ionic crystal, is shown in Fig. 16.

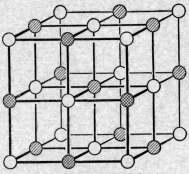

Fig. 15.—The rock-salt lattice.

Many metals possess lattices more complicated than the structures shown in Figs. 10 to 12. For example, Figs. 17 to 19 show the structures of white tin, manganese, and bismuth. The last structure, which is also formed by arsenic and antimony, is not a typical metallic structure, for, as the figure shows, it may be

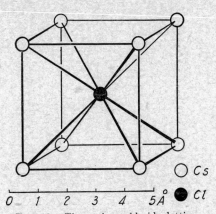

Fig. 16.—The cesium chloride lattice.

viewed as if the lattice were divided into layers in which each atom is surrounded by three nearest neighbors. Since the electro-negative valence of arsenic, antimony, and bismuth is 3, this implies that these atoms form a valencelike structure.

The simpler alloys possess typical metallic lattices. For example, Fig. 20 shows the lattices of CuZn (β brass). In this

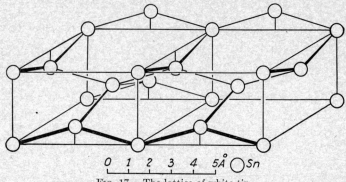

Fig. 17.—The lattice of white tin.

case the structure exhibits a striking change in going from low to high temperatures. At high temperatures the cube-corner and body-center positions of the block of atoms are occupied at

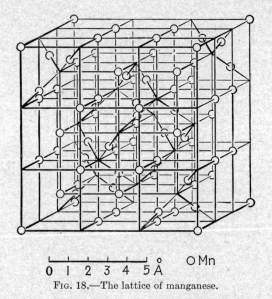

Fig. 18.—The lattice of manganese.

random by both copper and zinc atoms, whereas at low temperatures the two types of site become preferentially occupied with atoms of opposite kinds. Ordering is very common, though it does not occur in all alloys.

Figure 21 shows the structure of the alloy of composition Cu_5Zn_8 (γ brass). In this case the unit cell is very large, containing fifty-two atoms.

Much useful information may be derived from crystal-structure data. For example, if we assume that the atoms are rigid spheres and that nearest neighbors are in contact with one another, we may equate the distance between nearest neighbors to the atomic diameter. Values of this quantity for most monatomic metals are given in Fig. 22, in which the order of atomic

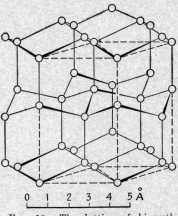

0 1 2 3 4 5 Å

Fig. 19.—The lattice of bismuth.

arrangement is that of increasing atomic weights. It may be observed that the atomic diameters vary periodically with increasing atomic number. It follows that the atomic diameter

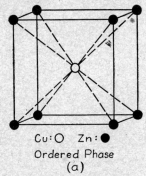

Cu:O Zn:●
Ordered Phase
(a)

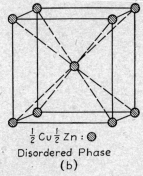

$\frac{1}{2}$ Cu $\frac{1}{2}$ Zn : ◎
Disordered Phase
(b)

Fig. 20.—The lattice of β brass. The left-hand figure represents the low-temperature ordered phase, whereas the right-hand figure is the high-temperature disordered phase.

is not a precisely defined quantity, for the values obtained from different phases of the same metal are not precisely equal.

4. Crystalline Textures.—It is advisable at this point to discuss briefly the various forms or textures in which crystalline materials may be obtained. The most common type is of course the polycrystalline form, such as is produced by freezing a melt under normal conditions. In cases of this type the individual crystals are usually visible either to the naked eye or under a microscope. If a polycrystalline specimen has not been subjected to mechanical working, such as drawing or rolling, the individual crystals, or *grains*, are usually oriented at random. In special cases, the mold in which an ingot is cast may have an effect on the relative orientation of the crystals near the boundary. This occurs commonly, for example, in die-casting. If a polycrystalline specimen in which the orientation is random is subjected when either cold or hot to drawing, rolling, or any of the other common working processes, the grains frequently exhibit types of *preferred orientation* about which we shall have more to say in later chapters. Such orientation may vary from a distribution nearly random to one in which all the crystals have almost exactly the same orientation. It is clear that in extensive deformation of a specimen the individual crystals must alter their shape. We shall discuss the details of this change in Chaps. VI and VII.

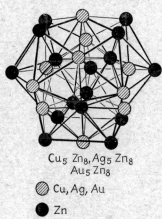

Cu$_5$ Zn$_8$, Ag$_5$ Zn$_8$
Au$_5$ Zn$_8$

◍ Cu, Ag, Au

● Zn

Fig. 21.—The γ brass lattice.

If the temperature of a cold-worked specimen is raised sufficiently after the cold-working, the crystalline texture may change. This process is known as *recrystallization*, and its implications will be discussed in Chap. IV. If the specimen showed preferred orientation before recrystallization, the recrystallized texture also exhibits preferred orientation, although the new orientation is usually different from the original.

It is possible by judicious cooling of a melt or by properly cold-working and annealing a specimen to obtain large single crystals. Such crystals have provided a great deal of fundamental information concerning the properties of metals, and much of our discussion will deal with them.

In forming a concept of a single crystal, it is important to realize that a specimen having this form generally is not strictly homogeneous, as one might think. It is true that the structure is far more uniform than in a polycrystalline specimen; however, it approaches true perfection closely only in cases seldom met in practice, namely, in cases of rare mineralogical specimens grown under exceptional conditions. The artificial single crystals used in metallurgical studies usually have imperfections on two sepa-

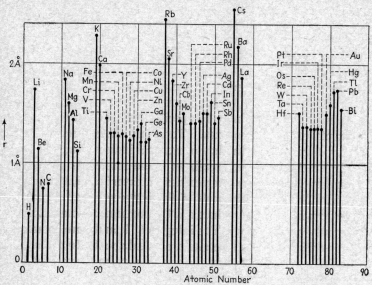

FIG. 22.—The half-distance between the centers of neighboring atoms in a number of metals. In cases in which the metal exists in two or more structures, more than one value is given.

rate scales of size, namely, a scale of about 1 micron (10^{-4} cm) and a scale of about 0.1 cm. The first type of irregularity, which is usually called *block structure* or *mosaic structure*, appears as an interruption of the basic periodicity of the lattice. There has been much speculation concerning the cause of this interruption. The most plausible explanation, suggested by Buerger,[1] is that it occurs as the result of accidents during growth and is not an inherent characteristic of the material, that is, it would not appear if the crystal were grown with sufficient care. The second type

[1] M. J. BUERGER, *Z. Kryst.*, **89**, 195 (1934).

of imperfection appears as a slight angular disorientation of neighboring domains of the crystal about 0.1 cm in size and probably is also explained as the result of irregularity in the growth process.

5. Crystallographic Notation.—We shall have frequent cause to consider particular crystallographic planes and directions in the simpler types of lattice. The notation used almost universally to designate the orientation of such planes and directions is as follows: Consider a system of three axes parallel to the edges of a unit cell of the lattice. If these happen to be orthogonal, as in cubic crystals when referred to a cubic unit cell (not the basic cell) or tetragonal crystals, the axes are a Cartesian set. This is generally not the case, however. Next, units of length along these axes are chosen equal to the corresponding lengths of the edges of the unit cell. When referred to this system of axes, any crystallographic plane may be specified uniquely in terms of its intercepts on the three axes. These are three numbers, a, b, and c. According to the law of rational indices, which is based on observation, the reciprocals of these intercepts are always rational fractions whose common denominator is a relatively small integer. Thus the reciprocals of the intercepts may be written in the form h/x, k/x, l/x where x is the common denominator and h, k, and l are integers. The integers h, k, and l are commonly used to designate the plane and are called the *Miller indices*.

Similarly, any direction in the crystal may be represented by a line, or vector, of arbitrary length pointing in the given direction. This line may be resolved into components along the three axes. It is found that whenever the direction is parallel to a line of atoms, the components are in the ratio of three integers r, s, and t. These integers may be used as a convenient representation of the direction. In crystals for which the axes discussed above are orthogonal, the indices specifying a direction are the same as the Miller indices of the plane normal to the direction.

Let us consider specific examples. Let us suppose the crystal is cubic; and, to begin with, let us represent the faces of the cube. Since each of these intersects only one axis, the intercepts are $(1, \infty, \infty)$, $(\infty, 1, \infty)$, and $(\infty, \infty, 1)$. The reciprocals of these numbers are $(1,0,0)$, $(0,1,0)$, and $(0,0,1)$; the corresponding Miller indices are usually designated as (100), (010), and (001). Simple consideration shows that the planes corresponding to the faces of the unit cell always are represented by these indices although the intercepts for the three opposite faces should have opposite signs.

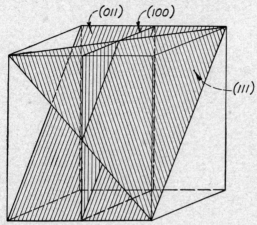

Fig. 23.—The principal crystallographic planes in cubic crystals.

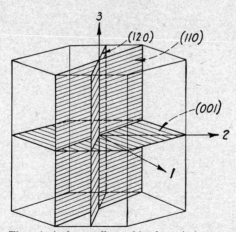

Fig. 24.—The principal crystallographic planes in hexagonal crystals.

The indices for these planes are commonly written as $(\bar{1}00)$, $(0\bar{1}0)$, $(00\bar{1})$ in which the negative sign is placed above the integers for convenience. Other planes that are particularly interesting in cubic crystals are the (110) type planes and the (111) type planes shown in Fig. 23. There are six independent planes of the first type and four of the second as illustrated. Planes in sets such as these, that are symmetrically disposed in the crystal, are called *equivalent* planes. Inspection of Fig. 10 shows that the (111) planes are the planes of closest atomic packing in the face-centered cubic lattice. They are commonly known as the *octahedral* planes.

The axes affording greatest convenience in the close-packed hexagonal lattices are the set shown in Fig. 24. The horizontal planes, which possess greatest atomic density, are represented by the indices (001) in this scheme. They are commonly called the *basal* planes.

CHAPTER II

THE PERIODIC CHART

6. The Valence Electrons in Atoms.—It was discovered in the early days of the development of chemistry that the properties of the elements vary periodically when plotted as functions of the atomic weight. This variation is exhibited clearly in Fig. 22, in which the atomic diameters of the metallic elements are plotted in sequence.

This periodic behavior has given rise to the periodic chart of the elements given on the back cover of this book. In it the elements appear in a sequence of increasing atomic number running from left to right. The entire group is divided into ten rows comprising six periods, which terminate with the rare gas elements. Elements in the same vertical column usually have closely similar properties.

The chart has received complete interpretation with the development of the modern picture of atomic structure. As we saw in the previous chapter, each atom consists of a central nucleus surrounded by electrons. The essential difference between atoms lies in the number of electrons circulating about the nucleus of each. In all cases these electrons move in orbits analogous to the planetary orbits. There are, however, important differences between the electronic orbits and planetary orbits, apart from size. First among these is the energy limitation occurring in atoms. The energy of any planet, though fixed, could, at least in principle, be altered by an arbitrary amount. The energies of the orbital electrons in atoms, however, are restricted to definite, or *discrete*, values. For example, it is possible for a planet to move in any elliptical orbit that might be drawn with the sun at one focus, whereas only a comparatively few such orbits are allowed in the atomic case. This discreteness of energy states is characteristic of atomic systems and is evidence of the now established fact that Newton's laws of motion must be modified when such systems are discussed. The modified version of the laws of motion is now completely known but need not concern us here.

The simplest manner of discussing the electronic orbits is in terms of the *energy-level diagram*, in which the energies of the allowed states of motion, or orbits, are represented as horizontal lines in a vertical energy scale (Fig. 25). It is customary to

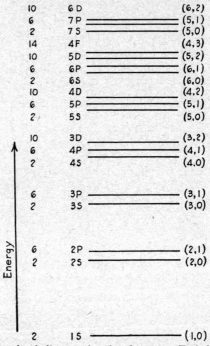

FIG. 25.—Energy-level diagram for the elements. Each level represents a possible energy state for an orbital electron. The numbers on the extreme left represent the degeneracies of the various levels. These numbers give the number of electrons that may reside in each level. The other symbols are conventional designations for the levels.

associate with each level two positive integers n and l, which are related, respectively, to the energy of the electron and to its angular momentum relative to the nucleus. These are commonly called the *total quantum number* and the *angular-momentum quantum number*. The allowed values of n range from 1 to infinity and those of l from zero to $n - 1$ for given n. Thus if we use the notation (n,l) to designate the pair of numbers characterizing a given level, there is a (1,0) level, but no (1,1) level. Similarly, there are (2,0) and (2,1) levels, but no (2,2) or (2,3) levels. Generally speaking, the orbits for which n and l are smallest lie nearest the nucleus and have the lowest energy, as is shown in Fig. 25.

In the course of unraveling the facts associated with atomic motion different investigators introduced different ways of designating the orbits. Though all such schemes of notation are essentially equivalent, so that only the one given above is necessary, there is another used so frequently that we shall present it here. In this, the integers l are replaced by letters in accordance with the following scheme:

$$l:\quad 0\quad 1\quad 2\quad 3\quad 4\quad 5\quad 6$$
$$\text{Letter:}\quad s\quad p\quad d\quad f\quad g\quad h\quad i$$

Thus the level designated by (2,0) in the previous scheme is also designated by $2s$, etc. Both schemes of notation are used in the figure.

Let us consider the manner in which the levels are occupied by electrons when we consider the elements in a sequence of increasing atomic number, as they appear in the periodic chart. The first element, hydrogen, has one electron, which occupies the lowest, or $1s$, level. Helium has two electrons, both of which occupy the $1s$ level. If more electrons could enter this level, lithium would have three $1s$ electrons. Actually, it is found that only a limited number of electrons may occupy any given atomic orbit. This restriction is a special case of a general rule, called the *Pauli exclusion principle* in honor of its discoverer. According to this rule, the maximum number of electrons that may occupy an orbit of given l is $2(2l + 1)$. These numbers, which are known as the *degeneracies* of the levels, are shown on the left-hand side of the figure. Thus we see that only two electrons are allowed in the $1s$ state and that the third electron of lithium must enter a level of higher energy. Actually, it enters the next lowest, or $2s$ level. The inert characteristics of helium are associated with the fact that its two electrons occupy completely the $1s$ level, which is widely separated from the $2s$ and $2p$ group. A completed group of levels that is widely separated from other groups is usually called a *closed shell*. Only the electrons outside closed shells determine the chemical properties of the element for reasons we shall discover presently.

Beryllium possesses two electrons in the $2s$ level. This element is not a rare gas, however, because of the proximity of the $2p$ level. Only when we reach neon, in which both the $2s$ and $2p$ levels are filled, do we again obtain a rare gas. The next element, sodium, has, like lithium, one electron outside a closed shell. This fact is intimately related to the similar chemical properties of the two elements. There is a one-to-one correspondence between the sequence of elements ranging from magnesium to argon and the sequence ranging from beryllium to neon in which the $3s$ and $3p$ levels are filled. The element following argon, namely, potassium, is again an alkali metal.

Before continuing this discussion, let us pause to consider the origin of the chemical properties of an element. When two atoms are brought in contact, they exert forces on one another as a result of the charged particles they contain. It is clear that the electrons in the largest occupied orbits of the atoms should be most affected by these interatomic forces, for they are farthest from the nucleus of their own atom and hence least under its force. Investigation shows that the orbits of electrons in the closed shells are practically unaltered by the proximity of other atoms. On the other hand, the electrons occupying the unfilled shells usually take new orbits that course about both atoms and thus establish a chemical bond. The magnitude of this bond is intimately related to the extent to which the electrons are influenced. Thus, when an alkali atom comes near a halogen atom, the single electron the former possesses outside closed shells is so strongly attracted to the halogen atom that it takes up a new orbit in which it spends most of its time about the halogen. For this reason the bond between the two atoms is very strong.

We may see from these principles that the electrons outside closed orbits are those involved in chemical reactions and that hence they may be called *valence electrons*. Generally speaking, these are the electrons which metallic elements lend in combining with nonmetals such as the halogens, oxygen, sulphur, selenium, nitrogen, and phosphorus. It follows at once that the chemical similarity of the alkali metals or of the alkaline-earth metals occurs because the atoms of elements in these groups have the same number of valence electrons. In combining with metals, the nonmetallic elements borrow electrons from the former and thus tend to fill the vacant levels they possess. As soon as their incompleted shells are filled, they become saturated in the sense that the pattern of filled orbits resembles that of the rare gases. Thus a halogen, such as fluorine, which has one electron less than the number required to fill the $2p$ level, becomes stable as soon as it has borrowed one. Similarly, oxygen becomes stable after borrowing two. We see that the common valence of the non-metals is determined by the number of electrons required to complete a shell.

To return to the discussion of the filling of levels, we see that a new type of element enters the picture in the sequence between potassium and the next rare gas, namely, krypton. At this point the $3d$ shell, which lies near the $4s$ and $4p$ shells, begins to be occupied. The elements having partly filled d shells are usually magnetic and include the useful iron-group metals, iron, cobalt, and nickel. Moreover, one or more of the d electrons are some-times lent in many of these elements, which, as a result, exhibit several valences. As the $3d$ level fills, its position drops relative to the $4p$ and $4s$ levels for reasons too complicated to discuss here. Thus, when the element nickel, which has ten electrons outside the argon group of shells, is reached, the $3d$ level is below the $4p$ and $4s$ levels. The next element, namely, copper, has one electron in the $4s$ level and, in consequence, has properties that resemble in part those of the alkali metals. The filled $3d$ shell is not so stable as the closed shells of the rare gases, however, and electrons contained in this shell are sometimes lent in reactions. For this reason, copper is often divalent.

With the filling of the $4s$ and $4p$ shells, we reach the rare gas krypton.

The sequence from potassium to krypton repeats itself in the period extending from rubidium to xenon in which the $5s$, $5p$, and $4d$ levels become occupied. A group of magnetic elements somewhat resembling the iron-group elements appears in this series just before silver.

Beyond xenon, the sequence from rubidium to xenon essentially repeats itself, although the $4f$ shell of fourteen electrons is filled just after lanthanum, giving rise to the fourteen rare-earth elements. The chemical properties of these elements are closely alike because they differ only with regard to the number of comparatively inert $4f$ electrons they possess.

The atomic nuclei beyond lead are relatively unstable. The instability is made evident by the presence of radioactive elements in this sequence. Apparently the cessation of known elements at atomic number 92 results from the onset of complete instability. Were it not for this, there apparently would be an unending sequence of longer and longer periods of elements.

7. The Electromotive Series.—As we have seen above, different atoms exert different forces on their valence electrons. As a result, atoms differ in regard to the readiness with which they lend or borrow their valence electrons in chemical reactions. This difference has been studied by chemists on a purely experimental basis. The results of their work are most conveniently summarized in terms of the *electromotive series*[1] of the metallic elements, given below, in which a number of metallic elements are plotted in a sequence representing decreasing tendency to lose electrons.

TABLE II.—AN ELECTROMOTIVE SERIES OF THE METALLIC ELEMENTS

Lithium	Cobalt
Potassium	Nickel
Sodium	Tin
Barium	Lead
Calcium	Antimony
Magnesium	Bismuth
Aluminum	Arsenic
Manganese	Copper
Zinc	Mercury
Chromium	Silver
Iron	Platinum
Cadmium	Gold

Independent physical experiments, in which the energy required to remove valence electrons completely from the atom is determined, show that this energy actually increases in going down the sequence given above.

[1] The electromotive series is commonly used in electrochemistry to indicate the manner in which elements replace one another from solution. Usually a metallic element lying higher in the series will displace one beneath it.

If any two atoms, *A* and *B*, the first of which lies higher in the series, are brought together to form a bond, the valence electrons in *A* alter their orbits in such a way as to spend a larger fraction of their time about *B* than the valence electrons of *B* do about *A*. In other words, the atom lying higher in the series loses some negative charge to the other, thus becoming positively charged. For this reason, an atom is said to be "electropositive" relative to those lying below it in the series; conversely, it is said to be "electronegative" to those lying above it.

The nonmetals, such as the halogens, oxygen, sulphur, carbon, and nitrogen, are not included in the preceding table. They are, however, generally electronegative relative to the metals and could be added in an additional column. If so, the order would be approximately as follows:

> Hydrogen
> Boron
> Silicon
> Carbon
> Phosphorus
> Nitrogen
> Sulphur
> Oxygen
> Bromine
> Chlorine
> Fluorine

CHAPTER III

SUBSTITUTIONAL AND INTERSTITIAL ALLOYS

8. The Phase Diagram.[1]—The crystals or grains of a specimen of pure metal composed of one atomic species have the same structure under normal conditions. The exceptional case will be discussed in the next chapter in connection with allotropy. In alloys, however, different grains may have different structures over certain ranges of composition. This topic is most conveniently discussed in terms of the conventional scheme for representing an alloy system, namely, the phase diagram, which we shall consider for a binary, or two-component, alloy.

In this diagram the ranges of temperature in which all grains have the same structure, that is, in which the alloy is homogeneous, are plotted as functions of composition. Figure 26 shows a typical case, the areas α, β, and γ marking regions of temperature and composition in which the alloy is homogeneous. It is to be emphasized, of course, that the structure is generally different in each of these regions, but it does not change as long as the point representing temperature and composition remains within one of these domains. If one attempts to make an alloy that corresponds to a point such as X not in one of these regions, the result is a mechanical mixture of the two structures, or *phases*, that lie on each side of the domain containing the point. These are the α and β phases in the case of the point X. It should be added that this statement is rigorously true only if truly stable phases are implied, for it is possible to prepare an unstable phase that corresponds to a point such as Y_2. Suppose, for example, that the α phase corresponding to the point Y_1 is formed and is then rapidly cooled to the relatively low temperature T_2, so that the temperature-composition point corresponds to Y_2. Under

---

[1] A discussion of phase diagrams is given in the book by G. Tammann, *The States of Aggregation* (translated by R. F. Mehl, D. Van Nostrand Company, Inc., New York, 1925). A very complete survey of binary alloys is given in the book by M. Hansen, *Aufbau der Zweistofflegierungen* (Verlag Julius Springer, Berlin, 1936).

these conditions the crystals of the β phase may form so slowly that they are not observed in a measurably interesting period of time. Although the alloy thus formed consists only of the α phase, it is basically unstable since it would revert to a mixture of the α and β structures, given sufficient time. This manner of obtaining a homogeneous phase in a region where it is not stable is known as *quenching* and serves a very useful purpose in practice. For example, the face-centered cubic form of steel (an iron-carbon alloy), namely, austenite, which is unstable at

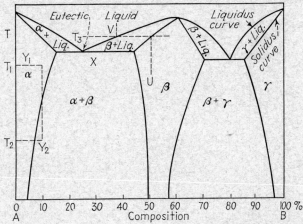

Fig. 26.—A typical phase diagram. The horizontal axis represents the composition, and the vertical axis represents the temperature (see text).

room temperature, may be preserved by quenching when the steel contains small amounts of alloying elements other than carbon.

It may be observed that the structures of phases such as α and γ which occupy positions on either side of the diagram are, respectively, the same as those of the pure metals A and B. Such phases are called *terminal solid solutions*.

The liquidus curve, shown in the figure, marks the temperature at which a solid phase begins to separate from the molten solution of two metals. This curve has significance only over a range of composition in which the molten metals are miscible. The solidus curve, on the other hand, marks the temperature at which a solid phase of given composition begins to melt. The two curves coincide only at special points such as at the ends of the diagram. At a temperature such as T_3 the liquid and solid phases that may be in equilibrium with one another are given, respectively, by the two intercepts that the temperature line T_3 makes with the liquidus and solidus curves. Consider, for example, the case of Fig. 26 again. Starting with the solid of composition U, we find that this begins to melt at temperature T_3 and that the composition of the first sample of molten metal corresponds to the point (V,T_3). Conversely, if we start with the liquid of composition V and cool it to temperature T_3, the solid that forms has composition U. It follows that the compositions of the solid and melt usually change as the process of melting or freezing proceeds, for the newly formed phase usually has a different composition from the old and thus induces a change in the composition of the latter.

Compositions for which the liquidus curve has cusped minima are called *eutectics* (see Fig. 26). They have considerable interest in many applications such as the making of solders, for their compositions remain constant during the freezing process. Moreover, a eutectic has a lower freezing point than any liquid of neighboring composition.

From the standpoint of crystal structure, alloys may be divided into two main classes, namely, *substitutional* and *interstitial* types. The structure of any phase of the first may be viewed as though derived from a lattice of one of the constituents by replacing some atoms of this metal with atoms of the alloying metal. Thus, as the composition is varied within the solubility limits of a given phase of a substitutional alloy, the variation takes place by the replacement of one kind of atom by the other. For example, α brass may be regarded as a face-centered lattice of copper in which atoms of copper have been replaced by atoms of zinc. β brass and γ brass have the structure neither of pure copper nor of pure zinc; however, atoms of zinc replace atoms of copper as the zinc content of either alloy is increased within the concentration in which each phase is stable. Many common alloys are substitutional. Examples other than the brasses are the bronzes (the copper-tin system), the Duraluminum system (aluminum-copper alloys), the Fernico system (alloys of iron, nickel, and cobalt), and Invar (60Ni40Cu). Most of the specific alloying elements that dissolve in steel, apart from carbon, nitrogen. and hydrogen, are substitutional constituents.

In interstitial alloys, one or more of the constituent atoms enter into the interstitial positions of the lattice of another metal. Examples are iron alloys containing carbon, nitrogen, and hydrogen.

We shall now survey in more detail the principles governing the formation of substitutional and interstitial alloys.

9. Substitutional Alloys.[1]—It was recognized long ago that the atomic volume of the metals entering into substitutional alloys is usually about the same. This rule has been formulated most carefully by Hume-Rothery[1] and his associates on the basis of careful statistical analysis. They found that those atoms whose diameters differ by less than 15 percent usually form substitutional-alloy systems with wide solubility limits, whereas those whose diameters differ by more than 15 percent do not. In applying this rule, it is essential to consider atoms that possess similar crystal structures and lie near one another in the electromotive series. Thus, antimony and bismuth have atomic diameters which are very nearly the same as that of magnesium; however, they do not alloy with this more electropositive atom in a manner typical of substitutional alloys. On the other hand, they do alloy with one another. We may see from Fig. 22 (page 19) that a large number of atoms near the center of the long periods have favorable sizes. This explains why metals such as iron, cobalt, nickel, and copper form alloy systems and thus explains in part the intricacy of ferrous metallurgy.

It is interesting to speculate briefly on the fact that elements which alloy well, that is, for wide ranges of composition, must lie near one another in the electromotive series as well as have nearly equal radii. We shall see that this principle operates in the field of interstitial alloys as well as substitutional. If elements are widely separated in the series, as, for example, the alkali metals and the halogens, they become strongly charged during combination since they lend or borrow electrons strongly and exert strong electrostatic forces on one another. Moreover, the process of lending or borrowing is carried out most efficiently when the electropositive element lends all its valence electrons and the other borrows enough to fill its incompleted shells. As

[1] See, for example, the book by Hume-Rothery, *The Structure of Metals and Alloys* (Institute of Metals Monograph, London, 1936).

a result, the atoms become strongly bound and obey the rules of ordinary chemical valence. On the other hand, if the elements lie near to one another in the electromotive series, they become much less strongly charged in alloying and behave more nearly as if they were of the same chemical species. As a result they do not obey valence rules rigidly and are able to combine for a wider range of composition. In this connection it is interesting to note that the metals magnesium and antimony, which are widely spaced in the electromotive series, form a single compound Mg_3Sb_2 for a very narrow range of composition. It is evident that antimony is behaving like a trivalent electronegative element in this case.

TABLE III.—SOLUBILITY LIMITS OF THE PRIMARY PHASES OF SEVERAL COPPER ALLOYS

(The solubilities are expressed in atom percentage of the solute.)

System	Size factor	Solubility in Cu	Solubility of Cu
Cu-Be	Favorable	16.5Be	2.0Cu
Cu-Mg	Unfavorable	6.5Mg	0.01Cu
Cu-Zn	Favorable	38.4Zn	2.3Cu
Cu-Cd	Unfavorable	1.7Cd	0.12Cu
Cu-Ga	Favorable	20.3Ga	Very small
Cu-Tl	Unfavorable	Small	Small
Cu-Ge	Favorable	12.0Ge	Small

Table III contains the solubility limits of the end phases of a number of copper alloys. It may be seen that atoms having favorable size factors almost invariably have wide limits whereas those whose sizes are unfavorable do not. Borderline cases in which the difference in atomic diameter is nearly 15 percent require individual consideration. For example, copper and silver do not alloy appreciably, whereas gold, which has the same size as silver, alloys in nearly all proportions with copper.

In the ideal case, alloys of atoms having the same valence and distinctly favorable size factors tend to form a continuous solid solution for the entire range of composition. Typical examples are the gold-silver system, the gold-copper system at high temperatures, and the bismuth-antimony system. In cases such as that of the cadmium-mercury system in which the constituent metals have different structures, the phase diagram is broken by one or two phases whose solubility limits are very broad.

The phase diagrams of alloys of metal atoms not having the same valence but having sizes favorable for substitution show several striking regularities, first emphasized by Hume-Rothery.[1] Let us consider the brass system (Fig. 27) and the copper-aluminum system (Fig. 28) which are typical examples of such alloys. We may note that a definite phase pattern appears in both these diagrams on the copper-rich side. First, there is an

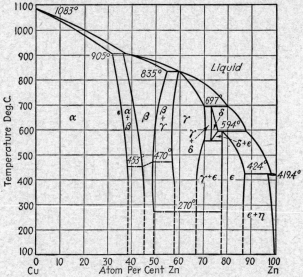

FIG. 27.—The phase diagram of the brass system (Cu-Zn). The horizontal axis represents the atom percentage of zinc in the alloy.

extensive α, or face-centered cubic, phase on the left. Next to these is a β, or body-centered cubic, phase whose solubility limits form a characteristic V-like pattern. Next there is a γ phase which invariably possesses a complex cubic structure, such as that shown in Fig. 21 (page 18) and which is usually comparatively hard and brittle. Finally, there is the ϵ, or hexagonal close-packed, phase. Table IV contains a list of the approximate compositions of a number of alloys that possess these characteristic phases. It is readily seen from this table that the alloys possessing a given structure do not all possess the same composition. For example, the β phase occurs for the compositions

[1] HUME-ROTHERY, *op. cit.*

CuZn and AgCd in the copper-zinc and silver-cadmium systems, whereas it occurs for the composition Cu_5Sn in the bronze system. Moreover, it is evident that none of these alloys, when regarded as chemical compounds, conforms to the ordinary rules of valence chemistry.

TABLE IV.—PHASES THAT CONFORM TO HUME-ROTHERY'S ELECTRON-ATOM RATIO RULE

Electron-atom ratio	1.5	1.61	1.75
Structure	β brass	γ brass	Hexagonal
Nontransition cases	CuZn	Cu_5Zn	$CuZn_3$
	CuBe	Cu_5Cd_8	$CuCd_3$
	AgZn	Ag_5Zn_8	$AgZn_3$
	AgCd	.....	$AgCd_3$
	AuZn	Au_5Zn_8	$AuZn_3$
	AuCd	.....	$AuCd_3$
	Cu_3Al	Cu_9Al_4	Cu_3Sn
	Cu_3Ga	Cu_9Ga_4	Cu_3Ge
	Cu_5Sn	Cu_9In_4	Ag_3Sn
	.....	$Cu_{31}Sn_8$	Au_5Al_8
Transition cases	CoAl	$CoZn_3$	
	NiAl		
	FeAl		

The rule for systematizing data such as those given in Table IV was discovered by Hume-Rothery. He observed that each structure occurs for *a fixed ratio of valence electrons to atoms.* Let us consider the β-brass phase, which occurs for the composition CuZn. Since there are equal numbers of atoms of each kind and since each zinc atom contributes two valence electrons, whereas each copper atom contributes one, it follows that the ratio of valence electrons to atoms is 3:2, or 1.5. The composition associated with this structure in the bronze system is Cu_5Sn. In this case, each copper atom contributes one electron, as before, and each tin atom contributes four. Thus the ratio of valence electrons to atoms is $9:6 = 1.5$. It is readily seen that the corresponding phase in the copper-aluminum system satisfies the same rule.

Similarly, it turns out that the γ-brass type of phase is characterized by the electron-atom ratio 1.61, and the hexagonal close-packed phase is characterized by the ratio 1.75.

This electron-atom ratio rule should be regarded as the analogue of the rules of combining proportions, such as the "rule of eight," that are commonly used in ordinary valence chemistry.

Hume-Rothery has also pointed out that the transit on metals such as iron, cobalt, and nickel enter into substitutional alloys as if they possessed valence zero. Table IV contains alloys that involve these metals and conform to the electron-atom ratio rule.

The various characteristic phases are not the only features of phase diagrams for ideal substitutional alloys that may be correlated with the use of the electron-atom ratio. For example, Hume-Rothery has shown that the liquidus and solidus lines of the end phases of such alloys may be made to coincide by plotting these lines as functions of the electron-atom ratio rather than of the weight or atomic percentage of alloying element.

We shall return to this subject in a later chapter and discuss the more basic principles underlying the electron-atom ratio rule.

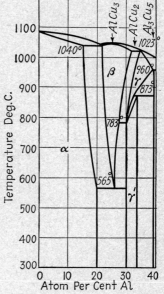

FIG. 28.—The copper-aluminum phase diagram. It may be seen that the copper-rich end of this diagram, which is shown, resembles closely the brass diagram.

It is worth remarking in passing that the phenomenon of ordering, mentioned in the first chapter, is characteristic of substitutional alloys alone since it can be observed only when two different atoms may occupy the same type of position in the lattice.

10. Interstitial Alloys.[1]—A systematic survey of the available experimental data for interstitial alloys, analogous to that described in the previous section for substitutional alloys, has been made by Hägg.[1] Unfortunately, in the experimental work more emphasis has been placed upon the variety of phases that

[1] The fundamental investigations of the rules obeyed by interstitial

are formed among the interstitial systems than upon the limits of solubility in any one phase. As a result, Hägg's work deals mainly with the systematization of the structures of the phases lying between the end phases of the temperature-composition diagram. We shall, however, discuss the end phases briefly near the conclusion of the section.

As might be expected from the fact that one type of atom fits into the interstices of the lattice of another in interstitial alloys, Hägg found that an essential characteristic of these alloys is that one of the atoms be small in comparison with the other. In fact, he found that the interstitial alloys obey comparatively simple rules if the following two conditions are satisfied:

1. The ratio of the atomic diameter of the interstitial atom to that of the atoms of the solvent must be less than about 0.59, that is, the difference in atomic diameter must be larger than 41 percent of the diameter of the larger atom. If the diameter ratio is larger than 0.59, the alloys either do not form or, in the relatively few cases when they do, obey no definite rules.

2. The larger constituent must be one of the transition metals, that is, one of the polyvalent metals such as vanadium, chromium, manganese, iron, cobalt, nickel, molybdenum, palladium, tungsten, osmium, iridium, and platinum.

Only four interstitial atoms are small enough to satisfy both conditions 1 and 2, namely, hydrogen, carbon, nitrogen, and boron (see Fig. 22). These atoms are sometimes called "metalloid" atoms since they do not possess ideal metallic properties in the pure solid form and yet are able to form metallic compounds with transition metals.

Metals other than the transition metals in general seem to form compounds with the metalloids that are similar to ionic solids. Typical of such compounds is CaC_2, which has a high electrical resistivity and in which carbon is apparently behaving like a tetravalent electronegative atom. The reason for the difference in behavior between the transition metals and the others when they combine with the metalloids is not difficult to find. A glance at the electromotive series (see Chap. II, page 28) shows that

---

alloys were first carried out by G. Hägg, *Z. physik. Chem.*, **6(B)**, 221 (1929); **7(B)**, 339 (1930); **8(B)**, 445 (1930).

the transition metals are only slightly more electronegative than the metalloids, whereas calcium and similar metals are much more strongly so. Thus the metalloids meet the transition atoms on a more nearly equal footing, which, as we have seen in the case of the substitutional alloys, seems to be an essential condition for extensive alloying.

Since the range of diameter ratio extending from zero to 0.59 is that for ideal interstitial alloys and the range from 0.85 to 1.00 is that for ideal substitutional alloys, it follows that the range from 0.59 to 0.85 is one in which alloying is not favored.

It is interesting to note that the ratio of the diameter of carbon to that of iron is 0.63. Thus steel is a borderline case. Were the ratio slightly larger, it is possible that iron would have little tendency to dissolve carbon and we should have been deprived of the use of the most important of all alloys!

The metalloid atoms scatter X rays so poorly that they cannot be detected by use of X-ray analysis when in combination with the transition metals. For this reason, their positions cannot be located precisely. The positions of the metal atoms can be located easily, however, and it is found that the most common arrangements are the face-centered cubic lattice (Fig. 10, page 12) and the hexagonal close-packed lattice (Fig. 12, page 13). It is not difficult to understand why these two lattices are so definitely preferred if we regard them as though formed of close-packed spheres. For a given atomic diameter they possess interstitial spaces having larger linear dimensions than other common lattices. For example, the linear dimensions are nearly 10 percent larger in these lattices than in the corresponding body-centered cubic lattice (Fig. 11, page 12). It should be emphasized that the total interstitial *volume* actually is greater in the body-centered lattice and that the close-packed lattices are preferred only because they accommodate a larger interstitial body of *spherical* shape. Incidentally, the diameter ratio, 0.59, which enters in Hägg's rule actually corresponds to the largest sphere that will fit interstitially into a close-packed lattice of spheres.

Although the face-centered and hexagonal close-packed metal lattices predominate, the body-centered and simple hexagonal lattices (Fig. 29) occur in a few cases. Table V contains a list of the interstitial alloys in which the four lattices have been observed. End phases such as austenite, which are not included in this table, will be discussed below. It may be seen that

TABLE V.—DIAMETER RATIOS AND COMPOSITION OF INTERSTITIAL ALLOYS HAVING DIFFERENT STRUCTURES

Diameter ratio	Alloy
Hexagonal Close-packed Lattice	
0.29	Zr_2H
0.32	Ta_2H
0.32	Ti_2H
0.53	Ta_2C
0.55	Mn_2N
0.55	W_2C
0.56	Cr_2N
0.56	Mo_2C
0.56	Fe_2N
0.58	V_2C
Body-centered Cubic Lattice	
0.32	TaH
Simple Hexagonal Lattice	
0.52	MoN
0.58	WC

Face-centered Cubic Lattice

Diameter ratio	M_4X	M_2X	MX	MX_2
0.29	Zr_4H		ZrH	
0.32			TiH	TiH_2
0.34		Pd_2H		
0.45			ZrN	
0.47			ScN	
0.48			ZrC	
0.49			CbN	
0.49			TiN	
0.59		W_2N		
0.53			Vn	
0.53			CbC	
0.53			TiC	
0.53			TaC	
0.55	Mn_4N			
0.56			CrN	
0.56	Fe_4N			
0.58			VC	

carboloy (WC) is one of the cases in which the metallic atoms are distributed in a simple hexagonal lattice. Cementite (Fe_3C) does not appear in this table since it possesses a more complex structure, in keeping with the fact that the iron-carbon system is a borderline one.

The somewhat meager available data concerning the solubility of the metalloid atoms in the end phases indicate that the radius ratio and the structure play a role in the manner which the rigid sphere concept of atoms suggests. The most striking example of this occurs in the iron-carbon system. As we remarked above, for a given size of sphere the close-packed lattices will accommodate larger interstitial spheres than the body-centered lattice. In agreement, we find that face-centered γ iron dissolves about 8.5 atom percent of carbon, whereas the solubility in the body-centered α form is only a few tenths of a percent. Actually, the ratio of radii for iron and carbon is 0.63, which is larger than the maximum of 0.59 allowed in the rigid sphere picture. However, we should not expect the relatively crude rigid sphere concept to apply too closely. In similar manner, we find that a number of body-centered cubic metals for which the diameter ratio is near 0.59

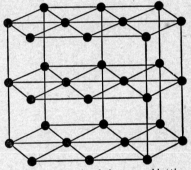

FIG. 29.—The simple hexagonal lattice.

do not dissolve an appreciable amount of carbon. In this category we may mention tantalum, molybdenum, tungsten, and vanadium. On the other hand, both nickel and cobalt, which have close-packed structures and diameter ratios larger than iron, dissolve carbon to the extent of about 0.4 percent. Platinum and palladium, however, seem to violate the rules, for they do not dissolve carbon even though they have face-centered cubic structures and favorable diameter ratios.

It is interesting to note that the iron-nitrogen system furnishes another excellent example of a case, like that of the iron-carbon system, in which the face-centered cubic phase of the metal has a far higher solubility for the interstitial constituent than the body-centered cubic phase (see Fig. 120, page 198).

We shall have cause to return to this topic in the discussion of the solubility of gases in metals.

CHAPTER IV

THE PHYSICAL FORM OF ALLOYS

11. The Thermodynamical Principles Governing Equilibrium.[1]
Let us consider an oscillatory mechanical system, such as a simple pendulum, that is at least slightly damped. If the system is made to oscillate and is then left alone, the amplitude of its oscillations decreases, because of the influence of friction, and eventually becomes very small. The system comes to rest at the position of lowest energy if all heat is removed, whereas it undergoes oscillations about the point of lowest energy if heat is not removed. The amplitude of these thermal oscillations is usually negligible for a system of ordinary size, for it may be shown that the mean oscillational energy of a one-dimensional system is of the order kT, where T is the absolute temperature and k, which is called "Boltzmann's constant," is about 10^{-23} ft-lb per deg ($1.39 \cdot 10^{-16}$ erg per deg). Thus at room temperature the thermal oscillations of a 1-ft pendulum weighing 1 lb correspond to a swing of about 10^{-10} deg.

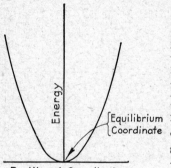

Fig. 30.—The energy of an atom as a function of its position for small displacements.

The atoms in solids are bound to equilibrium positions by forces, similar to those acting on a pendulum bob, that arise from the interaction between neighboring atoms. Thus, if an atom is displaced from its equilibrium position, it vibrates back and forth like the bob of a pendulum. In an energy diagram, the potential of an atom varies as shown in Fig. 30 when it is displaced

---

[1] The basic relations of thermodynamics are derived in a number of textbooks. See, for example, P. S. Epstein, *Textbook of Thermodynamics* (John Wiley & Sons, Inc., New York, 1937).

from its equilibrium position. Because of the coupling between atoms, the vibrational energy given to one atom when it is displaced is dissipated to others. If the solid is at absolute zero of temperature, this vibrational energy eventually leaves the solid in the form of heat. Hence, at the absolute zero of temperature, the state of a solid is determined by the condition that its *energy be a minimum*. This condition is not valid at higher temperatures because the amplitudes of thermal oscillation of atoms are not negligibly small. In ordinary metals the amplitude of atomic oscillations at room temperature is, in order of magnitude, about 10 per cent of the interatomic spacing.

The appropriate condition for equilibrium at temperatures above absolute zero may be determined by the use of thermodynamics—a subject that we shall not attempt to develop in detail here. The important quantity that enters into the new equation for equilibrium is the *entropy*, which is usually designated by the symbol S. It may be defined in the following way.

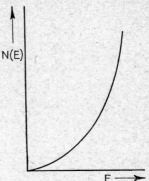

Fig. 31.—Schematic diagram showing the increase of $N(E)$ with E.

If we endow a system, such as a solid, with an amount of energy $(E - E_m)$ above the minimum value E_m, it may oscillate in a variety of different ways. We shall designate the number of different ways by $N(E)$. The problem of computing N is one that requires the use of atomic mechanics; however, the solution can, at least in principle, be carried through for any system. Usually the number of modes of motion increases as $(E - E_m)$ increases, and, as a result, $N(E)$ is a monotonically increasing function of E of the form shown in Fig. 31. It may be added that $N(E)$ is unity when E equals E_m since the atoms are at rest at their equilibrium positions when there is no extra energy. The entropy $S(E)$ associated with the system when it has energy E is given in terms of $N(E)$ by the equation

$$S(E) = k \log_e N(E) \tag{1}$$

where k is Boltzmann's constant.

It turns out that the condition for equilibrium at absolute temperature T is that the quantity

$$A(E) = E - TS(E) \tag{2}$$

be a minimum. This quantity, which is called the *free energy*, becomes equal to the mechanical energy E when T is zero, for TS then vanishes. We see that, the more rapidly S increases with E and the larger T is, the more the equilibrium state of the system deviates from the state of lowest energy.

It is not difficult to see in a qualitative way why the quantity (2) determines the equilibrium state of the system. If a system has several modes of vibration with one energy and only one mode with another, the first energy would certainly be preferred purely on the basis of probability for the same reason that it is more probable that one will draw a spotted card from a deck than a picture card, namely, there are more of the former. Since the entropy S depends only upon the number of modes of motion associated with a given state [see Eq. (1)], it provides a measure of this inherent probability of each state. This probability, however, can determine the likelihood that a system will be in a given energy state only when the magnitude of the energy does not matter, that is, when the temperature is very high. At very low temperatures there is, in addition, a preference for the states of lower energy. This tendency of the system to prefer simultaneously the state of low energy and of high entropy appears in the condition that (2) be a minimum, for A is decreased both by decreasing E and increasing S. The fact that S is more important at high temperatures than at low appears quite naturally since S contains T as a coefficient.

Just as changes in the mechanical energy of an ordinary mechanical system measure the amount of work done on the system, the changes in free energy, which take place as a result of chemical change in a system, measure the amount of work that may be derived from the chemical change at given temperature. In one of the simplest types of system, namely, an electrolytic cell, the work done as the chemical constitution of the system changes may be measured by determining the amount of electrical energy produced or consumed as the reaction proceeds. If the amount of substance that undergoes the reaction is one electrical equivalent, the total current that flows is the Faraday (96,500 coulombs), which is usually designated by F. Thus the electrical energy produced is VF, where V is the electromotive force (emf) of the cell. According to thermodynamics, this is equal to the change A_e of the free energy per equivalent, that is,

$$VF = A_e. \tag{3}$$

Since F is a constant, it follows that the emf of the cell is a direct measure of the change in free energy occurring when a standard amount of the materials in the cell reacts.

Let us now return to a discussion of the conditions for equilibrium of a solid phase. If we have a number of different crystalline modifications of the same substance at the same temperature, it follows from the condition for equilibrium quoted above that only that phase which has the lowest free energy is truly stable. All others are *metastable* at the given temperature and should revert to the stable form if given sufficient time. In particular, let us suppose that the stable phase and one of the metastable phases are used as opposite electrodes in a simple electrolytic cell in which the only change that takes place when a current flows is the transfer of material from one electrode to the other. In this case the sign of the emf of the cell should be such that the stable electrode grows at the expense of the other when the cell is short-circuited. Cells of this type in which one electrode is gray tin and the other is white tin actually have been made. It turns out, in this case, that the emf of the cell has a sign corresponding to the stability of gray tin below 18°C and has opposite sign above this temperature. We may conclude that the free energy versus temperature curves of the two phases cross at 18°C, that of gray tin being lower below this temperature and higher above it.

The fact that the free energy versus temperature curves of different phases may cross accounts for allotropy. An existing crystalline phase can change to another crystalline form only when it is unstable in some temperature range. It does not follow that every observed crystalline form is stable in some temperature range, for an unstable structure may be produced temporarily during the transition from one phase to another. For example martensite, which is apparently metastable at all temperatures, is produced during the transition from austenite to the low-temperature phases of the iron-carbon system.

Let us now consider the relative stability of two phases of a binary-alloy system. Let the two curves of Fig. 32 represent the two free-energy versus composition curves per gram atom of substance at a given temperature. We shall designate the atomic percentage of the component C by x. The system illustrated corresponds to a case in which the two curves cross and possess a common tangent. This situation does not always

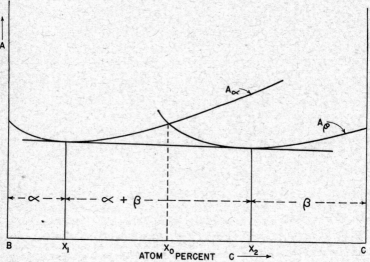

Fig. 32.—The free-energy versus composition curves for two-alloy phases. The phase boundaries are determined by the points x_1 and x_2 at which the curves have a common tangent. The heterogeneous system is more stable than either phase alone for the range of composition between the points of tangency.

occur, but does occur in the most interesting cases. From composition $x = 0$ to composition $x = x_0$, where the two curves cross, the α phase is more stable than the β because the free-energy curve of the former is lower. Similarly, the β phase is more stable in the range from x_0 to 1. It may be shown by the use of simple mathematics, however, that neither the α nor the β phase is stable relative to the inhomogeneous alloy consisting of a mixture of the two in the range from $x = x_1$ to $x = x_2$ where the common tangent to the two curves is lower than either curve. In the case shown, the α phase would be stable in the range from

$x = 0$ to $x = x_1$, the β phase would be stable from $x = x_2$ to $x = 1$, and the mixture of the two phases having compositions x_1 and x_2, respectively, would be stable in the intermediate range. It follows from the figure that the points x_1 and x_2 can coincide only in the improbable case that the curves have the same slope at the crosspoint x_0. As a result, alloy phases are usually separated by a region in which the inhomogeneous alloy is stable.

The solubility limits of a possible third phase may be determined by plotting its free-energy curve for the same temperature

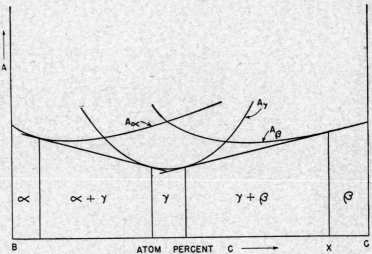

FIG. 33.—This figure is similar to that of Fig. 32; however, it corresponds to a case in which there are three phases under consideration.

in the same diagram and determining the points of common tangency for all pairs of the three curves (Fig. 33).

As the temperature is varied, the free-energy curves of the various possible phases may be expected to vary, so that the solubility limits of the phases should usually vary. Now it may be shown by the use of statistical mechanics that the entropy changes with composition in the manner $-x \log_e x$ in the region where x is very small and in the manner $-(1 - x) \log_e (1 - x)$ in the range where x is nearly unity. Thus the curves representing free energy *versus* composition usually vary with temperature in the manner shown in Fig. 34. Since the points of common tangency of the end phases tend to shift nearer the center of the diagram as the temperature is raised, it follows that the solubility limits of the end phases usually increase with increasing temperature. This is a thermodynamical explanation of a commonly observed fact. The exceptional cases, such as that of the α-brass system (see Figure 27, page 35), occur when a terminal solid solution is crowded closely by an intermediate phase.

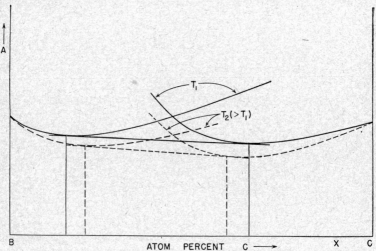

Fig. 34.—The free-energy versus composition curves for the phases usually decrease with increasing temperature in the manner shown and bring the points of tangency closer together.

Since any single phase, liquid or solid, has associated with it a free-energy curve similar to the preceding ones, it follows that the transition between liquid and solid can be described in the terms used above. The phase boundaries are called the "liquidus" and "solidus curves" in this case.

12. Transition from One Stable Phase to Another.—We have seen above that a phase is thermodynamically unstable in a given temperature range if another phase has a lower free energy in the same range. It does not follow that the transition takes place as soon as the existing phase becomes unstable; in fact, all transitions require a finite amount of time, which actually may be unobservably long. For example, many commonly used phases of alloys are unstable phases that have been quenched from elevated temperatures. Although white tin is theoretically unstable below 18°C, tin disease does not set in until well below 0°C. Martensite, which is an unstable phase of steel, has been found in prehistoric tools.

The reason for delay in phase transitions may best be appreciated by realization of the following fact: even in an unstable

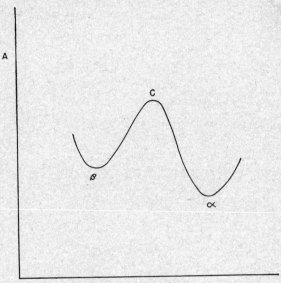

ATOMIC COORDINATES

Fig. 35.—Variation of the free energy of a system as the coordinates of the atoms are changed from the values corresponding to one phase to those corresponding to another (schematic). In the case illustrated the configuration α has a lower free energy than β, so that the former is the stable phase. The free energy passes through the maximum C during the transition, so that the transition may occur only if energy sufficient to carry the system over C is available.

range a metastable phase is stable for small displacements of many atoms or for relatively large displacements of a few atoms. In other words, the free energy is increased as a result of small displacements of atoms—a decrease can occur only when the atoms undergo extensive rearrangement. This principle is illustrated schematically in Fig. 35. The ordinate in this figure is the free energy at a given temperature; the abscissa represents schematically the coordinates of the atoms in the solid. The point α corresponds to the stable phase at which the free energy is a minimum. The point β corresponds to the unstable phase. The free energy increases initially for all displacements from β, so that, if the atoms are given small displacements, their coordinates will oscillate about β. Only if the system is given an amount of distortional energy sufficient to carry it over C will the phase transition take place. Distortional energy of this type, which must be supplied before a reaction may proceed, is commonly called the *activation energy* for the process.

The normal source of distortional energy is, of course, temperature agitation. If the amount of such agitational energy in a small region of the solid were a fixed quantity at any given temperature, the system would not pass over C until a definite temperature were reached, at which point the transition from β to α would take place abruptly. Actually, however, the amount of thermal energy in a given region continually fluctuates, even at constant temperature. Statistical analysis shows that these fluctuations are small compared with the total heat energy for a solid of ordinary size but that they are appreciable compared with the average thermal energy per atom. Thus, if the energy of thermal agitation of an atom could be observed, it would be found to vary by a comparatively large fraction of the average from one instant to the next.

It may be added that the fluctuations are not entirely unobservable, for if individual smoke particles are watched through a microscope they are found to execute an irregular motion, called "Brownian movement," which originates in the variations in heat energy. As a result of such variations, the system discussed in connection with Fig. 35 has a finite chance of passing over the barrier C at any temperature above absolute zero. Since the magnitude of the fluctuations increases with temperature, this probability also increases.

Generally speaking, it is not necessary for the entire system to go from β to α at one jump for the transition to occur. It can easily be shown that, if this were necessary, phase changes would practically never occur, for the probability that a large number of atoms will do the same thing at the same time is extremely small. Actually, a small group of atoms pass from β to α to form a *nucleus* of stable phase. The nuclei then grow until all the β

phase is exhausted. Thus the factors that determine the rate of phase changes in practice are the rate of nucleation and rate of growth of the nuclei.[1] The rate of nucleation may be conveniently expressed in terms of a quantity N that measures the rate at which new nuclei are formed in unit time. Similarly, the rate of growth may be conveniently expressed in terms of a quantity G that measures the rate at which layers of atoms are transformed from the β phase to the α phase at the interface between the two.

Both the process of nucleation and that of growth involve activation energies, which in general are not equal. Both these activation energies, however, are far smaller than that required to change the entire lattice from the β phase to the α phase in one step, for a much smaller number of atoms is involved in each step of the processes of nucleation and growth.

Since the nucleus of the new phase is in a foreign environment, namely, the unstable phase, it follows that the surface atoms of the nucleus are out of place in the surrounding lattice. On the other hand, the atoms inside the nucleus are in proper places for the new phase and hence are more stable than those in the old phase. If the increase in free energy associated with the misfit surface atoms is small in comparison with the decrease associated with internal atoms, the nucleus is stable—otherwise not. Estimates of nuclear size, based on a study of these energies, indicate that under ordinary conditions the smallest stable nuclei contain of the order of twenty-five atoms.

Experiments on supercooling show that the rate at which nuclei form below the transition temperature increases with decreasing temperature. The explanation of this probably is as follows: A nucleus of a given size is relatively more stable the lower the temperature; for whereas the energy of the misfit atoms on the surface is practically independent of temperature, the relative stability of the internal atoms increases with decreas-

---

[1] Detailed theories of the processes of nucleation and growth have been developed by M. Volmer and A. Weber, *Z. physik. Chem.*, **119**, 277 (1926); I. STRANSKI, *Z. physik. Chem.*, **17**(B), 127 (1932); and R. Becker, *Ann. Physik*, **32**, 128 (1938). These have been carefully reviewed by R. F. Mehl and L. K. Jetter, *Age Hardening Symposium* (American Society for Metals, Cleveland, Ohio, 1940).

ing temperature. Thus a nucleus of given size that is not stable at the freezing point may be stable at a temperature below the freezing point. Moreover, the smaller the nucleus the lower the temperature at which it becomes stable, since it has a proportionally higher ratio of surface atoms. Thus, at the freezing point, only infinitely large nuclei, which require an infinite activation energy and hence have a small probability of occurring, are stable.

The rate of formation of all nuclei eventually decreases if the temperature is lowered sufficiently far below the thermodynamic transition temperature, for fluctuations are less likely to occur.

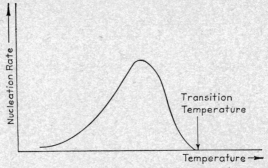

Fig. 36.—The schematic variation of nucleation rate with temperature for a phase that is formed *during cooling*. This rate passes through a maximum and then drops with decreasing temperature because all rates decrease with temperature.

Thus the rate of nucleation has the form shown in Fig. 36. Incidentally, the shape of this curve explains in part the observation that ingots which are cooled very slowly are more coarsely crystalline than those which are cooled more rapidly. If a melt is cooled very slowly, the material has sufficient time to crystallize completely around the few nuclei that are produced just below the melting point, whereas, if it is cooled more rapidly, many nuclei may form before crystallization is complete. If the melt is supercooled below the temperature corresponding to the peak of the curve of Fig. 36 before many nuclei have formed, the size of the crystals that finally form will depend upon the rate at which nuclei form and the rate at which they grow.

It is interesting to note that there are many cases on record in which the mechanism for establishing the stable phase has such low probability of occurring when all the material is in the unstable form β that a transition to a second unstable phase occurs first and is followed by a transition to the stable phase. For example, β quartz becomes unstable relative to cristobalite above 1060°C; yet the transition does not take place directly. Quartz first melts and the melt then devitrifies, forming cristobalite. Thus although the melt is not stable relative to cristobalite, it forms first. Similarly, at sufficiently low temperatures the precipitation of cementite and ferrite from austenite takes place via the formation of unstable martensite, which subsequently decomposes.

This type of behavior may be explained as follows: Of all sequences of atomic rearrangements leading from the unstable to the stable phase, that for which the barrier height is lowest involves formation of the nucleus of the intermediate unstable phase. This nucleus is stable, of course, only when the intermediate phase is stable relative to the original one.

13. The External Form of Crystalline Materials.—The principles that determine the relative stability of different crystalline phases also determine the external form of crystals. Generally speaking, surface atoms are not so tightly bound as internal atoms because they do not have neighboring atoms on one side of the surface. In liquids, this fact is made evident by the tendency of drops to reduce their area to a minimum by pulling themselves into spherical form. The difference between the energy of surface atoms and internal atoms is expressed in terms of the energy required to form a unit area of the surface, that is, the *surface energy*. Since the creation of surface requires work, it follows that the process must be accompanied by a force. This force is, in fact, the surface tension. As in other cases with which we shall deal, work done at temperatures above absolute zero actually appears as free energy in the system on which the work is done. Unless the contrary is stated, we shall usually imply free energy per unit area when using the term "surface energy."

Since crystals do not have the same properties in all directions, it follows that the energies of different surface crystalline planes usually are different. Thus there are forces acting on most crystalline aggregates to change the form of each crystal to that corresponding to lowest energy. Let us consider the single crystal shown diagramatically in Fig. 37, and let us assume that the horizontal and vertical faces such as a and b have lower surface energy than the diagonal faces c and d. It follows that, if the temperature is sufficiently high so that atoms may move about on the surface, atoms in faces of the type cd move to surfaces of the type ab more frequently than the reverse. Hence, the area of the diagonal faces decreases at the expense of the others. Actually, if the difference in surface energy between the two types is sufficiently great, this process probably takes place in the manner shown in Fig. 37. In other words, the

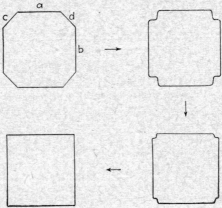

Fig. 37.—The attainment of equilibrium form for a crystal. The original crystal has the unstable faces c and d, which disappear as equilibrium is attained.

diagonal faces are first hollowed out, turning into two surfaces of the type ab. These are then decreased, and the crystal eventually becomes a cube.

Wulff[1] has proved an interesting theorem relating to the equilibrium form of a crystal. Suppose that the magnitude of the surface energy of a given crystal surface is plotted as the radius vector in a polar diagram, the direction of the vector being that of the normal to the surface. Typical diagrams of this kind corresponding to hypothetical two-dimensional crystals having square symmetry are shown in Fig. 38. It may be demonstrated that the ultimate stable form of a single crystal is obtained by taking the envelope of planes that are normal to the radius

[1] G. Wulff, Z. Kryst, **34**, 449 (1901).

vectors at the points where these vectors intersect the surface-energy curve. Thus in Fig. 38a the stable form is a square, whereas in Fig. 38b it is an octagon. It may be seen that the relative lengths of the diagonal sides and the horizontal sides are determined by the distances of points a and b from the origin. As b recedes from the origin, the length of the diagonal side evidently decreases, and vice versa.

It should be emphasized in passing that the surface energy of a given plane depends upon the medium in which a crystal is

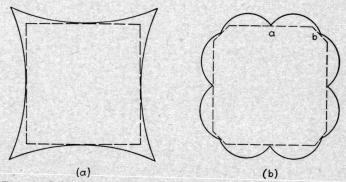

(a)   (b)

Fig. 38.—Polar plots showing the variation of the free energy of crystalline surfaces in two hypothetical cases. The length of a line extending from the center of the diagram to a point on the full curve is proportional to the free energy of the crystallographic surface normal to the line. The envelope of the planes that are normal to these lines at the point of intersection with the full curves determines the equilibrium form of the crystal. This form is represented by the square in the first case and by the octagon in the second.

immersed, for the surface atoms react in different ways with different exterior atoms. Thus the free-energy diagrams of the type shown in Fig. 38 may be completely different for crystals in a vacuum and in an acid medium. This explains in part the heterogeneous results that are possible when metal crystals are etched with different solutions, for surfaces may have different relative stabilities in different solutions.

We may conclude that in a given medium a crystal has a definite equilibrium form. It need hardly be mentioned that in most cases the time required to establish equilibrium is so long that it never is completely obtained in practice.

Since surface atoms have higher free energy than internal atoms, it follows that any aggregate of crystals tends to unite in order to decrease the amount of surface, even though each crystal of the aggregate may have the equilibrium form. This tendency is responsible for the fact that large crystals usually grow at the expense of smaller ones when free interchange of atoms is possible, as occurs when solids are at such high temperatures that diffusion or evaporation may occur. Given sufficient time, any aggregate of crystals would form one very large crystal having a definite geometrical shape. This seldom occurs in practice, although it may be observed in special cases. For example, a quantity of powdered iodine will grow into a single crystal if left in a closed container at constant temperature for a period of months. In this case, vaporization provides the mechanism for growth.

One of the processes by which powdered solids are commonly united into a firm mass is sintering. The procedure consists of pressing the powder and heating it to an elevated temperature. The temperatures involved frequently are below the values at which appreciable evaporation or diffusion can occur. Apparently it must be assumed in these cases that the grains of material flow plastically under the forces which the faces of neighboring particles exert on one another and that a large fraction of the free faces are thereby able to weld together. Direct evidence for the plastic flow is provided by the fact that the density of the pressed powder rises during sintering and, in some cases, attains very nearly the value of the ideal solid.

14. Recrystallization after Plastic Deformation.—If a material is deformed plastically and the external stresses are then removed, some of the internal stresses produced during deformation remain. The stressed regions possess a higher energy than unstressed regions and hence are thermodynamically unstable relative to unstressed material. This means that a transformation from the stressed to the unstressed state is permissible thermodynamically and should take place in the course of time if the temperature is sufficiently high. We shall refer to this process as *recrystallization*. As in the case of crystallization from a melt, the transformation may be expected to occur via the formation of nuclei of unstressed material and the subsequent growth of these nuclei (see Sec. 12). Thus, as in the case of a phase change, the process may be described in terms of quantities

N and G that provide a measure of the rate of nucleation and rate of growth of the nuclei. The present case provides an interesting difference, however. N and G are functions of the temperature alone in the case of a phase change, if all other things remain equal, whereas they will, in general, be functions of the degree of cold-work as well in the process of recrystallization. As the amount of cold-work increases, the free energy of the material may be expected to rise, for experience shows that the disorder of the lattice increases with increasing cold-work. Thus we may expect the size of the smallest nucleus of the unstressed phase that is stable at a given temperature to decrease with increasing cold-work; and, as a result, we may expect N to increase with increasing amounts of cold-work. Experiments actually show that the crystal size of recrystallized materials is smaller the larger the stresses. It is likely that this is primarily a result of the increase in the rate of nucleation which accompanies increasing degrees of cold-work.[1]

It should be noted that the "driving force" for recrystallization in stressed and unstressed materials arises from essentially different origins. In stressed materials, it is probably the stored energy of deformation of the stressed material, which decreases with the amount of new unstressed material. In unstressed materials, on the other hand, it is the surface energy, which varies inversely as the dimensions of the crystals and is largest when the crystals are very small. Hence the driving force is larger for large crystals in the case of stress recrystallization. For this reason, it is possible to obtain larger crystals in a given time by appropriately stressing and crystallizing a given material than by annealing it in the unstressed form.

15. The Specific Heats of Solids.—Much useful information concerning the fundamental constitution of solids can be gained from a study of their specific heats. This field has been exploited with particular interest by the thermochemists, for it is possible to compute the differences in the free energies of different phases

---

[1] A yet unpublished work by R. F. Mehl and W. Anderson indicates that G also increases with increasing amounts of cold-work in the case of aluminum; however, the relative increase of N is greater and presumably is the factor deciding the relation between recrystallized-grain size and the degree of cold-work.

of a substance by the use of the experimentally determined specific heats of the phases and the experimentally determined heat of transformation. In fact, the equation that may be used for this purpose is the following:

$$\Delta A(T) = \Delta E_0 - T \int_0^T \frac{dT'}{T'^2} \int_0^{T'} \Delta C(T'')dT''. \qquad (1)$$

Here $\Delta A(T)$ is the difference in molar free energy of one phase at temperature T (in degrees absolute), ΔE_0 is the difference in

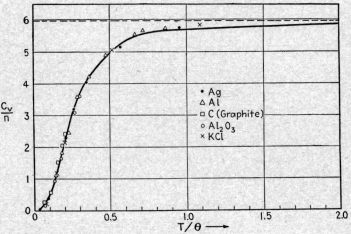

Fig. 39.—The specific-heat versus temperature curve for solids that obey Debye's theory. The horizontal axis is the ratio of the absolute temperature to the characteristic temperature of the solid. The vertical axis is the atomic heat expressed in calories.

energy of the phases at the absolute zero of temperature, and $\Delta C(T)$ the difference in molar heat of the phases at temperature T.

There are a number of ways in which the constituents of solids conceivably may absorb thermal energy. The most common processes are the following: (*a*) stimulation of atomic vibration, (*b*) stimulation of electronic motion or excitation, (*c*) stimulation of molecular rotation. The first of these is common to all solids since the atoms in all may be set into vibration. The problem of determining the type of specific-heat versus temperature curve which occurs when this is the only process by which heat may be absorbed has been subject to much investigation and is fully understood. Figure 39 shows the type of curve for this case.

TABLE VI.—THE DEBYE CHARACTERISTIC TEMPERATURES OF SOLIDS

Substance	θ	Substance	θ
		Metals	
Na	150	Al	390
K	100	Ga	125
Cu	315	In	100
Ag	215	Tl	100
Au	170		
Be	1,000	Ti	350
Mg	290	Zr	280
Ca	230	Hf	213
Sr	170	Ge	290
Zn	250	Sn	260
Cd	172	Pb	88
Hg	96		
		Sb	140
		Bi	100
Cr	485	Ta	245
Mn	350	W	310
Fe	420	Re	300
Co	385	Os	250
Ni	375	Ir	285
Mo	380	Pt	225
Ru	400		
Rh	370		
Pd	275		
		Ionic Crystals	
KCl	227	CaF_2	474
NaCl	281	FeS_2	645
KBr	177		
AgCl	183		
AgBr	144		

It may be seen that the specific heat is very small at temperatures near absolute zero and rises to a *saturation value* at elevated temperatures. The temperature at which the specific heat is 0.96 times the saturation value is commonly called the *characteristic temperature* and is usually designated by the symbol Θ. Values of Θ for a number of salts and metals are given in Table VI. It may be shown that the characteristic temperature is proportional to the natural frequency of oscillation of the atoms, so that this frequency is highest for those solids in which Θ is high.

The saturation value of the specific heat obeys a simple rule that was first observed experimentally by Dulong and Petit. It is found that the product of the saturation value of the specific heat and the molecular weight of the substance is equal to $n3R$, where n is the number of atoms per molecule and R is the gas constant, namely, 2.00 cal per deg. Since this is equal to $3Nk$, in which k is Boltzmann's constant and N is the number of atoms per molecular weight, it follows that the saturation value of the vibrational heat of various substances is the same for amounts containing equal numbers of atoms.

If it is found that the specific heat curve of a given substance has the form shown in Fig. 39 and that it obeys Dulong and Petit's law, it is invariably safe to assume that the principal mechanism for absorption of heat is atomic oscillation. This is true for the simpler metals and the salts listed in Table VI. On the other hand, it is not true for substances such as the ferrous metals or the salts of the iron group, in which there are atoms or ions that contain groups of unfilled d shells. For example, Fig. 40 shows[1] the atomic heat of α and γ iron as a function of temperature. It may be seen that the saturation value is much larger than $3R$, the value to be expected from Dulong and Petit's law. In other words, we must conclude that, in cases such as this, atomic oscillation is not the only mechanism by which heat is absorbed. As we shall see later, there is good reason for believing that the electrons absorb the thermal energy not accounted for on the basis of Dulong and Petit's law.

Before leaving this subject, it is interesting to examine Eq. (1) from a qualitative viewpoint. It may be noted that the free energy of a given phase decreases relative to that of another phase if the specific heat of the former is larger than that of the latter. The reason for this is not difficult to find. The phase

[1] After J. B. AUSTIN, *Ind. Eng. Chem.*. **24** 1225 (1932); **24**, 1388 (1932).

with the larger specific heat has a larger number of ways of absorbing heat and, as a result, has a greater degree of randomness, or larger entropy. In view of this, let us examine the specific-heat curves for the two phases of iron (Fig. 40). There is little doubt that the α phase is the more stable at the absolute zero of temperature. As a result, we may conclude that the free energy of the α phase is initially lower than that of the γ phase. In Fig. 40, we note that below 350°C the specific heat of the γ phase is larger than that of the α phase. Thus in this region the difference in free energy of the two phases decreases.

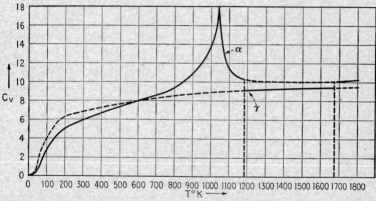

FIG. 40.—The atomic heats of α and γ iron as functions of temperature. The full portions of the curves correspond to ranges of temperature in which the phase is stable. The peak in the curve for α iron occurs at the temperature at which ferromagnetism disappears.

Since the shape of the curves below 350°C is much the same as would be expected if the specific heat were of vibrational origin, it may be concluded that the characteristic temperature is lower for γ iron than for α iron. There seems little doubt that the transformation from α to γ iron that occurs at 930°C arises from this difference in vibrational specific heat below 350°C. We may note, however, that the specific heat of the α phase is the larger in the range above 350°C where Dulong and Petit's law is violated. It follows from Eq. (1) that the free energy of the α phase decreases again relative to that of the γ phase at sufficiently high temperatures. We may conclude that this decrease is responsible for reversion of the γ phase to the body-centered cubic phase at 1400°C. In other words, the change from α to γ iron occurs

CHAPTER V

THE ELASTIC PROPERTIES OF CRYSTALS

16. Stress and Strain.—We shall now discuss the relationships between force and displacement in crystals, with the intention of applying the results in a discussion of the elastic and plastic properties of polycrystalline aggregates.

a. Stress Components.—Let us consider a material that is under stress and discuss the components of force acting on a small cube whose edges are parallel to an arbitrarily chosen set of coordinate axes, labeled x, y, and z. Since the medium is stressed, it follows that the cube is exerting forces on the surrounding medium and that the medium is exerting equal and opposite forces on it. At equilibrium, the forces acting on opposite faces of the cube are balanced and hence equal. As a result, the forces acting on the cube may be completely specified by the magnitude and direction of those acting on three perpendicular faces of the cube. We shall designate the forces *per unit area* acting on the cube across the x, y, and z planes, respectively, by X, Y, and Z. Each of these forces may be resolved into three components parallel to the three coordinate axes. If the components of X, Y, and Z parallel to the x axis are written as X_x, Y_x, and Z_x, respectively, and if the components parallel to the y and z axes are written as X_y, Y_y, Z_y and X_z, Y_z, Z_z, the stresses on the cube are completely specified by nine numbers

$$X_x, Y_x, Z_x$$
$$X_y, Y_y, Z_y$$
$$X_z, Y_z, Z_z.$$

It may be noted (Fig. 41) that X_x, Y_y, and Z_z are normal to the three surfaces of the cube and hence are compressional or tensional stresses, depending upon whether they are positive or negative. The other six stress components are the forces parallel to the plane faces and hence are shearing stresses.

63

More careful analysis shows that the condition that the cube be at equilibrium under torsional forces requires the relations

$$X_y = Y_x, \qquad Y_z = Z_y, \qquad Z_x = X_z$$

on the six components of shearing stress. It follows that only three of the six are independent. For this reason, it is common to abbreviate the notation by replacing the nine components given above by the following six:

$$\sigma_x = X_x, \qquad \sigma_y = Y_y, \qquad \sigma_z = Z_z,$$
$$\tau_{yz} = Y_z = Z_y, \qquad \tau_{xy} = X_y = Y_x, \qquad \tau_{xz} = X_z = Z_x.$$

The first three are the compressional stresses and the last three the shearing stresses. For convenience we shall commonly desig-

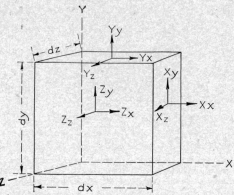

Fig. 41.—The components of stress referred to a simple Cartesian set of axes.

nate a given component of stress by S when it occurs frequently in a discussion.

If the nine stress components are the same at each point of the body, it is said to be *homogeneously* stressed. We shall usually be concerned with homogeneous stresses.

If we consider an arbitrary plane in a specimen that is under homogeneous stress, the forces acting across the plane may be resolved into a normal component and a shear component. As this plane is rotated about a point, the values of the two components change. It is possible to show that three orthogonal orientations of the plane can always be found for which the shear stress is zero. The values of the normal stresses across these three *principal planes* are called the *principal stresses*. As a particular example, let us consider a uniform cylindrical rod that is under axial tension. It is obvious that in this case the three planes for which the shearing stress is zero are the plane normal to the axis and two perpendicular planes passing through the axis (Fig. 42). The second pair of planes can be oriented arbi-

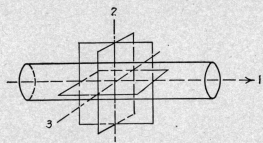

Fig. 42.—A set of principal planes of stress for a rod under tension. One of the planes is normal to the axis of the bar, and the other two are parallel to this axis. In this case the second pair may be chosen to be any orthogonal pair containing the axis. This, however, is not generally possible.

trarily in a direction around the rod in this example; however, this is not the general rule. The principal stress for the plane normal to the axis evidently is equal to the load divided by the cross-sectional area, whereas the other two values are zero. The shearing stress across any plane other than the principal planes is not zero. A simple analysis shows that the values of the

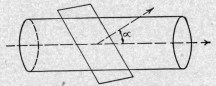

Fig. 43.—Plane making an angle α with the axis of a rod.

normal stress and shearing stress, S_n and S_t, in a plane whose normal makes an angle α with the axis of the rod (Fig. 43) are

$$S_n = S \cos^2 \alpha,$$
$$S_t = S \cos \alpha \sin \alpha,$$

where S is the principal stress for the plane normal to the axis. S_t takes its maximum value when $\cos \alpha \sin \alpha$ is a maximum, that is, when α is 45 deg. There is no essential change in this analysis when the rod is under compression rather than tension, for then S merely reverses its sign.

b. Strain Components.—When a medium is distorted, or *strained*, the relative positions of the particles of the substance are changed. Thus the distortion may be described by giving the relationship between the coordinates of a point of the medium before and after the strain. If x, y, and z are the coordinates of a point before the strain and x', y', and z' are the coordinates after, the displacement of the point along the three coordinate axes is given by the three quantities

$$a = x' - x,$$
$$b = y' - y,$$
$$c = z' - z.$$

When a, b, and c are constants, the deformation is a pure translation since each point of the medium is displaced by the same amount. The most interesting case to consider is that of *homogeneous distortion* in which a, b, and c are proportional to x, y, and z.

$$a = e_{xx}x + e_{xy}y + e_{xz}z,$$
$$b = e_{yx}x + e_{yy}y + e_{yz}z,$$
$$c = e_{zx}x + e_{zy}y + e_{zz}z.$$

Here the nine quantities

$$e_{xx}, \ e_{xy}, \ e_{xz},$$
$$e_{yx}, \ e_{yy}, \ e_{yz},$$
$$e_{zx}, \ e_{zy}, \ e_{zz}$$

are constants, called the "components of strain." A simple interpretation of these constants may be obtained by considering several special cases. In the case of the particle at the origin, it is readily seen that its position is unchanged by the distortion, for a, b, and c are zero when x, y, and z are zero. The particle a unit distance along the x axis ($x = 1$, $y = z = 0$) is displaced to a point having the coordinates $(1 + e_{xx}, e_{yx}, e_{zx})$. Hence, e_{xx}, e_{yx}, e_{zx} give the displacement of this point. Similarly, the sets of numbers e_{xy}, e_{yy}, e_{zy} and e_{xz}, e_{yz}, e_{zz} give, respectively, the amounts by which the coordinates of points a unit distance along the y

and z axes are displaced. It can easily be shown that points along a line passing through the origin are displaced by amounts proportional to their distance from the origin. Since e_{xx}, e_{yy}, and e_{zz} give, respectively, the amounts by which the particles lying along the three axes are displaced along these axes, they are commonly called the "tensional" or "compressional" components of strain. The remaining six components, which give the displacements of the points normal to the axes, are called the "components of shearing strain."

In the case in which we shall be principally interested, namely, that in which the body is distorted without a net rotation, the strain components satisfy the relations

$$e_{xy} = e_{yx}, \qquad e_{yz} = e_{zy}, \qquad e_{zx} = e_{xz}.$$

Hence, in this case, as in the case of the stress components, only six of the nine are independent. As a result, it is convenient to introduce the simplified notation

$$\epsilon_x = e_{xx}, \qquad \epsilon_y = e_{yy}, \qquad \epsilon_z = e_{zz},$$
$$\gamma_{yz} = e_{yz} = e_{zy}, \qquad \gamma_{zx} = e_{zx} = e_{xz}, \qquad \gamma_{xy} = e_{xy} = e_{yx}.$$

c. Hooke's Law.—A medium is said to be elastic, or to obey Hooke's law, if the components of stress are linearly related to the components of strain. In this case the stresses are zero if the strains are zero and, in general, are proportional to the amount by which particles are displaced relative to one another. In the perfectly general case, each of the six independent stress components is written as a linear equation involving the six strain components. For example, σ_x is given by the equation

$$\sigma_x = c_{11}\epsilon_x + c_{12}\epsilon_y + c_{13}\epsilon_z + c_{14}\gamma_{yz} + c_{15}\gamma_{zx} + c_{16}\gamma_{xy} \qquad (1)$$

in which c_{ij} are the *elastic constants*. Since there are six different equations of this type, it follows that there would be $6^2 = 36$ constants c_{ij}. Fortunately, most of these either are zero or are interrelated in the materials of most common interest. Thus in isotropic media, such as glasses or finely grained polycrystalline metals, in which the crystal orientation is random, there are only two independent values of the elastic constants. Similarly, in cubic crystals, such as those possessing the face-centered and body-centered cubic structures, there are at most three independent elastic constants, whereas in hexagonal crystals there are at most five.

In isotropic media the two independent constants are directly connected with the well-known tensional modulus (Young's modulus) and the shear modulus, which may be determined by placing the specimen under tension and under torque.

In the cubic case, the three constants may be determined by making the following three measurements: (1) measurement of the tension strain when the crystal is compressed along a cubic axis, (2) measurement of the transverse strain induced when a crystal is compressed along a cubic axis, and (3) measurement of the shearing strain when the crystal undergoes a shearing stress normal to a cubic axis. The three independent constants are commonly taken as c_{11}, c_{12}, and c_{44}.

In the hexagonal case the five elastic constants may be determined by appropriate computation from the following five experiments: (1) tension test normal to the hexagonal axis, (2) measurement of the transverse strain normal to the hexagonal axis when the specimen is compressed normal to the hexagonal axis, (3) tension test parallel to the hexagonal axis, (4) measurement of the strain normal to the hexagonal axis when the specimen is compressed along the hexagonal axis, (5) measurement of the shearing strain normal to the hexagonal axis when a specimen is sheared in a direction perpendicular to that axis. The five elastic constants obtained from these five experiments are commonly taken as c_{11}, c_{12}, c_{33}, c_{13}, c_{44}.

In several cubic crystals, such as pyrites and sodium chlorate, c_{12} is negative, a fact showing that these materials undergo a transverse contraction when compressed along a cubic axis.

The equation inverse to (1) which gives the dependence of strain on stress is also linear when Hooke's law is obeyed. The equation for ϵ_x is, for example,

$$\epsilon_x = C_{11}\sigma_x + C_{12}\sigma_y + C_{13}\sigma_z + C_{14}\tau_{yz} + C_{15}\tau_{zx} + C_{16}\tau_{xy}.$$

The constants C_{ij} are commonly called the *elastic moduli*. They may always be expressed in terms of the elastic constants, so that the two sets are not independent. Measured values of the independent values of the moduli for a number of crystals are given in Table VII.

TABLE VII.—THE ELASTIC CONSTANTS OF CRYSTALS
(In 10^{-12} cm²/dyne)

Metal	C_{11}	C_{12}	C_{44}
Face-centered Cubic			
Al	1.59	−0.58	3.52
Au	2.33	−1.07	2.38
Ag	2.32	−0.993	2.29
Cu	1.49	−0.625	1.33
Pb	9.30	−4.26	6.94
Body-centered Cubic			
Fe	0.757	−0.282	0.862
Na	48.3	−20.9	16.85
K	83.3	−37.0	38.0
W	0.257	−0.073	0.660

Hexagonal

Metal	C_{11}	C_{12}	C_{13}	C_{33}	C_{44}
Mg	2.23	−0.77	−0.45	1.98	5.95
Zn	0.84	+0.11	−0.78	2.87	2.64
Cd	1.23	−0.15	−0.93	3.55	5.40

Lower Symmetry

Metal	C_{11}	C_{33}	C_{44}	C_{12}	C_{13}	C_{14}
Sb	1.77	3.38	4.10	−0.38	−0.85	−0.80
Bi	2.69	2.87	10.48	−1.4	−0.62	+1.6
Sn	1.85	1.18	5.70	−0.99	−0.25	$C_{66} = 13.5$

Alloys

Alloy	C_{11}	C_{12}	C_{44}
100Ag- 0Au	2.37	−0.993	2.29
75Ag- 25Au	2.07	−0.891	2.05
50Ag- 50Au	1.97	−0.852	1.97
25Ag- 75Au	2.05	−0.909	2.06
0Ag-100Au	2.29	−1.04	2.34
Cu₃Au	1.34	−0.565	1.508
72Cu-28Zn	1.94	−0.84	1.39
50Cu-50Zn	3.88		
95Al-5Cu	1.5	−0.69	3.7

Ionic Crystals

Salt	C_{11}	C_{12}	C_{44}
NaCl	2.27	−0.476	7.89
KBr	3.17	−0.462	16.1

CHAPTER VI

THE PLASTIC PROPERTIES OF SINGLE CRYSTALS[1]

17. The Stress-Strain Curve.[2]—If sufficiently large stresses are applied to any crystal, it remains at least partly deformed when the stresses are removed. Such a relation between stress and strain evidently cannot be described by Hooke's law. The material is said to be plastically deformed under these conditions.

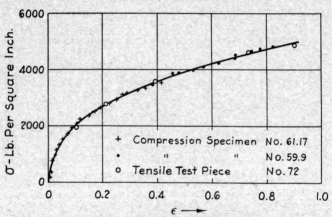

Fig. 44.—The stress-strain curve of a single crystal of aluminum. In this figure (see text) the abscissa is the shearing strain in the plane of easy slip and the ordinate is the shearing stress in the same plane. (*After G. I. Taylor.*)

In the present chapter we shall discuss some of the properties of single crystals during the course of plastic deformation.

If a pure single crystal of one of the cubic metals, such as copper or aluminum, is submitted to a gradually increasing stress,

---

[1] Extensive summaries of the plastic properties of crystals are to be found in the following books: C. F. ELAM, *The Distortion of Metal Crystals* (Oxford University Press, New York, 1936); E. SCHMID and W. BOAS, *Kristallplastizität* (Verlag Julius Springer, Berlin, 1936); A. NADAI, *Plasticity* (McGraw-Hill Book Company, Inc., New York, 1931).

[2] Unless the contrary is stated, "stress" will be used to mean true stress, that is, the force per unit of actual area.

the elongation follows a curve of the type shown in Fig. 44. In the region very near the origin, that is, for low stresses, the deformation is reversible and linear and thus corresponds to Hooke's law. As soon as the stress exceeds a certain value, which is to some extent dependent upon the sensitivity of the measuring instrument, part of the elongation is permanent. The most common mode of deformation of this type is the process known as *slip*, which is characterized by the displacement of one part of

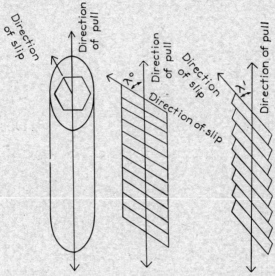

Fig. 45.—Schematic appearance of a crystal in which slip has occurred. Blocks of the material are displaced relative to one another along the slip planes giving rise to slip bands on the surface of the specimen. (*After Elam.*)

the crystal relative to another along particular crystallographic planes. These planes may be detected by the presence of step-wise discontinuities on the surface of the specimen that are known as *slip bands*. In many cases, these bands run continuously around the crystal, their spacing and orientation depending greatly on the conditions under which the plastic flow is carried out. Careful experiments[1] on lead and brass have shown that the slip bands are randomly spaced, the mean separation being of the order of 1 micron.

[1] N. DA C. ANDRADE and R. ROSCOE, *Proc. Phys. Soc.*, **49**, 152 (1937); R. G. TREUTING and R. M. BRICK, *Trans. A.I.M.E.*, **147**, 128 (1942).

The form of the slip bands is usually simplest in hexagonal crystals such as zinc and magnesium in which the slip planes are the parallel set normal to the hexagonal axis. The appearance of the slip bands in such crystals is shown schematically in Fig. 45. The pattern of the bands is usually not so simple in cubic crystals since they contain sets of symmetrically equivalent planes that make angles with one another [for example, the four sets of (111) planes in face-centered cubic crystals].

Let us return to the discussion of the stress-strain curve and consider its form when the stress is temporarily relieved during the elongation of an ideal specimen. Suppose that we start with a virgin specimen and deform it to the point A in Fig. 46. When

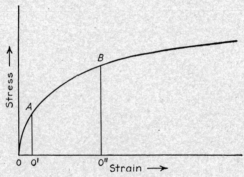

Fig. 46.—Stress-strain relations in a crystal during intermittent plastic flow.

the stress is released, the specimen contracts to O' along a line and satisfies Hooke's law during the contraction. The slope of the line AO' is practically the same as that of the line in the region near the origin where Hooke's law is satisfied. If the specimen is reloaded, the stress-strain curve follows the line AO' almost to the point A and then bends to the right again in the manner shown. If the specimen is unloaded again before the stress-strain curve deviates from the line AO', the system returns to O' along the line AO'. Thus in the vicinity of the point O' the specimen behaves in much the way that it did about the origin. The principal difference is that the previous plastic flow has extended the range of stress and strain in which Hooke's law is valid. This phenomenon is known as *work-hardening*. The process may be repeated by deforming the specimen to the point B and again releasing the stress. In this case the system contracts in accordance with Hooke's law to O'' and behaves elastically over a much wider range of stress than when it was in the condition corresponding to point O'. The slope of the line BO'' is essentially equal to that of AO'.

The foregoing process cannot be continued indefinitely if the specimen is deformed by tension, for stretching is invariably terminated by rupture when carried sufficiently far. On the other hand, it is possible to compress a specimen between parallel plates almost indefinitely if the plates are properly lubricated. Experiments[1] in compression of this type show that work-hardening does not continue indefinitely. Figure 47, for example, shows the flattening of the stress-strain curve observed in copper. It should be noted that the compression extends over a fifty-fold range in this case.

18. The Slip Process.—We remarked above that the most common mechanism of plastic flow in crystals is the slip process illustrated in Fig. 45 for the comparatively simple hexagonal crystals. In these materials, flow occurs in much the way that cards slide over one another when a deck is deformed. It might be supposed that, from the atomic viewpoint,

[1] G. I. TAYLOR and H. QUINNEY, *Proc. Roy. Soc.*, **143**, 307 (1934).

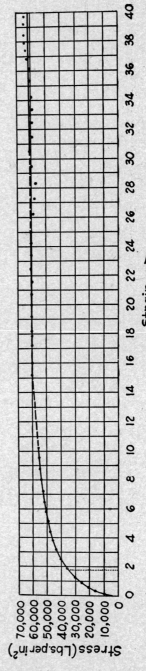

FIG. 47.—The stress-strain curve of copper obtained during extensive compressive plastic flow. It may be seen that the curve flattens for large strains, showing that work-hardening ceases.

slip occurs as the result of planes of atoms sliding past one another in a manner closely analogous to the cards. In general, the experiments support this picture; however, there is good evidence to show that the process is not quite so simple as this naïve viewpoint suggests. One of the most striking phenomena not explained on this basis is the fact that the slip bands are separated by distances of the order of magnitude 10^{-4} cm instead of 10^{-8} cm, which is the distance between neighboring atomic planes. In this connection it is interesting to note that careful measurements by Andrade and Roscoe[1] on the spacing of slip bands in lead show that the distance of spacing is random in this metal, one average value being 4 microns. We shall survey the most promising theory of the slip process in a later section in this chapter.

The slip process in crystals other than hexagonal ones is more complicated only because slip may occur in several nonparallel sets of planes. Generally speaking, it is found that only one set of planes operates at any given time during a deformation; however, different sets may operate at different stages of the deformation process.

The law governing the relation between slip and applied stress is a very simple one. For any given specimen, slip occurs along a given crystallographic plane when the component of shearing stress in that plane reaches a critical value, which is greatly dependent upon the previous history of the specimen and which also depends upon the rate of loading, as we shall see below. It should be noted that the normal stress on the plane does not play a role in determining slip in single crystals. It is probably true that there is a critical shearing stress for each plane in the crystal and that slip occurs in practice only in the observed slip planes because the shearing stress invariably reaches the critical value in the latter first. Since the stress in a given plane depends upon the orientation of this plane, it follows that the geometrical arrangement of the crystal specimen relative to the applied stresses is an important factor in determining which planes actually will slip.

The planes of easiest slip and the lowest observed values of the critical shearing stress of these planes are given in Table VIII.

[1] ANDRADE and ROSCOE, *op. cit.*

TABLE VIII.—DATA CONCERNING SLIP IN SOLIDS
Pure Metals

Metal	Impurity content	Slip plane	Direction	Critical stress kg/mm²
Cu	0.001	(111)	(10$\bar{1}$)	0.10
Ag	0.0001	(111)	(10$\bar{1}$)	0.060
Au	0.0001	(111)	(10$\bar{1}$)	0.092
Ni	0.002	(111)	(10$\bar{1}$)	0.58
Mg	0.0005	(001)	(100)	0.083
Zn	0.0004	(001)	(100)	0.094
Cd	0.00004	(001)	(100)	0.058
	......	(100)	......	<0.03
Na	......	(110)		
	......	(112)	(111)	
	......	(123)		
Mo	......	(112)	(111)	
	......	(110)		
K	......	(123)	(111)	
W	......	(112)	(111)	
Fe	......	(110)		
	......	(112)		
	......	(123)		
	......	(100)	(001)	0.19
β Sn	0.0001	(110)	(001)	0.13
	......	(101)	(10$\bar{1}$)	0.16
	......	(121)	(10$\bar{1}$)	0.17
Bi	~0.001	(111)	(10$\bar{1}$)	0.221
Hg	~10^{-8}	Complex	......	0.007

Composition	Slip plane	Slip direction	Critical stress, kg/mm²
	Alloys		
99.4Zn0.6Cd	(001)	(1$\bar{2}$0)	2.7
6.8Al93.2Mg	(001)	(1$\bar{2}$0)	1.4
85Al15Zn	(111)	(10$\bar{1}$)	8
72Cu28Zn	(111)	(10$\bar{1}$)	1.5
AuCu₃ (ordered)	......	......	2.2
AuCu₃ (disordered)	......	......	4.4
	Ionic Crystals		
NaCl	(110)	(1$\bar{1}$0)	~0.2
AgCl	(110)	(1$\bar{1}$0)	~0.1
KCl			
KBr	(110)	(1$\bar{1}$0)	
KI			
RbCl			

The directions in which slip occurs in the easiest planes are also given. It is interesting to note that the octahedral and basal planes, which are those having closest atomic packing, are the easiest planes of slip in face-centered cubic and hexagonal close-packed lattices. In general, metals having body-centered cubic

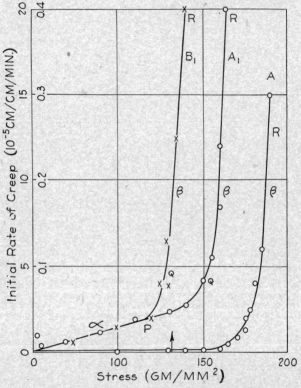

FIG. 48.—The rate of plastic flow in a single crystal of tin as a function of stress. The strain rate is expressed in units of 10^{-5} sec^{-1}. The stress is the resolved component of shear in the slip plane. Note the two ordinate scales. Curves *A* and *B* are for different specimens.

lattices possess at least two types of planes of easiest slip. These are usually not only the planes of highest atomic density but also planes having nearly equal atomic density.

It is worth emphasizing that the values of the critical shearing stress not only are greatly dependent upon the purity and annealing condition of the specimen but also are dependent upon the lowest strain rate which the apparatus is capable of measuring. The values given in the table were determined in almost all cases with a machine capable of measuring a strain rate of about 10^{-6} per sec. That is, 1 cm of the specimen elongates by 10^{-6} cm in 1 sec. When this machine was used, the strain was immeasurably small for stresses below the critical values. More careful measurements indicate that a small and gradual plastic flow occurs in single crystals of metals at arbitrarily small values of the stress. However, the same work indicates that there is a rather sharply defined value of the stress at which this flow rapidly increases. Figure 48 shows, for example, the rate of plastic flow in very pure tin as a function of stress, when measured[1] with an apparatus having about a hundred times the sensitivity of that for which the values in Table VIII were obtained. It may be seen that the stress for tin given in Table VIII corresponds very closely to the value at which the rate increases very rapidly. It was found that the flow continued for a much longer time for values of the stress above the critical value than for values below it, which indicates that this stress has absolute meaning.

It follows from the facts discussed in connection with Fig. 46 that the critical shearing stress increases with the degree of cold-work. It is also found that the presence of impurity or alloying elements raises the critical shearing stress, particularly when such elements are dissolved in the lattice. Figure 49 shows, for example, the influence on the critical shearing stress of annealed zinc, of cadmium, and of tin. It may be seen that the first agent, which is soluble to the extent of about 1.5 percent, is much more effective in raising the shearing stress than the second, which is soluble to the extent of only about 0.1 percent. This indicates that the hardening effect is to be associated with changes in the interior of the crystal lattice and not merely with changes induced in the surface or at block boundaries.

It is natural to ask how slip in one set of crystallographic planes affects the critical shearing stress for crystallographically equivalent planes. Planes of the latter type are said to be *latent* slip planes if slip is not actually occurring on them. The most

[1] B. CHALMERS, *Proc. Roy. Soc.*, **156,** 427 (1936); *J. Inst. Metals*, **61,** 103 (1937).

reliable evidence[1] on single crystals of pure metals indicates that the latent planes harden at the same rate as the actual slip planes. In other words, if slip occurs first in one set of planes and then in an equivalent set, the critical shearing stress for the second at the instant slip begins in them has the same value as for the planes in which slip has just ceased. There is evidence, which we shall

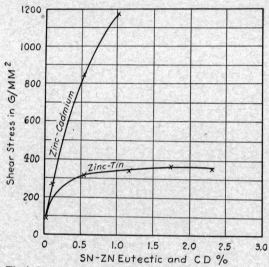

Fig. 49.—The influence of soluble and insoluble impurities on the critical shearing stress of zinc. The upper curve shows the increase of shearing stress for varying concentration of cadmium, which is soluble for the range of composition shown, whereas the lower curve shows the influence of tin, which is soluble to the extent of 0.1 percent. (*After Schmid and Rosbaud.*)

discuss later, to show that, in brass, latent slip planes harden more rapidly than the actual slip planes.

19. The Change in Energy and the Distortion Accompanying Cold-work.—Since cold-work hardens metals, it is natural to expect that the associated change would be accompanied by a change in energy of the material. A change of this type has, in fact, been measured by a number of workers, notably Taylor and his associates,[2] who studied the difference between the work done

---

[1] Elam, *op. cit.;* Schmid and Boas, *op. cit.*

[2] G. I. Taylor and H. Quinney, *Proc. Roy. Soc.*, **143**, 307 (1934); **163**, 157 (1937). Earlier work of lower accuracy was carried out by G. I. Taylor and W. Farren, *Proc. Roy. Soc.*, **107**, 422 (1925).

on a specimen during cold-work and the amount of heat evolved. They found that the latter is always less than the former, a fact which shows that a part of the energy of cold-work is stored within the material. Figure 50 shows the ratio of the stored energy to the total work done on copper during cold-work. It may be seen that this is constant for the early stages of the process, which illustrates the fact that the amount of energy stored is proportional to the amount of working in this range. The decrease in the ratio for values of strain greater than 1.2

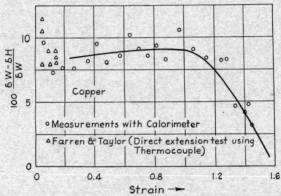

Fig. 50.—The ratio of the stored energy to the total work done during the cold-working of copper. The triangles refer to tension tests and the circles to torsion tests. The falling portion of the curve indicates that the stored energy approaches a saturation value. (*After Taylor and Quinney.*)

shows that the stored energy eventually approaches a constant value. It is not unlikely that work-hardening ceases when this stage is reached, for, as Fig. 47 illustrates, the stress-strain curve flattens during extensive plastic flow. Table IX lists the maximum value of the stored energy during the cold-working of several metals.

TABLE IX.—VALUES OF THE MAXIMUM ENERGY STORED DURING WORK-HARDENING

(The values are expressed in units of calories per gram.)

Aluminum	1.1
Copper	0.5
Iron	1.2
Nickel	0.78
Brass	0.49

These energies are sufficient to warm the materials by several degrees if released in the form of heat.   There are two conceivable ways in which this energy may be stored, namely, in the form of residual strains on a scale of the order of 1 micron or larger, which we shall call a macroscopic scale for present purposes, or in the form of distortion on an atomic scale.   Measurements[1] of the distortion in the X-ray diffraction patterns of cold-worked materials provide a method for determining the fraction of energy stored in either of these ways.   In the first place, large-scale distortion causes a broadening of the diffraction lines, for the distorted regions behave as if they possessed a lattice constant different from that of the undistorted ones.   Careful work shows that the observed distortion of this type is sufficient to account for only about $\frac{1}{10}$ percent of the energy stored during cold-work. In the second place, the distortion on an atomic scale causes incoherent scattering, which dissipates the intensity of the incident and diffracted beams and thereby decreases the efficiency of the diffraction process.   Measurements of this effect show that such distortion can account for practically all the stored energy.

It must not be supposed that cold-work does not appreciably deform the X-ray diffraction pictures of crystals.   The effect is, in fact, a relatively large one, even though the associated distortional energy is small.   One of the common methods of exhibiting the distortion is to take a Laue photograph by sending a beam of continuous radiation through the crystal (cf. Chap. I).   It is found that the spots observed in an unstrained crystal become deformed into streaks extending radially from the central beam (Fig. 7, page 10).   This streaking is known as asterism.

There has been considerable speculative research on the nature of the distortion giving rise to asterism.   Two viewpoints are held at the present time.   According to the older of these, the distortion is pictured as a rotation of submicroscopic blocks of the crystal about an axis lying in the slip plane and normal to the slip direction.   The dimensions of the blocks involved in the "rolling" motion have not been specified exactly in this picture,

---

[1] W. Boas, Z. Kryst., **96**, 214 (1937), **97**, 354 (1937); G. R. Stibitz, Phys. Rev., **52**, 619 (1937); F. E. Haworth, Phys. Rev., **52**, 613 (1937); G. W. Brindley and P. Ridley, Proc. Roy. Soc., **50**, 501 (1938); U. Dehlinger and A. Kochendörfer, Z. Metallkunde, **31**, 231 (1939).

but they must contain many thousands of atoms, for otherwise the distortion would produce incoherent scattering, as does the distortion responsible for the stored energy of cold-work. Andrade[1] and his coworkers have carried out a large amount of research in support of this viewpoint. The alternative picture, first proposed by Barrett and Levenson,[2] is based on the observation that regions of a crystal observable to the eye become tilted relative to one another during the slip process. Neighboring regions of this type are found to be separated by a sharply defined line of demarcation, which is called a *deformation band*. Barrett has suggested that this kind of distortion is responsible for asterism. It is evident that these two pictures would be identical if the rolled blocks of the first could be identified with the units separated by deformation bands in Barrett's picture. The evidence bearing on this point is not yet sufficiently clear to settle the question, however.

20. Recrystallization and Resoftening.—The application of heat serves to reverse the effects of cold-work through two processes, which we shall term *recrystallization* and *resoftening*. (Resoftening is also commonly called *recovery*.) The first, discussed in Chap. IV, is accompanied by a complete change in the crystalline texture of the material. It follows the normal procedure of a phase change in that it begins by formation of nuclei, which subsequently grow to new crystals. As we saw previously, the resulting texture is determined by the rate of nucleation and the rate of growth, which, in turn, depend upon the amount of cold-work, the temperature to which the specimen has been raised, the original grain size, and the purity of the material.[3] Presumably the energy stored during cold-work furnishes the driving force for the reaction, and the most highly worked regions produce the nuclei as the result of thermal fluctuations.

As was remarked in Sec. 14, the process of recrystallization can be viewed as if it were a transition from a thermodynamically

---

[1] See, for example, E. N. DAC. ANDRADE, *Proc. Phys. Soc.*, **52** (1940).

[2] C. S. BARRETT and L. H. LEVENSON, *Trans. A.I.M.E.*, **135**, 327 (1939). Deformation bands were apparently first observed by Pfeil, *Iron Steel Inst.* (*London*), *Carnegie Schol. Mem.*, **16,** 153 (1927).

[3] See the survey by R. F. Mehl in the *A.S.M. Handbook* (1939).

unstable phase to a stable one. Evidently the cold-worked metal is unstable relative to the unworked metal at all temperatures, so that the transition should take place at a finite rate at any temperature above absolute zero. However, since the process requires nucleation and growth of nuclei and therefore requires thermal fluctuations (see Sec. 14), the rate of recrystallization will be extremely slow at very low temperatures. The lowest temperature at which recrystallization can occur in a readily measured time under the normal conditions of cold-work employed in commercial fabrication is called the *recrystallization temperature*. Typical values[1] of this temperature are given in Table X. It is to be emphasized that these values are *greatly* dependent upon the previous history of the particular specimens on which the measurements were made and that the numbers in the table are not to be regarded as invariants in the same sense as are the melting and boiling points of metals. The principal factors upon which the recrystallization temperature depends are the degree of cold-work and the length of time the specimen is held at temperature.

TABLE X.—RECRYSTALLIZATION TEMPERATURES OF SEVERAL METALS
(In deg C)

Aluminum	150	Nickel	620
Cadmium	50	Platinum	450
Copper	200	Silver	200
Gold	200	Tantalum	1020
Iron	450	Tin	0
Lead	0	Tungsten	1210
Magnesium	150	Zinc	15

It may be seen that tin, zinc, and lead recrystallize at room temperature. It should be added that higher temperatures are required to produce recrystallization in slightly worked single crystals.

Resoftening is the process by which the effects of cold-work are partly or fully removed by temperature without recrystallization. It is found to occur most rapidly at temperatures just below the recrystallization temperatures given in Table X and to decrease rapidly with decreasing temperature. Figure 51

[1] R. S. ARCHER, *A.S.M. Handbook* (1939), 198.

shows[1] the progress of the resoftening process in a single crystal of zinc. In the case corresponding to Fig. 51*a* the specimen was given a succession of 50 percent extensions, after each of which the load was removed for a "rest period" of about one minute. In the second case, the extensions were identical, but the rest period was a day. It may be seen that the first rest period was not sufficiently long for very extensive resoftening to occur, whereas resoftening was almost complete after the second.

It is reasonable to suppose that the tendencies toward both resoftening and recrystallization occur at all temperatures and

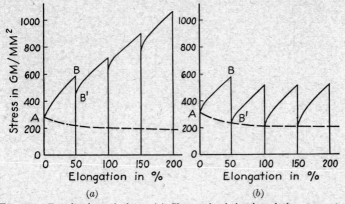

Fig. 51.—Resoftening of zinc. (*a*) Shows the behavior of the stress-strain curve when the crystal is unloaded for about 1 minute during plastic flow and indicates that negligible resoftening occurs during the rest period. (*b*) Shows the behavior when the period of rest is increased to a day. In this case the resoftening is nearly complete. (*After Haase and Schmid.*)

that the rates of both processes increase with increasing temperature. Resoftening is the more rapid process below the recrystallization temperature, whereas recrystallization is more rapid above it.

21. The Influence of Temperature on the Critical Shearing Stress.—The influence of temperature on the critical shearing stress of well-annealed single crystals has been studied[2] for zinc and cadmium for a wide range of temperature. The result is shown in Fig. 52 for the range extending from values close to absolute zero to about 300°C. It may be seen that there is a gradual drop in the curve as the temperature is increased.

[1] O. HAASE and E. SCHMID, *Z. Physik*, **33**, 416 (1925).
[2] W. BOAS and E. SCHMID, *Z. Physik*, **61**, 767 (1930); **64**, 845 (1930).

The actual form of the stress-strain curves of zinc at various temperatures is shown in Fig. 53.   It should be noted that these

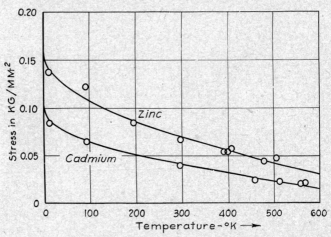

Fig. 52.—The critical shearing stress of single crystals of zinc and cadmium as functions of temperature.

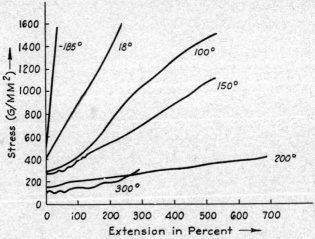

Fig. 53.—The stress-strain curves of zinc at various temperatures.

curves vary approximately linearly with stress rather than in the parabolic manner of cubic crystals (Fig. 44).   This type of linear behavior is characteristic of hexagonal crystals.   Figur

54 shows the variation with temperature of the slope of these curves near the stress axis for the case of cadmium.

The change of the stress-strain curves of aluminum[1] with temperature is shown in Fig. 55.

22. Hypothetical Mechanism of the Slip Process.—We are now in a position to consider the slip process from an atomic viewpoint. The simplest hypothesis for explaining slip is to suppose that parallel planes of atoms in the crystal behave like cards in a deck and slide past one another as rigid units in the manner suggested in Fig. 45. There are two major flaws in this

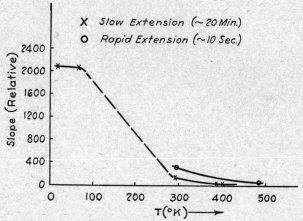

Fig. 54.—The variation of the initial slope of the stress-strain curves of cadmium with temperature.

picture. In the first place, we have seen that the major part of the distortion produced by cold-work occurs on an atomic scale rather than on the scale which would result if large areas of planes behaved rigidly and moved as units. In the second place, it may easily be shown that the shearing stresses required to cause planes to move bodily past one another are far larger than the critical shearing stresses actually observed in well-annealed single crystals of pure metals. We shall consider this point in detail.

Let us consider two neighboring atomic planes. It is clear that if one plane is pushed past the other by one atomic spacing

[1] W. BOAS and E. SCHMID, *Z. Physik*, **71**, 703 (1931).

the over-all relative position of atoms does not change because of the periodicity of the atomic arrangement in the direction of motion. The atoms in each plane are subject to two types of force, namely, the forces exerted by atoms in the same plane and those exerted by atoms in the neighboring plane that moves relative to it. The former remain approximately fixed if the planes move rigidly, for the interatomic spacing in the direction of the planes does not alter during the motion. On the other

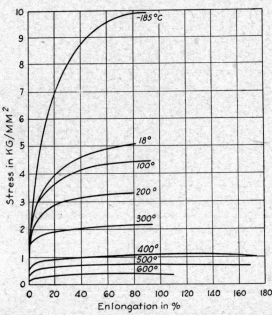

FIG. 55.—The dependence of the stress-strain curves of aluminum on temperature.

hand, the force between planes does change and varies in the manner represented schematically in Fig. 56. The force is zero at the equilibrium position and is such as to oppose the displacement until the planes have been pushed halfway from one equilibrium spacing to the next. At this point it reverses sign and then assists the two planes in moving to the next equilibrium spacing, in which the planes are displaced by one atomic distance. This variation in force may also be considered conveniently from the standpoint of energy.

The energy of the system is a minimum when the planes are at their normal positions. It reaches a maximum when the planes have been pushed past one another by one-half an atomic spacing and then drops again to the equilibrium value when the displacement is one atomic distance. This variation repeats itself indefinitely as the displacement is increased by successive interatomic distances.

We are interested in the maximum shearing stress required to cause a unit displacement and may estimate this in the following way: In the linear range of the force versus distance curve shown in the figure, which is valid for small displacements from the

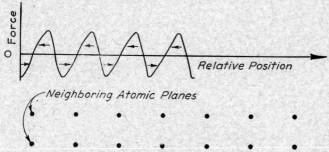

FIG. 56.—Schematic representation of the forces between two atomic planes when they are displaced relative to one another.

equilibrium position, the relation between stress and strain corresponds to Hooke's law and satisfies the equation

$$S_s = c_s e_s.$$

Here S_s and e_s are the shearing stress and strain and c_s is the corresponding elastic constant, which is of the order of magnitude 10^{11} dynes per cm^2 (about 10^6 lb per in.^{2}). We shall consider the case of zinc in detail for illustrative purposes. The value of c_s for this metal is $3.5 \cdot 10^{11}$ dynes per cm^2 ($5.3 \cdot 10^6$ lb per in.^{2}). If we assume that Hooke's law is valid for a relative interatomic displacement of about one-tenth the displacement from one equilibrium position to the next, the shearing strain at the point where the displacement is a tenth is 0.1, for this strain is just the ratio of the relative displacement of the planes divided by the spacing between planes. Thus, at the corresponding point, the shearing stress is about $3.5 \cdot 10^{10}$ dynes per cm^2, which is at least a thousand times larger than the observed critical shearing stress (see Table VIII).

Actually, our estimate of the maximum shearing stress occurring during the relative displacement of the two planes is conservative, for we have determined the stress only at the point where the force versus distance curve ceases to be linear, and not at the maximum. Moreover, the restriction of the actual calculation to zinc is not an important limitation, for the shearing constant c_s is the same to within a factor ten for almost all metals and would in each case lead to a value of S_s of about 10^{10} dynes per cm^2 or larger.

We may conclude with certainty that the slip process does not consist of the rigid motion of atomic planes relative to one another. Moreover, we may be sure that the actual process involves lattice distortion or imperfection on an atomic scale.

The most promising alternative mechanism for the slip process that has been suggested[1] up to the present time is based on the assumption that slip occurs as a result of the motion of a linear type of lattice imperfection known as a *dislocation* which is shown in cross section in Fig. 57. We shall leave the question of the production of such imperfections open until later and shall consider their properties at the moment. Other types of lattice imperfections were used in earlier work; however, the theory based on dislocations has made more noteworthy progress.

It is assumed that the dislocation extends indefinitely in the slip plane in a direction normal to the slip direction. Figure 57 represents a cross section of the crystal in a plane normal to the length of the dislocation. This plane contains the normal to the slip plane (vertical direction) and the slip direction AB. The distortion is assumed to be the same in each of the atomic planes parallel to the one shown. It may be observed that the section

---

[1] This theory may be regarded as the combined work of several investigators. The basic papers that deal with it are as follows: L. PRANDTL, *Z. angew. Math. Mech.*, **8**, 85 (1928); U. DEHLINGER, *Ann. Physik*, **2**, 749 (1929); E. OROWAN, *Z. Physik*, **89**, 634 (1934); M. POLANYI, *Z. Physik*, **89**, 660 (1934); G. I. TAYLOR, *Proc. Roy. Soc.*, **145**, 362 (1934); F. SEITZ and T. A. READ, *J. Applied Phys.*, **12**, 100, 170, 470, 538 (1941); J. S. KOEHLER, *Phys. Rev.* **60**, 397 (1941). Earlier theories are reviewed in the book by Z. Jeffries and R. S. Archer, *The Science of Metals* (McGraw-Hill Book Company, Inc., New York, 1924).

of the crystal above the slip plane contains one more vertical atomic plane than that below it. The vertical planes above and below the plane are in step at large distances to the left and right of the center of the diagram, but become increasingly more out of step toward the center of the diagram. We shall call the point at the center of the imperfection, where the vertical planes are just one-half an atomic spacing out of step, the *center of the dislocation*. It is clear that the region of the crystal above the center of the dislocation is under sidewise compression, whereas the region below the center is under tension.

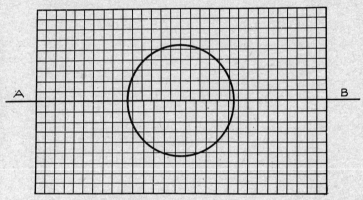

Fig. 57.—A schematic picture of a dislocation of the type considered in the theory of slip. Within a circular region there is one more atom in the line of cells above *AB* than in the line below it. (*After Orowan.*)

Figure 58 shows what occurs when a dislocation is produced at one side of a crystal and moves across a slip plane. It may be seen that the end result is the displacement of the part of the crystal above the slip plane relative to that below by one atomic distance. The lower group of pictures (Figs. 58d, e, and f) shows that the same end result may be produced by forming a dislocation on the opposite side and moving it in the opposite direction. The second dislocation differs from the first in that the tension is above the slip plane rather than below it. To distinguish between the two, the first dislocation is said to be "positive" and the second "negative."

Thus we see that the phenomenon of slip may be explained on the assumption that dislocations are produced in the crystal and move in the slip planes in the manner shown in Fig. 58.

It is evident that the low values of the observed critical shearing stress can be explained on this basis only if it can be shown that the force required to move a dislocation from one equilibrium position to the next, that is, to move the center of the dislocation one atomic distance in the slip direction, is much smaller than the force required to move two planes rigidly past one another.

Actually, it is easy to demonstrate this fact. Let us consider the forces between two neighboring parallel planes, first when no dislocation is present (Fig. 59a) and second when a dislocation

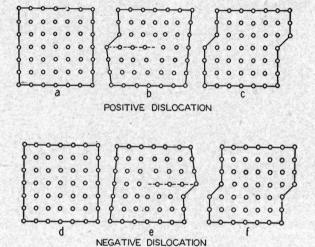

POSITIVE DISLOCATION

NEGATIVE DISLOCATION

Fig. 58.—The strain produced in a crystal when dislocations pass along its atomic planes. In the upper set of pictures a positive dislocation moves from left to right, whereas in the lower one a negative dislocation moves from right to left. (*After Taylor.*)

is present (Fig. 59b). For simplicity, we shall assume that the upper planes are the same in the two cases. The uppermost curve in Fig. 59 illustrates schematically the energy of an atom in the lower plane as a function of its position relative to the upper plane. It may be seen that in the normal arrangement (Fig. 59a) all the atoms in the lower plane are at positions corresponding to minima of this curve. Thus, if these atoms are displaced simultaneously in the same direction, they encounter equal forces opposing the displacement. In the case shown in the lower figure, in which a dislocation occurs, the atoms at large distances from the center of the dislocation are at positions corresponding to minima of the energy curve; however, the atoms near the center are not. It may be seen that pairs of symmetrically disposed atoms on opposite sides of the center of the dislocation encounter forces arising from the upper plane which are equal and opposite. As a consequence, if the atoms near the center of the dislocation are displaced by equal distances, one half encounter opposing forces whereas the other half encounter assisting forces, and the net work required to produce the displacement is zero in first approximation. It follows that the stress required to move the dislocation an atomic distance is very small com-

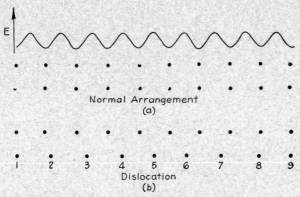

FIG. 59.—Schematic representation of the fact that a dislocation moves easily. The upper curve represents the potential energy of an atom in a given plane arising from the atoms in the plane above it (see text).

pared with the stress required to move planes bodily. The actual magnitude of the ratio of the two stresses is very difficult to compute but has been estimated[1] to be of the order of 10^{-6} for an ideal crystal. It is to be hoped that more accurate estimates will be available in the future; however, at present it seems beyond reasonable doubt that there is no outstanding discrepancy between the stresses required to move dislocations and those required to cause slip in actual crystals.

It is clear that a crystal containing a dislocation possesses a higher energy than one which does not because of the distortion associated with the dislocation. As a result, we may attempt to identify the energy stored during cold-work with the energy

[1] R. PEIERLS, *Proc. Phys. Soc.*, **52**, 34 (1940).

required to produce dislocations. Estimates based on atomic theory show[1] that the energy stored in a dislocation 1 cm long should be of the order of magnitude of 10^{-5} erg. From this estimate and the data of Table IX, it follows that the number of dislocation lines cutting across 1 cm^2 of a highly cold-worked metal is about 10^{12}. We shall see below that this value may be obtained from independent estimates.

Since the energy stored during cold-work increases with increasing strain during the early stages of deformation, it follows, from our picture, that the density of dislocations must increase at

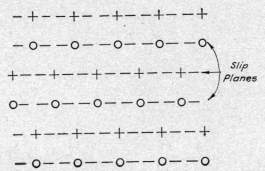

Fig. 60.—A stable array of dislocations. The negative dislocations are indicated by circles, the slip planes by dashes.

the same time. G. I. Taylor,[2] one of the founders of the dislocation theory, suggested that the interference of dislocations with one another as their number increases is responsible for the phenomenon of work-hardening. He pointed out that dislocations exert comparatively strong forces on one another as a result of the distortion they produce in the lattice. These forces vary inversely as the first power of the distance between the dislocations, are attractive for dislocations of opposite sign, and are repulsive for dislocations of the same sign. In these respects they resemble closely the electrostatic forces between charged rods. Taylor suggested that both types of dislocation are produced in equal number and that the two types arrange themselves into a stable latticelike array, such as that shown in Fig. 60. Since the density of dislocations increases with increasing

[1] J. S. Koehler, *Phys. Rev.*, **60**, 397 (1941).

[2] Taylor, *op. cit.*

cold-work, it follows that the force exerted on a dislocation by other dislocations increases and that, as a result, the stress required to cause the dislocation to move should increase.

Taylor also assumed that dislocations are generated at the imperfections associated with mosaic structure, which are presumably separated by a distance of the order of 1 micron, and move an average distance λ comparable with the separation before becoming stuck as a result of the interaction with other dislocations. Moreover, he assumed that the spacing of dislocations is the same in the slip direction and in the direction normal to the slip plane. From this assumption, it follows readily that the total shear strain e_s is related to the density of dislocations by the equation

$$e_s = ca\lambda N. \tag{1}$$

Here c is a numerical constant of the order unity, the precise value of which depends upon the form of the dislocation lattice, a is the distance by which two planes are displaced when a dislocation moves across one, and N is the number of dislocation lines per unit area. It may be noted that the spacing between dislocations varies as $1/N$ as their density increases. Since the force between dislocations varies inversely as the first power of this spacing, it follows that the stress required to make dislocations move varies as $\sqrt{N}$. If the proper proportionality factor is determined and the resulting equation is used to eliminate N in Eq. (1), the resulting relation between stress and strain is

$$S = kG(ae_s\lambda)^{\frac{1}{2}} \tag{2}$$

in which k is a constant of the order unity that is closely related to c in Eq. (1) and G is the shear modulus of the crystal.

All the constants appearing in Eq. (2) are known accurately except λ, which, according to Taylor's assumption, should be of the order of 1 micron. Figure 61 shows the degree of accuracy with which the parabolic type of stress-strain curve of cubic crystals may be fitted with the relation (2). The experimental curve is for aluminum, and the value of λ required to give the fit shown is $5.3 \cdot 10^{-4}$ cm. Thus Taylor's picture appears to work very well in these materials.

It follows readily from Eq. (1) that the density of dislocations introduced as a result of a strain of ten is about 10^{12} per cm^2. It has proved possible to determine the energy per unit volume stored in lattices of dislocations of the type shown in Fig. 60. On the basis of such calculations and the experimental data given in Table IX, Koehler[1] has found that the separation of dislocations in the most highly worked state of the metals is about thirty atom distances. The corresponding density of lines of dislocation agrees closely with the value derived from Eq. (1).

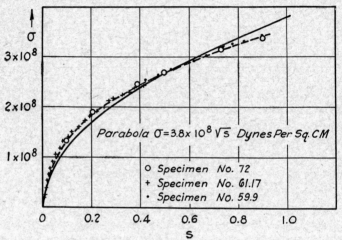

Fig. 61.—Comparison of the observed stress-strain curve of aluminum with that obtained from Taylor's theory for $\lambda = 5.3 \cdot 10^{-4}$ cm.

The fact that the stress-strain curves for hexagonal crystals are linear instead of parabolic (Fig. 53) does not contradict the basic qualitative assumptions of Taylor's theory, for a very simple modification of the steps leading to Eq. (2) produces a linear relation. In deriving (2) it is assumed that the spacing between dislocations in the slip direction is the same as in the normal direction. It turns out that the parabolic relation (2) is closely connected with this assumption and that linear curves would have been obtained if the spacing in the direction normal to the slip plane were taken as constant. At the present time there is no a priori basis on which to decide which of the two assumptions is better in a given case, so that we must base our judgment on

[1] Koehler, *Phys. Rev.*, **60**, 397 (1941).

the form of the observed curves. This is, of course, an inherent weakness in Taylor's picture of work-hardening; however, it must be admitted that the theory does a good job of interpreting work-hardening on the basis of a few well-defined and unambiguous assumptions which will eventually be tested experimentally.

The basic principles involved in Taylor's theory are more general than the particular application given above, as was pointed out by Mott.[1] Let us assume that at any point in a crystal there is a residual shearing stress S in the slip plane. This may result from a near-by dislocation, as in the case considered above, from an impurity atom, which expands or contracts the lattice in a given region, or from any other type of lattice imperfection that distorts the crystal. If external forces are applied to the crystal, the stresses resulting from these forces add to those already present. Now let us suppose that a dislocation has reached the region where the residual stresses occur and is moving in such a direction that it is opposed by these stresses. Unless the applied forces have the proper sign and direction at least to neutralize the residual stresses, the dislocation becomes stuck. It is obvious that if the residual stresses are directed in such a way as to aid the dislocation in moving they may assist it even when the external forces are released. However, in many of the cases that occur in practice, residual stresses of both signs appear in closely neighboring regions and external stress must be applied to make dislocations move continuously.

We may conclude from this discussion that residual stresses which alternate in sign over distances of the order of magnitude of those in which dislocations move, namely, 10^{-4} cm, should have a hardening effect. Among such stresses are included the residual stresses produced by neighboring dislocations, dissolved impurity atoms, or clumps of misfit atoms, the linear dimensions of which are 1 micron or less in size. On the other hand, residual stresses that alternate in sign only over distances much larger than 1 micron, such as those produced during large-scale punching or drawing operations, should aid plastic flow of one sign and inhibit that of the opposite sign.

It is interesting to consider further Taylor's assumption that dislocations are produced only at "weak spots" in the crystal.

[1] N. F. Mott, *Proc. Roy. Soc.*, **175**, 519 (1940).

Later in the section, we shall give additional reasons why this hypothesis is inescapable. It may be remarked now, however, that this hypothesis suggests a rudimentary explanation of the fact that slip bands are separated by distances of the order of 1 micron rather than of the order of an atomic distance. It is possible that the observed slip bands are planar regions in which many weak spots occur simultaneously and hence in which many dislocations are produced during strain. It is not clear, of course, just why such a confluence of weak spots should exist, and it is very likely that the solution of this problem must await a better understanding of the mosaic structure of crystals.

Up to this point, the discussion has dealt with the manner in which dislocations move. Let us now consider the probable mechanism by which dislocations are produced. The stresses required to form a dislocation in a region where a crystal is perfect can be shown to be comparable with those required to push atomic planes directly past one another, namely, about 10^{10} dynes per cm^2 or larger. As a result, we must conclude that the process of formation is assisted by a type of lattice imperfection. There are two reasonable possibilities:

1. It is possible that temperature fluctuations play an important role in the process. At any temperature above absolute zero, atoms undergo thermal oscillations, and this vibration obviously is accompanied by local variations in stress. It is conceivable that these stresses might occasionally attain sufficient magnitude to produce a dislocation. Close examination of the problem, however, shows that at normal temperatures the fluctuations are not sufficiently large to produce a dislocation which extends for more than a few atom distances, so that this mechanism alone cannot be responsible.

2. It is possible that local variations in stress occur as a result of cracks already present in the lattice and that in localized regions the stresses may be as much as a thousand times higher than the average stress at particular spots in the crystal. The basis for this possibility is illustrated in Fig. 62. If a tensile specimen contains an elliptical crack of the type shown in the figure, the lines of stress avoid the open space and concentrate at the end points of the ellipse. It may be shown[1] by suitable

[1] A. A. GRIFFITH, *Trans. Roy. Soc.*, **221**, 163 (1921).

stress analysis that the ratio of the stress in these regions and the average stress is $2a/b$, where a is the major diameter of the ellipse and b is the minor diameter. Hence, if a crystal contains a long narrow crack for which a/b is of the order of 1,000, the stress at the ends of the crack is sufficient to produce dislocations when the average stress is equal to the observed critical shearing stress. At the present time, the assumption that such cracks exist in

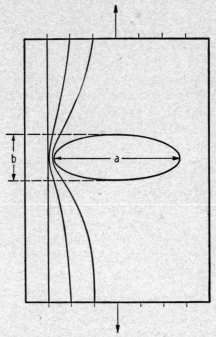

FIG. 62.—Stress concentration about a crack.

ordinary metal specimens provides the most reasonable explanation of the formation of dislocations. As will be seen later, this hypothesis also plays an important role in the theory of rupture. Since the required cracks are not observable under an ordinary microscope, it is generally supposed that their length is of the order of 1 micron and their width no more than a few atomic diameters.

Evidently one weak spot may act as the source for an unlimited number of dislocations; for, as is shown in Fig. 63, the dislocations produced by a given crack are formed in planar regions parallel to the slip planes bounding the crack and not in planes intersecting the crack. As a result, a given weak spot may be effective during an extensive range of flow.

It cannot be stated with certainty that temperature fluctuations play a significant part in the region where the stresses are large. Figure 52 shows that the critical shearing stress definitely varies with temperature and suggests that temperature fluctuations at least aid the dislocations in moving from one equilibrium position to the next. However, experiments that would permit a clean-cut analysis of the slip process into a part dealing with the production of dislocations and a part dealing with their subsequent motion have not yet been carried out. In this connection, it should be added that the dislocation picture offers two possible explanations of the fact that slip may occur more easily in one set of crystallographic planes than in another. It is possible either that the dislocations are easier to produce in the planes of easy slip or that when produced the stress required to make them move is much lower. We cannot decide between these at the present time.

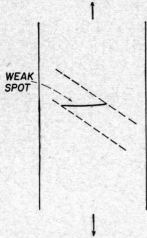

WEAK SPOT

Fig. 63.—Schematic diagram showing the relation between a crack and the slip planes produced by the dislocations generated at its edges. The dotted lines represent slip planes.

It is interesting to note that whereas single dislocations can be produced at the surface in the manner suggested in Fig. 58 it is more likely that in the interior of crystals pairs of dislocations having opposite sign are produced. This possibility was first pointed out by Orowan.[1] Figure 64 shows such a pair of dislocations. It may be noted that the deformation associated with the dislocations is appreciable only for a distance comparable with their separation because of their mutually compensating effects at larger distances. It is easy to see that the result obtained by producing such a pair in the interior of a crystal

[1] Orowan, *op. cit.*

and allowing them to move to the surfaces in opposite directions is the same as that obtained when a dislocation is produced at a surface and moves entirely across the specimen to the opposite side. As the dislocations separate, the over-all distortion of the lattice increases so that the energy of the crystal increases. This

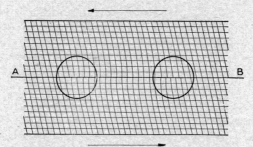

FIG. 64.—A pair of dislocations generated at the same point. They are of opposite sign and move in opposite directions.

means, on the other hand, that the members of a pair of dislocations attract each other—a result already discussed more generally in connection with Taylor's theory of work-hardening.

Since the ratio of the number of surface atoms to the number of interior atoms is very small for a specimen of ordinary size, it is natural to suppose that the majority of dislocations are produced pairwise in the volume of the material. Moreover, it is not

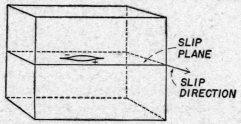

FIG. 65.—Suggested relation between a pair of dislocations and the slip plane (see text). The pair will spread and lengthen as they separate.

unreasonable to expect that at the start they are comparatively short and elongate in the manner suggested in Fig. 65 as they separate.

We are now in a position to consider the processes that occur during the annealing of a cold-worked specimen. It is evident that resoftening can be represented very simply in the dislocation picture as a process in which pairs of dislocations of opposite sign diffuse together under the action of their mutual attractive force and the activation energy furnished by thermal fluctuations. On the other hand, recrystallization is a process in which extensive changes in lattice structure take place in the regions where dislocations are present before sufficient time has elapsed to allow them to flow together. Since the forces required to move dislocations are very small, we may expect the activation energy required to assist such motion to be small compared with that required to nucleate extensive atomic rearrangement. This being the case, it is not surprising that resoftening occurs at much lower temperatures than recrystallization.

There are two important observations that have not yet been given an adequate explanation in terms of the concept of dislocations. The first of these is the fact that latent slip planes appear[1] to harden at least as rapidly as the actual slip planes. The second is the fact that work-hardening approaches a constant after sufficient cold-working (Fig. 47). It is not difficult to understand why the distortion produced by dislocations in one set of slip planes should make it more difficult for dislocations to move in equivalent sets, but it is not easy to see why the hardening should be practically the same in both sets, as work with pure metals indicates. It is entirely possible, however, that the experimental work bearing on this point is not sufficient to reveal all the facts of the matter and that additional work should be done. The leveling of the critical shearing stress for large strain and the associated leveling of the stored energy of cold-work (Fig. 50) imply, according to the dislocation picture, either that dislocations eventually disappear as rapidly as they are formed or that a new mechanism for flow occurs. Here again additional experimental work on the mechanism of plastic flow in the region where the stress-strain curve flattens may prove illuminating.

Another weakness of the theory of dislocations, in its present stage of development, is that the evidence for the model of a dislocation we have used is almost entirely indirect. It is true that the X-ray evidence implies that the unit of distortion extends over atomic dimensions, but this evidence does not favor one

[1] ELAM, *op. cit.*, SCHMID and BOAS, *op. cit.*

type of atomic distortion over another. Among the fields of experimental work that could be explored to cast light on the actual geometrical pattern of the distortion, two should be mentioned. In the first place, studies of the influence of cold-work on the magnetic properties of ferromagnetic material provide a method of inferring this pattern. In fact, experiments[1] of this kind have already given fairly convincing evidence that the actual pattern is as we have supposed and that the density of dislocations in highly worked materials is 10^{12} per cm^2. In the second place, studies of the change in electrical resistance of single crystals induced by cold-working should furnish additional evidence. Comparatively rough experiments with polycrystalline materials have been carried out and show that the change in resistance is of the order of 0.1 percent for extensive working. This value is readily explained on the basis of the theory. However, more careful work with single crystals should provide a much more stringent test of the model.

23. Twinning.—Slip is not the only process by which a crystal may deform plastically; an alternative one, called "twinning," is commonly observed. In this process a long sequence of neighboring atomic planes move relative to one another by distances *not* equal to an integer multiple of an atomic spacing. Moreover, the relative motion of successive parallel planes is not random but takes place in such a homogeneous fashion that the region in which the distortion occurs remains a single crystal even though it does not have the same orientation as the original crystal. Since the new orientation may be derived from the old by rotation or reflection, the new crystal is commonly called a "twin." This process is to be contrasted with the slip process in which comparatively large blocks are translated parallel to one another along randomly oriented slip planes.

When twinning is observed, it is not always the result of ordinary applied stress. For example, it frequently occurs in grains obtained as a result of recrystallization or as a result of a phase change. In fact, it appears that in face-centered cubic crystals, such as copper and α brass, visible twinning has never been produced by mechanical means although it is commonly observed in recrystallized and transformed specimens.

[1] W. F. BROWN, *Phys. Rev.*, **58**, 736 (1940).

In the simplest case of twinning the twinned region may be
viewed as though derived from the original crystal by the displacement of a sequence of parallel planes by the same relative
distance.   In the face-centered cubic crystals this displacement
is a fictitious one; for, as mentioned in the preceding paragraph,
visible twinning actually cannot be produced by mechanical
deformation in these crystals.   However, the relative orientation
of the crystal and its twin in such cases is the same as if the latter
were produced by the relative displacement of a sequence of
octahedral planes through a distance equal to one-third a complete translation (Fig. 66).   In this case, the new orientation

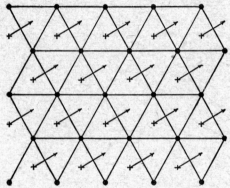

Fig. 66.—Motion of atoms in neighboring (111) planes of a face-centered cubic
crystal that will produce twinning.

may be derived from the old by reflection in a plane parallel to
the plane of motion.

In body-centered cubic metals and in the simple hexagonal
metals, such as zinc and cadmium, in which twinning can be
produced mechanically, the process actually occurs by the relative
displacement of a sequence of atomic planes in a manner closely
resembling that shown in Fig. 66.   Twinning does not always
occur in such a simple manner, however.   For example, it has
been shown[1] that twinning in tin produced by impact probably
occurs as the result of the motion of two different systems of
planes through different distances.

It is found frequently that twinning occurs during the elongation or compression of specimens in slip experiments.   In all

[1] B. CHALMERS, *Proc. Phys. Soc.*, **47**, 733 (1935).

these cases, the appearance of twinning is marked by a discontinuity in the shearing stress. Thus Fig. 67 shows[1] the form of the stress-strain curve of cadmium obtained under conditions in which twinning occurs most easily. The irregularities observed for elongations greater than twenty are associated with twinning.

Examination of the specimen after each discontinuous jump shows that a new region of twinning has been produced.

Stress-strain curves for bis muth exhibit irregularities of this type for the entire range of strain, a fact indicating that twinning is almost entirely responsible for the plastic flow in this metal.

As the curve for cadmium illustrates, the stresses required to produce twinning are roughly comparable with those required to produce slip. It does not seem to have been established, however, whether or not the effective component of stress is the shearing stress in the planes in which translation occurs.

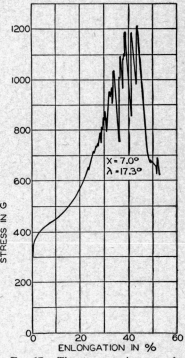

FIG. 67.—The stress-strain curve of a cadmium crystal in which twinning occurs. The irregular peaks are associated with twinning.

Chalmers[2] has suggested, as a result of extensive work on the twinning produced in tin by means of impact, that twinning requires the existence of a definite amount of available elastic energy per unit volume (Fig. 68). In the case he studied, it was found that this threshold energy is $8 \cdot 10^5$ ergs per cm³, which would be attained by a stress of the order of magnitude 10^8 dynes per cm². Most of this elastic energy is converted into heat, within the accuracy of his measurements; this accuracy,

[1] SCHMID and BOAS, *op. cit.*

[2] B. CHALMERS, *Proc. Phys. Soc.*, **47**, 733 (1935).

however, is not sufficiently high to indicate whether or not the fraction stored in the specimen is comparable with that stored during slip. There is, of course, no reason for expecting it to be.

It should be emphasized in passing that twinning can be produced by static load in only a comparatively few substances. In many metals, of which iron is an example, it may be produced by shock. The twinning of iron was first observed in meteoric

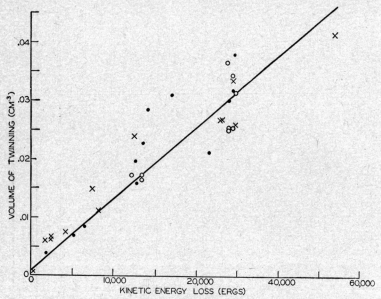

Fig. 68.—Relation between the energy transmitted to a crystal of tin during twinning and the volume of twinned material. (*After Chalmers.*)

specimens in which the impact terminating the fall is probably the source of deformation.

The mechanism of the twinning produced by mechanical means has been subject to much less theoretical investigation than the mechanism of slip. There are many similarities between the processes, however, for in both cases plastic flow is produced by stresses many times smaller than the critical shearing stress required to translate planes as a unit. As a result, it has been suggested that twinning is caused by the passage through the planes in which relative motion occurs of dislocations that resemble closely those responsible for slip. If this is true, the case of twinning must differ from that of slip in that the plane neighboring a plane through which a twin dislocation has passed must become relatively unstable if the crystal is under stress, so that a twin dislocation is readily generated in it. It is also possible that the thermal energy released by the passage of the first dislocation furnishes the activation energy for the next, so that an avalanche of twin dislocations passes through a long sequence of neighboring planes.

CHAPTER VII

THE PLASTIC PROPERTIES OF POLYCRYSTALLINE MEDIA

24. Introduction.—The properties of polycrystals are influenced by two separate factors: (1) by the intrinsic properties of the single crystal constituents, or grains; (2) by the restrictions neighboring grains exert on one another. If it were not for (2), all properties of polycrystals could be derived by taking some simple average of the properties of corresponding single crystals for various orientations. This procedure actually is possible for some properties, which, as a result, are sometimes called *structure-insensitive properties*. For example, the elastic moduli and electrical resistivity of pure polycrystals may be approximated closely from the appropriate averages for single crystals. On the other hand, many properties of polycrystals such as shear strength and internal friction are affected by the discontinuities in structure that occur in polycrystals in a way that cannot be explained simply by treating the system as a set of disoriented isolated single crystals. Such properties are sometimes called *structure-sensitive properties*. We shall refer to the additional factor as *grain-boundary influence* and shall attempt to unify present knowledge of this factor in the present chapter. It should be borne in mind that by grain-boundary influence is meant not only the effect arising from the atoms in the transition region between two grains, but also the effect neighboring grains exert on one another.

It should be remarked that there is available at the present time a set of well-tested rules[1] concerning plastic flow in polycrystals in the formulation of which no attempt is made to understand the behavior of the individual grains of the material.

[1] See, for example, A. NADAI, *Plasticity* (McGraw-Hill Book Company, Inc., New York, 1931); M. GENSAMER, *Strength of Metals under Combined Stresses* (American Society for Metals, Cleveland, Ohio, 1941).

Although these rules have considerable practical interest, they do not provide us with fundamental information concerning the manner in which grain-boundary interaction affects the rules for single crystals discussed in the previous chapter. For this reason we shall not discuss them in detail here. When the principles concerning grain-boundary interaction are completely understood, these rules for polycrystals should be derivable from those for single crystals.

25. Grain-boundary Influence.—The various ways in which grain boundaries affect the properties of polycrystals may be summarized as follows:

a. The Impurities at Grain Boundaries as Barriers for Thermal and Electrical Flow.—Since different grains presumably grow from different nuclei during solidification of a melt, it follows that grain boundaries will naturally be the regions where impurities which are insoluble in the grains tend to aggregate during growth. This principle, of course, is not nearly so true for grains obtained as a result of a recrystallization process as it is for grains produced during the original solidification of a melt. In any case, this tendency has as a consequence the fact that grain boundaries may act as barriers to thermal and electrical currents, particularly in impure metals.

b. The Influence of the Transition Layer between Grains.—Even if the material of which polycrystals are made is very pure, or if all impurities are highly soluble, we may expect an abnormal arrangement of atoms in the immediate vicinity of the boundary between grains; that is, we may expect a transition layer of atoms that occupy positions resulting from a compromise between the forces of the atoms in both grains. These atoms are not so tightly bound as the atoms in the interior of the grains and, as a result, may be expected to be more mobile at a given temperature than interior atoms. This does not necessarily mean that slip should occur more easily along grain boundaries than within grains; for if the theory of dislocations is correct, slip should be determined by the ease with which dislocations form and move instead of by the ease with which individual atoms move. At most, we may conclude that the diffusion of a given atom would probably occur more readily at grain boundaries than in the interior of grains. In fact, it is possible that, as a result of the irregularities occurring in the intergranular regions, it would be difficult for dislocations to move through them.

The width of the transition region between grains in very pure crystals is not known from experimental work. We know from other sources, however, that the forces between atoms in solids are of short range, extending with appreciable intensity only over a few atom distances. For this reason it seems safe to conclude that the width of the intergranular region is of the order of five interatomic distances at most. This conclusion is not valid, of course, in materials containing a high percentage of insoluble impurities, for in such cases a large fraction of the insoluble material may be localized at grain boundaries.

From a study of the behavior of very pure tin at temperatures near its melting point, Chalmers[1] has concluded that the grain-boundary material has a slightly lower melting point than the bulk material. This conclusion was based on the fact that grains separate along their boundaries at temperatures somewhat below the melting point. The difference between the separation temperature and the true melting temperature for any pair of grains is found to be independent of the relative orientation of the two crystals and of the amount of impurity, provided that the latter does not exceed 0.02 percent. For highly pure tin the measured temperature difference is 0.14°C. Although it may be a matter of discussion whether Chalmers's experiments show that the material at grain boundaries becomes molten or merely highly plastic below the melting point of the bulk material, these observations are apparently in good accord with the conclusion drawn previously that the transition layer of atoms is thermodynamically less stable than interior atoms.

There is considerable evidence that the bond at grain boundaries is very strong at temperatures not too near the melting point, in spite of this lower thermodynamic stability. For example, fracture occurs most commonly *through* grains rather than at their boundaries in rupture tests performed well below the melting temperature. On the other hand, intercrystalline fracture is common near the melting point. On first consideration, observations of this kind seem to support the view that the intergranular material actually is stronger than the bulk material

[1] B. CHALMERS, *Proc. Roy. Soc.*, **A175,** 100 (1940).

at low temperatures and weaker at high. In fact, this view has often been advanced in the literature. It seems much more reasonable, however, to suppose that the less ordered regions at grain boundaries are weaker than the interior of grains and that rupture inherently tends to start at grain boundaries. The difference in strength is not so great, however, that a crack automatically follows the surfaces of grain boundaries regardless of their inclination relative to the plane of greatest tensile stress. In fact, once started a crack will occur in the plane of greatest tensile stress even if this plane cuts through grains. At high temperatures, it is possible that the greater relative instability of grain boundaries increases and that cracks follow such boundaries.

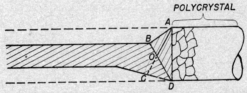

Fig. 69.—Slip in a single crystal of zinc bounded by a polycrystal. The heavy contour is the shape of the specimen after slip, the dotted line the shape before. The light lines show the positions of the slip planes in various regions (see text). (*After Miller.*)

Chalmers's experiments on tin indicate that the grain boundaries are extremely weak just below the melting point of the bulk material.

c. Slip Interference at Grain Boundaries.—Neighboring grains exert a strong restricting influence on the amount and kind of slip that may occur within the grains. A significant experimental investigation of this effect has been carried out by Miller[1] on specimens of zinc consisting of a large single crystal bounded by a polycrystal (Fig. 69). Measurements were made on specimens elongated at 180°C since slip occurs smoothly at this temperature. Miller found that those slip planes of the single crystal which intersect the polycrystalline region cannot operate as freely as those which do not. Thus in the typical case illustrated by the figure, stresses sufficient to cause slip in the uninhibited regions of the crystal were not sufficient to cause slip in the region OAD immediately bordering the polycrystal. Although

[1] R. F. MILLER, *Trans. A.I.M.E.*, **111**, 135 (1934).

slip occurred in the region *OBA*, which does not border the polycrystal, the deformation was highly restricted by the presence of the unstrained region, for the rotation of the slip planes in this region that would normally occur was not permitted. Similarly, slip occurred in the region *OCD* but was limited to the amount allowed by bending in the plane *BD*.

The fact that slip can occur in the region *OCD* makes it seem surprising at first sight that slip is absent in *OAD*; for if the shearing stress there had the same value as in the rest of the specimen, bending might be expected, as in *OCD*. A reasonable explanation of this fact is the following: Initially, the shearing stress is uniform throughout all planes in the single crystal (exclusive of

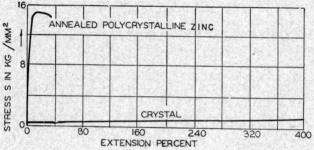

Fig. 70.—Comparison of the stress-strain curves of a single crystal and a polycrystal of zinc.

microscopic variations). After an undetectably small strain has occurred in *OAD*, however, the stress becomes redistributed in such a way that the shearing stress is lower in this region. This change evidently requires that the polycrystalline region exert a transverse tensile stress on the material to the left of the boundary *AD*, which thus reduces the shear in the slip planes. A condition sufficient for this is that slip does not occur in the intergranular surfaces along *AD*. Naturally, the transverse tension across *AD* would diminish if the polycrystal were to deform. It is clear, however, that in any case the motion occurring in *OAD* and that in the polycrystalline region must be closely correlated.

Now if a single crystal is favorably oriented for slip and is entirely surrounded by less favorably oriented grains, as can occur in the interior of a polycrystalline specimen, stresses similar to those occurring in Miller's specimens are exerted across the boundaries of this grain and slip occurs only when the stress is sufficiently large to allow all grains to deform. Naturally, the more numerous and randomly oriented the planes of easy slip, the more probable it is that one of the easy planes of slip of an arbitrarily chosen grain is favorably oriented for deformation. Thus the stresses needed to produce a given deformation should be smaller for cubic crystals, which have many easy planes of slip, than for hexagonal crystals, such as zinc, which have only one. Figures 70 and 71 bear out this conclusion by showing that the difference between the stress-strain curves for single and polycrystalline specimens is much greater in zinc, which is hexagonal, than in aluminum, which is cubic.

It is natural to ask at this point whether the actual stress-strain curves for polycrystals can be explained quantitively by regarding a polycrystal as a cluster of single crystals subject to a simple constraining condition such as the condition that there shall be no relative motion at the grain boundaries. This problem has not yet been sufficiently analyzed to allow us to say at present whether the condition is a simple one. We shall return to this topic briefly in the next section.

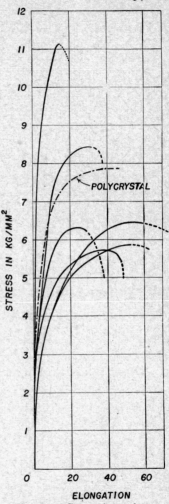

Fig. 71.—Comparison of stress-strain curves for single crystals of aluminum having various orientations with the stress-strain curve for a polycrystalline specimen.

One of the facts that indicates that the strength of polycrystalline specimens cannot be derived by the use of a simple constraining condition is the observation that the Brineli hardness and the form of the stress-strain curves of polycrystals seem to vary with grain size in a range in which the grain size is much smaller than the dimensions of the specimen. Figure 72, for example, shows the variation of the hardness of brass with grain size. Results of this kind are very surprising if taken at their

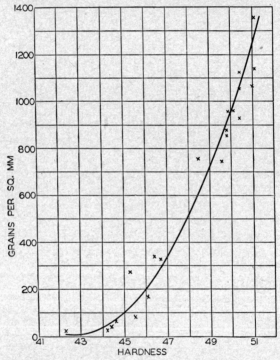

Fig. 72.—Dependence of the hardness of annealed brass upon grain size. It is to be noted that the horizontal scale shown does not begin at the origin. (*From Elam, The Distortion of Metal Crystals.*)

face value; for, if the width of the grain boundary region is as small as we have supposed, we should expect the mechanical properties of polycrystals to be independent of grain size as long as this size is small, compared with the dimensions of the specimen and of the device used in measurement, and large, compared with atomic dimensions. A possible explanation of this discrepancy lies in the fact that specimens must be treated in different manners in order to obtain different grain sizes. It is possible that this treatment has a profound effect upon the mechanical properties, particularly if the materials are not perfectly pure. Evidence for this viewpoint has been given by Corson[1] as the result of a study of very pure copper. He found that the tensile strength and hardness of coarse-grained ingots of very pure copper are practically the same as the corresponding properties of fine-grained specimens. He concluded that . the weakness ordinarily observed in large-grained materials can be attributed to the influence of impurities which congregate at grain boundaries and, for reasons not yet completely understood, weaken the bond between grains. According to this picture the weakening effect is larger for coarse-grained materials than for fine. because the total amount of grain-boundary area for a given weight of material is smaller for the former, whence there is a larger concentration of impurity per unit area of the boundary.

26. Slip in Polycrystals.[2]—Present knowledge of the basic principles of slip in grains was outlined in the previous chapter. Although this knowledge cannot be said to be complete, since the role of such factors as deformation bands is not yet completely understood, we at least have a qualitative formulation of the laws of plastic flow in single crystals. It is natural to hope to base a general discussion of the behavior of polycrystalline solids in various deforming processes, such as tension, compression, rolling, and drawing, on a few primary empirical laws by generalizing the laws for single crystals. Unfortunately, as we saw in the previous section, present knowledge of the influence of grain boundaries is not sufficient to complement the work on single crystals and so provide us with a good foundation for treating polycrystals. In spite of this, we shall outline briefly the experimental facts concerning slip in polycrystals.

a. Crystalline Orientation.—When polycrystalline specimens in which the grains are randomly oriented are uniformly deformed, several closely related changes occur. In the first place, the orientations of the grains become altered. This reorientation

[1] M. G. Corson, *Trans. A.I.M.E.*, **128**, 398 (1938).

[2] See, for example, C. F. Elam, *The Distortion of Metal Crystals* (Oxford University Press, New York, 1936; E. Schmid and W. Boas, *Kristallplastizität* (Verlag Julius Springer, Berlin, 1936).

frequently occurs in such a way that the resultant distribution of grains is no longer random but exhibits preferred orientation. The degree of preferred orientation is never nearly so great as that existing in a good single crystal and usually depends on the material of which the specimen is made, upon the method used to produce the deformation, and upon the amount of plastic flow. For example, when face-centered cubic metals are placed under tension, there is a tendency for both the [111] and [100] directions to become oriented parallel to the direction of tension. In aluminum the existing evidence indicates that most of the grains become oriented so that the [111] direction is along the axis of tension, but both the orientations occur in other metals having the same structure. Similarly, in simple compression, the [110] direction of face-centered cubic crystals tends to become aligned normal to the plane of compression. In some cases, the final orientations of the grains in polycrystals appear to be similar to those occurring in single crystals that have been subject to the same deformation, but more often they do not. This fact indicates once again the importance of the influence of grain boundaries in determining the actual stresses with the grains. For example, in tension tests on single crystals of aluminum, the [110] direction tends to become parallel to the axis of tension, whereas, as we have seen above, the [111] direction tends to become aligned in this direction in polycrystals.

TABLE XI.—THE PREFERRED ORIENTATIONS PRODUCED BY ROLLING AND
BY RECRYSTALLIZATION SUBSEQUENT TO ROLLING

Crystal	After rolling		After subsequent recrystallization	
	Rolling direction	Rolling plane	Rolling direction	Rolling plane
Aluminum........	[112], [111]	(110), (112)	[100]	(001)
Copper..........	[112], [111]	(110), (112)	[100]	(001)
Nickel..........	[112], [111]	(110), (112)	[100]	(001)
Cu85Zn15........	[112]	(110)	[112]	($\bar{3}$11)
Iron............	[110]	(100), (112)	[110], [112]	(001), (11$\bar{1}$)
Molybdenum.....	[110]	(100), (112)		
Zinc............	[100]	(001)		

The reorientations developed during rolling are of particular practical importance since a large fraction of useful metal is fabricated by this process. The stresses occurring during rolling are much more complicated than during simple tension or compression testing, for the surface of the rolled specimen is subject to shearing stresses both in the direction of rolling and at right angles to this direction, as well as to normal stresses. Although a high degree of preferred orientation can usually be produced by sufficient rolling, the results are greatly dependent upon the

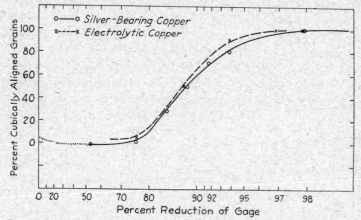

FIG. 73.—The variation of the preferred orientation of rolled copper with the degree of reduction. The degree of orientation was measured *after* recrystallization but is nearly the same as the degree before. Cubic axes are oriented parallel to the direction of rolling and normal to the rolling plane after recrystallization. (*After Baldwin.*)

particular material. Table XI shows, for example, the crystallographic direction that tends to become aligned parallel to the rolling plane in several metals and alloys possessing cubic structure. Figure 73 shows[1] the manner in which the degree of preferred orientation varies with the amount by which the thickness of the material is reduced during rolling.

It has been pointed out by Herrmann and Sachs[2] that the structures developed during the rolling of brass may be closely approximated by proper superposition of the orientations which occur during the compression and extension of the same material.

[1] W. M. BALDWIN, *Metals Tech. Pub.* 1455 (1942).
[2] L. HERRMANN and G. SACHS, *Metallwirtschaft*, **13** (1934).

Taylor has noted that the orientations developed by rolling can sometimes be reproduced in compression tests in which the specimen is constrained in such a way that it may spread in only one direction in the plane of compression. This work suggests that it may be possible in general to determine the orientations which occur when metals are subject to combined stresses from those produced during simpler operations.

The nature of the preferred orientation generally changes during recrystallization subsequent to any deformation in which preferred orientation is produced. Table XI, for example, shows the type of orientation observed in the rolled metals after recrystallization. It is an interesting fact that the degree of preferred orientation is often fully as high after recrystallization as before. This indicates that the nucleus of a recrystallized grain undoubtedly possesses a particular orientation relative to the lattice of the grain in which it was formed; moreover, this orientation is different from that of the cold-worked metal.

One of the interesting effects of extensive deformation on polycrystalline materials is the development of a gross fiber structure. This structure results from the elongation of individual grains in the direction of the deformation, which gives them the appearance of fibers of woven fabrics. In most materials that are used in practice, the neighboring grains appear to maintain close adhesion at their boundaries during the elongation, for the rupture strength of the material is not reduced except possibly in extreme cases of cold-working. This fact indicates once again the comparatively great strength of the intergranular bond. Moreover, it shows that the elongations of the grains take place under great restrictions. It can be shown that these restrictions are so severe that the development of gross fiber structure would not be possible in materials such as hexagonal metals whose grains normally possess only one parallel system of slip planes, if another mode of deformation were not possible. Actually, twinning seems to provide the additional degree of freedom in hexagonal materials such as zinc and cadmium. It is also possible that innercrystalline deformation of the type occurring during the development of deformation bands (see part b of this section) is an important means of deformation in many materials.

b. Nonuniform Distortion.—In the discussion of the deformation of single crystals in the previous chapter, we saw that recent work of Barrett and Levenson[1] has indicated that such deformation usually is not produced in a truly homogeneous fashion. They found, for example, that different parts of a single crystal of aluminum are disoriented by as much as 3 deg during a 50 percent compression between well-lubricated plates. Similar work on polycrystals of aluminum and iron shows that the disorientation within individual grains resulting from compression is even greater in materials having this texture. For example, in the case of aluminum the spread of orientation within a grain ranged from 7 to 10 deg for 10 percent compression, from 15 to 25 deg for 30 percent compression, and from 35 to 45 deg for 60 percent compression. This variation in orientation is accompanied by the appearance of narrow bands, termed "deformation bands," which sometimes separate regions having different orientation.

The source of this disorientation within grains has not yet been given a complete explanation. It seems possible, however, that the deformation bands correspond to regions such as the planar region *BD* in Fig. 69, which marks the place where bending occurs. If so, their appearance would indicate that the stresses are not uniform throughout individual grains. This conclusion would not be surprising in polycrystalline materials, for nonuniformity in these could possibly be related to the influence of different neighboring grains. However, the observation of bands in single crystals would then indicate that the grains themselves are intrinsically inhomogeneous on a scale of distance much larger than that of the spacing between slip bands.

c. Work-hardening.—Polycrystals harden with cold-work, as may be seen from the stress-strain curves shown in Figs. 70 and 71. Undoubtedly, work-hardening of the type observed in single crystals is appreciable in polycrystals; for the latter, like the former, may be softened by heating. It is possible, however, that additional factors related to the presence of grain boundaries enter into the hardening of polycrystals. For example, there are indications that in most metals complete softening of poly-

[1] C. S. BARRETT and L. H. LEVENSON, *Trans. A.I.M.E.*, **137**, 112 (1940).

crystals requres recrystallization of the specimen. In contrast with this, we have seen in the previous chapter (see Fig. 51, page 83) that single crystals can recover almost completely below their recrystallization temperature. It is not unlikely, however, that the temperature which accompanies recrystallization and not the change in grain texture is the important factor in determining softening. Since polycrystals recrystallize at far lower temperatures than single crystals for equivalent external strain, it is plausible to believe that the recrystallization which occurs in polycrystals in the temperature range most effective for softening is incidental.

A highly interesting analysis of the stress-strain curve for polycrystalline aluminum has been given by Taylor.[1] Briefly, he computed the stress-strain curve on the basis of the following assumptions:

a. The strain is uniform in all grains of the material. This evidently contains implicitly the assumption that no slip occurs at grain boundaries. It obviously is far more stringent, however, than a condition which merely excludes slip at grain boundaries would be, for it also rules out deformation bands of the type observed by Barrett and Levenson.

b. The deformation takes place in each grain as a result of slip on the octahedral planes, in the manner observed for single crystals, and, in addition, takes place in such a way that the work required for the deformation is a minimum.

On the basis of these assumptions, Taylor was able to compute the stress-strain curve for a polycrystal composed of randomly oriented grains by the use of curves for single crystals. The upper continuous curve of Fig. 74 is that derived in this way and is accompanied by experimental points. It may be seen that the computed curve agrees substantially with these points.

Unfortunately, the discovery of deformation bands indicates that assumption *a* is not correct and thus detracts from the significance of the agreement found by Taylor. Moreover, Barrett and Levenson[2] found that the average change in orientation of the grains during compression of aluminum is frequently different from that predicted on the basis of Taylor's theory.

[1] G. I. Taylor, *J. Inst. Metals*, **62**, 307 (1938).
[2] Barrett and Levenson, *op. cit.*

Thus assumption *b* is open to question. The constructive implications of Barrett and Levenson's work have not yet been determined, but it seems definite that Taylor's assumptions must be modified in some essential respects, at least in the case of compression.

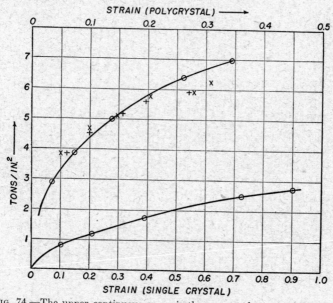

Fig. 74.—The upper continuous curve is the computed stress-strain relation found by Taylor, using the data obtained on single crystals of aluminum. The crosses and plus signs represent experimental values. The lower curve is a representative curve for a single crystal of aluminum.

27. Technical Hardness.[1]—Although a measurement of the critical shearing stress provides an excellent gauge of the "hardness" of a given single crystal specimen, such measurement cannot readily be carried out in the case of polycrystalline specimens. Since it is important in practical work to have a gauge of hardness that is applicable to any of the materials available for commercial use, engineers have developed several widely used devices of this type that require the minimum of effort.

[1] A discussion of the methods of hardness measurement may be found in the book by H. O'Neill, *The Hardness of Metals* (Chapman & Hall, Ltd., London, 1934), and that by S. R. Williams, *Hardness and Hardness Measurements* (A.S.M., Cleveland, 1942).

We shall not discuss machines of this type in detail but shall point out the qualitative connection between the hardness measured with them and the hardness that corresponds to the critical shearing stress. More complete information can be found, for example, in the *A.S.M. Handbook*. There are two principal types of hardness testers, namely, Scleroscope testers, which measure the energy lost by a hardened steel ball in bouncing from the surface of the metal to be tested, and indentation testers, which measure the geometrical dimensions of the indentation produced when a ball or a pointed instrument is pressed into the surface with standard load for standard length of time. In the Scleroscope tester, the bouncing ball loses energy if plastic flow occurs in the tested material as a result of the stresses produced during impact. It is evident that the energy lost bears an inverse relation to the critical shearing stress. As long as the depth of the pit produced by the ball is very small compared with the dimensions of the ball, the total strain is small. Thus, under this condition, the Scleroscope test corresponds to a measurement, on a relative scale, of the average critical shearing stress for a small range of strain.

On the other hand, much more plastic flow is produced near the tip of the indenter in tests of the Rockwell B type and Brinell type, in which an indentation is produced by a ball, and in the Vickers and Knoop tests, in which it has, respectively, the shape of a cone and the shape of a pyramid. That the strain is large in these cases is readily shown by the fact that, when an indented specimen is heated in the range where recrystallization occurs, the material near the indentation recrystallizes to a very fine grain size. Presumably the strain produced in this region is at least 30 percent. It follows that, in such cases, the indentation method provides a measure of the average shearing stress for plastic flow over an appreciable range of strain. While it is true that this average is of great practical interest, it must be kept in mind that the information obtained from it is not so specific as that obtained from stress-strain curves.

28. The Behavior of Metals at High Pressures.—The influence of very high pressures on the plastic properties of single crystals has not been studied; however, Bridgman,[1] who is responsible

[1] P. W. BRIDGMAN, *Phys. Rev.*, **48**, 825 (1935).

for most of what is known about the properties of matter at very high pressures, has investigated the influence of pressure on the shearing stress of polycrystalline specimens of a number of the softer metals. This work indicates that the plastic properties of metals usually are greatly altered by the application of sufficient pressure.

The method used by Bridgman to place combined pressure and shearing stress on the specimen is as follows: A thin disk of the material to be investigated is placed upon the end of a steel cylinder and another cylinder, or "anvil," is placed upon this.

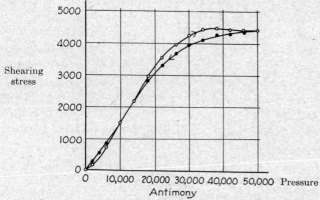

Fig. 75.—Curve for antimony showing the relation between shearing stress for plastic flow and the mean hydrostatic stress. The units for both axes are kg per cm². The white circles correspond to measurements made with increasing pressure and the darker ones to those made with decreasing pressure. (*After Bridgman.*)

A second specimen, identical with the first, is then placed on the upper side of the anvil; and a third cylinder, also identical with the first, is placed on top of this. The two end cylinders are then pushed together with a hydraulic press so as to press the specimens against the anvil. The materials used in these experiments were sufficiently soft for the pressure exerted upon them by the cylinders to be regarded as hydrostatic. The shear properties of the material under investigation may be determined by rotating the anvil, for this rests principally upon the specimens. Experience shows that, when the anvil is rotated, plastic flow occurs within the specimens rather than at the interface between the specimens and the steel cylinders, provided that the applied pressure is sufficiently high. Thus the torque required to rotate the anvil provides a measure of the critical shearing stress of the specimens.

Figure 75 shows the variation of the critical shearing stress of antimony with applied pressure as determined by the foregoing method. It may be seen that the curve starts out nearly linearly, with a slope of approximately 0.15. This indicates that the stress required to produce shear in a given plane of the material is not independent of the normal pressure exerted across this plane for sufficiently high pressures.[1] Bridgman has evidence to show that the flattening of the curve for pressures above 20,000 kg per cm^2 is related to the onset of a change in crystallographic structure induced by the pressure. Such phase changes were unmistakably found in other cases in which flat maxima of the same type occurred.

It is of passing interest to note that Bridgman observed that paraffin resists plastic flow as well as the metals at pressures of the order of 30,000 kg per cm^2. Moreover, he observed that, at pressures above 12,000 kg per cm^2, graphite behaves like an abrasive.

---

[1] Investigations by Schmid and Boas (*op. cit.*) indicate that the normal stress does *not* affect the shear stress for stresses in the atmospheric range.

CHAPTER VIII

THE PLASTIC PROPERTIES OF ALLOYS

29. Introduction.[1]—Alloys deserve individual treatment in our discussion of the plastic properties of metals because they possess a number of characteristic properties not found in pure metals.

As was pointed out in Chap. III, there are two types of alloy when viewed from the standpoint of the phase diagram, namely, homogeneous and heterogeneous. The grains appearing in the former possess the same composition and crystal structure, whereas they possess two or more compositions and structures in the second case. As Fig. 49 (page 78) shows, dissolved alloying elements generally harden a given pure metal more than undissolved ones so that it might be said that, for given composition, an alloy is in general harder when in the homogeneous than in the inhomogeneous form. There is a very important exception to this rule, namely, the case in which one or more of the constituent phases of the heterogeneous alloy is present as a phase which has precipitated from a solid solution stable at a higher temperature. In such cases, the hardness of the alloys increases as the size of the clumps of precipitate grows from groups of one or two atoms, passes through a maximum for particle size below the limits that can be resolved in a microscope, and then decreases again. This phenomenon of *precipitation hardening* is, of course, widely used both in ferrous and in nonferrous metallurgy.

30. Homogeneous Solid Solutions.—The regular manner in which the critical shearing stress increases with the amount of dissolved constituent is shown in Fig. 76 for the gold-silver

---

[1] See C. F. ELAM, *The Distortion of Metal Crystals* (Oxford University Press, New York, 1936); E. SCHMID and W. BOAS, *Kristallplastizität* (Verlag Julius Springer, Berlin, 1936); also S. SIEGEL, *J. Applied Phys.*, **13**, 84 (1942).

system,[1] which is homogeneous for the entire range or composition. The curve giving shearing stress as a function of composition is not always so symmetrical as in this case; however, it usually is continuous when only a single structure occurs.

It may be noted that the curve of Fig. 76 is essentially linear at both ends of the diagram. This fact allows us to describe the hardening influence of a given constituent, when its concentration is low, in terms of the slope of the stress-composition curve near the corresponding end point. A more practical equiv-

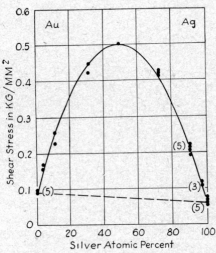

FIG. 76.—The critical shearing stress of a sequence of silver-gold alloys as a function of composition. The metals are miscible in all proportions. (*After Sachs and Weerts.*)

alent of this quantity is the increase in technical hardness of the solvent metal produced by a given amount of the dissolved metal. Norbury[2] has found, in fact, that the Brinell hardness of a sequence of copper alloys increases linearly with the atomic percent of alloying agent. Figure 77 shows the increase in hardness produced in copper by the separate addition of 1 percent of seven different metals. The hardness is plotted as a function of the relative difference in atomic volume of the dissolved metal

[1] G. SACHS and J. WEERTS, *Z. Physik*, **62,** 475 (1930).

[2] A. L. NORBURY, *Trans. Faraday Soc.*, **19,** 586 (1924). See also the more recent work by J. H. Frye and J. W. Caum, *Metals Tech. Pub.* 1554 (1943).

and copper. It may be seen that the points lie essentially on a straight line. This shows that the hardening influence of a given atom is at least approximately proportional to the amount of strain it produces in the solvent lattice. This fact strongly suggests that the increases in shear strength produced by the addition of soluble atoms are related to the residual stresses these atoms produce in the lattice, in general accord with the principles discussed in Sec. 22. In other words, the dislocations meet difficulty in attempting to move through the lattice unless the applied stress is sufficiently large to neutralize the local stresses produced by the dissolved atoms, which are somewhat misfit. The nearer the atomic volume of the solvent and solute elements coincide, the more closely does the dissolved atom simulate the effect of the atom for which it is substituted, the lower is the residual stress, and the lower need be the stress applied to produce slip.

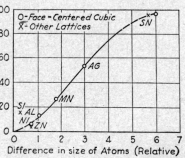

Fig. 77.—Relation between the increase in hardness and the fractional difference in sizes of the solvent and solute atoms for a number of copper alloys containing 0.1 atom percent of alloying metal. The abscissa is the difference in atomic volume of solvent and solute. This is proportional to the difference of atomic radii. (*After Norbury.*)

According to the first of Hume-Rothery's rules for the formation of ideal substitutional alloys, we expect the solubility limits of the primary phases to vary inversely as the difference in atomic radii of the solvent and solute atoms. As a result of this rule and Norbury's observation that the critical shearing stress increases with the difference in atomic radius of the two alloying atoms, we should expect the hardening influence of a given amount of dissolved atom to vary in an inverse manner with the solubility. Ludwick[1] has found such a relation to be valid for solid solutions of various elements in lead, as is shown in Table XII.

One of the important properties possessed by some alloys of the solid-solution type is that they usually harden by a larger

[1] P. LUDWICK, *Z. anorg. Chem.*, **94**, 161 (1917).

TABLE XII

Added metal	Increase in hardness, per atom percent	Solubility limit, percent
Bismuth...............	0.5	30
Tin..................	1.8	10
Cadmium.............	4.8	5
Antimony............	10.0	2.5
Magnesium...........	11	0.5

amount during cold-work than do pure metals. This fact is shown[1] in Fig. 78, which illustrates the Vickers hardness of a sequence of α brasses in the cold-rolled and annealed states, the

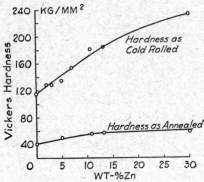

FIG. 78.—The Vickers hardness of α-brass in the cold-rolled and in the annealed state.

degree of cold-rolling being the same in all cases. It may be seen that the variation in hardness of the cold-rolled specimens is much larger than that of the annealed specimens, although the hardness increases with increasing zinc composition in both cases. A suitable explanation of this effect in terms of the theory of dislocations has not been given. It might be supposed that the work-hardened alloy possesses a larger number of dislocations than the work-hardened pure metal. In this case, the energy stored in the former as a result of cold-work should be larger than that in the latter. Unfortunately, a careful study of the varia-

[1] After Elam.

tion with work-hardening of the stored energy has not been made in a case such as this.

Figure 79 shows the hardness of well-annealed brasses as a function of their composition. It may be seen that the end

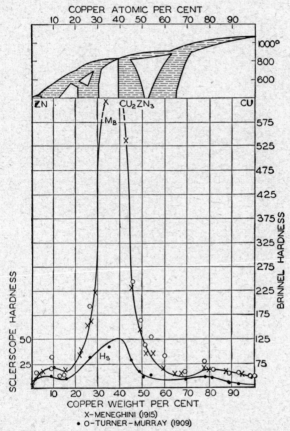

Fig. 79.—The hardness of the brasses as a function of composition. It may be observed that the hardness possesses a maximum in the region of the γ phase. (*After Elam.*)

phases are softest and that the hardness increases toward the center. Thus the β and γ phases are harder than the end phases. The high hardness of the β phase probably is a result of the fact that it contains more dissolved material than the α phase. However, the very high hardness of the γ phase undoubtedly is in part a result of its complex structure. As Fig. 21 (page 18) shows, the γ-brass lattice contains a large number of atoms per unit cell and no well-defined slip planes, as both the face-centered cubic and body-centered cubic lattices do. It seems safe to conclude that dislocations would find great difficulty in moving through this lattice even if they were formed easily.

31. Heterogeneous Alloys.—There are two types of heterogeneous alloys to be considered, namely, those which are so thoroughly annealed that any precipitation which might occur is complete, and those in which precipitation is incomplete. In the first case the dimensions of the grains associated with the precipitate are of the same order of magnitude as those of the solvent metal, whereas in the second case they are submicroscopic in size. If an alloy is heated to a temperature at which it is perfectly homogeneous and is then cooled so quickly that no precipitation whatever can occur, we might expect the quenched alloy to behave like the homogeneous alloys described in the preceding section.

A family of alloys that may be treated in this fashion are those of the copper-silver system. Although the constituent metals are completely soluble at elevated temperatures, they are soluble to the extent of only a few percent at room temperature. However, homogeneous alloys of arbitrary composition may be obtained by quenching. Figure 80 shows the difference in hardness of the quenched and annealed alloys. It may be seen that the maximum hardness of the annealed alloys is the same as that of the two homogeneous solid solutions corresponding to the compositions of maximum solubility, whereas the hardness of the quenched alloys increases uniformly at either end of the diagram and reaches a maximum near the center. The fact that this maximum actually occurs near the eutectic composition suggests that precipitation had already started in the quenched alloys having compositions in the region of the eutectic.

Results of this type show that the hardness of heterogeneous alloys which have been well-annealed is determined principally by the hardness of the constituent grains. There is no appreciable contribution to the hardness resulting from the fact that these alloys are composite. As we remarked in Sec. 29, the same cannot be said of alloys in which precipitation is in the early stages of development. For example, if one of the unstable quenched alloys that was used in obtaining Fig. 80 is warmed sufficiently to allow the formation of the end phases, the hardness does not decrease monotonically until it reaches the lower curve. Instead, it rises at first and drops only after a period of time which depends upon the temperature at which the specimen is held. This process is sometimes termed *age-hardening*.

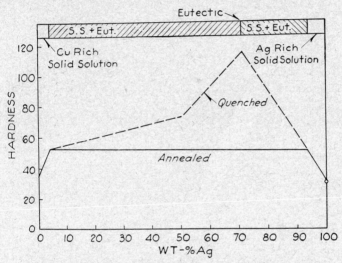

Fig. 80.—The variation of the Brinell hardness of Cu-Ag alloys with the silver content in the annealed and quenched states. (*After Siegel.*)

One of the alloys in which this process of age-hardening[1] has been extensively studied is that of aluminum and copper. At 400°C, copper is soluble in aluminum to the extent of 4.1 percent, whereas the solubility is less than 0.5 percent at room temperature. As a result, if an alloy containing between 0.5 and 4 percent of copper is annealed carefully at 500°C, it is perfectly stable at this temperature in the homogeneous form. On being cooled quickly to room temperature, it remains essentially homogeneous but is not thermodynamically stable. It is possible to accelerate

[1] This topic is surveyed in *Age Hardening of Metals* (American Society for Metals, Cleveland, Ohio, 1940); see particularly the article by R. F. Mehl and L. K. Jetter. Also see W. L. Fink, *J. Applied Phys.*, **13**, 75 (1942).

the precipitation considerably by raising the temperature somewhat above room temperature. Careful calorimetric work[1]
shows that this increase in hardness is accompanied by the evolu-
tion of heat and thus proves that precipitation occurs.

Figure 81 shows[2] the variation in hardness of a sequence of
aluminum-copper alloys resulting from age-hardening at 150°C.

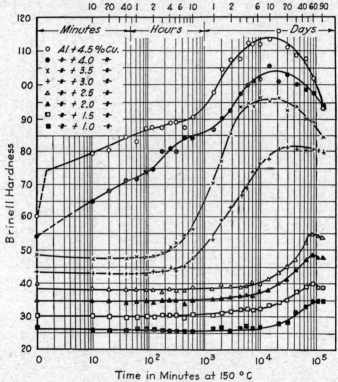

FIG. 81.—Precipitation-hardening curves for binary alloys of aluminum and
copper quenched in water at 100°C and aged at 150°C. (*After Hunsicker.*)

It may be observed that the curves drop after precipitation has
been allowed to proceed sufficiently.

X-ray measurements on the aluminum-copper alloys show that
during the earliest stages of precipitation very thin plates of a

[1] H. CALUS and R. SMOLUCHOWSKI, *Phys. Rev.,* **58,** 205 (1940).

[2] After H. Y. Hunsicker in *Age Hardening of Metals* (American Society
for Metals, Cleveland, Ohio, 1940).

new phase form on the (100) planes. These plates, which are known as *Guinier-Preston* aggregates in honor of their discoverers,[1] are so thin that only the diffraction pattern of a two-dimensional grating may be obtained from them. Although it is certain that the concentration of copper is higher in the plates than in the surrounding matrix, it is not yet known whether the copper atoms have diffused to these regions and arranged themselves in the new order or whether the crystallographic planes have undergone shear in regions where the density of copper atoms is accidentally high as a result of statistical fluctuations. If the temperature is sufficiently high to promote diffusion, the plates grow in thickness and eventually yield a three-dimensional X-ray pattern from which a lattice structure may be determined. This structure, which is commonly called the "θ' phase," may be regarded as derived by shear from the original face-centered cubic lattice. It is likely, however, that they are nucleated by the Guinier-Preston aggregates and that it is the latter which are derived by shear. Eventually the θ' phase is transformed to another phase, called the "θ phase," which in turn may be regarded as derived from the θ' phase by a shear process. It should be emphasized that the precipitation process does not proceed at exactly the same rate in all parts of a given specimen so that two and even all three of the products of the precipitation process may be found simultaneously during intermediate stages.

The hardness of the precipitating system appears to increase throughout the stages in which the Guinier-Preston aggregates and the θ' phase are forming and to drop at about the time the θ phase appears. Mott and Nabarro[2] have suggested that the precipitate produces residual stresses in the surrounding matrix during the earlier stages of the precipitation process and that the impediment which these stresses offer to dislocations accounts for the hardening. The primary source of the stress is, of course, the difference in volume of the copper and aluminum atoms and the strain produced when one is replaced by the other. Mott

---

[1] A. GUINIER, *Compt. rend.*, **204**, 1937, **206**, 1938; G. D. PRESTON, *Phil. Mag.*, **26**, 855 (1938).

[2] N. F. MOTT and N. F. R. NABARRO, *Proc. Phys. Soc.*, **52**, 86 (1940); N. F. R. NABARRO, *Proc. Phys. Soc.*, **52**, 90 (1940); *Proc. Roy. Soc.*, **175**, 519 (1940).

CHAPTER IX

CREEP AND SECONDARY PLASTIC EFFECTS

32. Creep in Single Crystals.[1]—In the range of stress below the critical shearing stress for slip, as determined by a machine capable of measuring rates of elongation only relatively crudely, solids extend or contract slowly under load. This effect, known as "creep," has been studied most extensively on commercially interesting materials, since it is highly important when metals are stressed at elevated temperatures, as in turbines and boilers. Fortunately, there are available in addition the results of a few enlightening experiments on single crystals.

It should be emphasized that there is ample room for ambiguity in the definition of creep, since the term is used loosely in the literature. Thus, a rate of flow that is regarded as slip by an investigator who uses a very precise measuring instrument would be called creep by a practical investigator making cruder measurements. This reflects the commonly accepted viewpoint that there is an intimate connection between slip and creep. Actually, the end results of creep in single crystals appear to be closely the same as those of slip, inasmuch as the elongation occurs in a manner implying relative motion along definite crystallographic planes.

One of the distinguishing features of the process of slip is the production of slip lines, so that if the processes occurring during slip and creep were identical in any given case we might expect to establish this by observing slip bands in a specimen that has undergone creep. This phase of the topic has not been investigated so fully as it should be; however, Dushman[2] has recently

---

[1] The practical aspects of creep are discussed in the book by H. J. Tapsell, *Creep* (Oxford University Press, New York, 1931) and in the review article by J. J. Kanter, *A.S.M. Handbook* (1939). A treatment of the topic of creep along the general lines of this section has been given by W. Kauzmann, *Trans. A.I.M.E.*, **143**, 57 (1941).

[2] S. Dushman, to be published shortly in *J. Applied Phys.* In this work

observed slip bands during creep in single crystals of
aluminum.

In this connection, it should be mentioned that creep has been
observed in bismuth, which apparently exhibits[1] twinning, not
slip, when strained beyond the elastic limit rapidly, as in ordinary
tensile tests.   It is possible that in this metal the mechanism

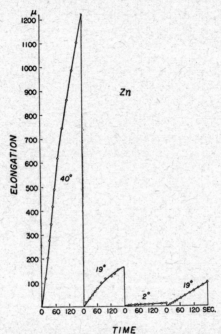

Fig. 82.—Creep curves for zinc obtained at several temperatures near room
temperature.   It may be observed that the rate of flow decreases with increasing
time during the initial stages of creep.

of creep has a closer resemblance to twinning than to slip; it is also
possible, however, that slip occurs along with twinning but is
responsible for only a small fraction of the elongation.   In the

Dushman and his associates have studied creep in recrystallized wires in
which the grain size is much larger than the diameter of the wires.   Measurements were made for various temperatures and various loadings (see Figs.
88 and 90).

[1] See C. F. ELAM, *The Distortion of Metal Crystals* (Oxford University
Press, New York, 1936); E. SCHMID and W. BOAS, *Kristallplastizität* (Verlag
Julius Springer, Berlin, 1936).

second case, the creep occurring at low stresses could be the residue of the slip occurring at high stresses.

The process of creep when regarded as a function of time can be divided into two ranges in the simplest cases. These ranges are clearly shown in Fig. 82, which shows[1] the elongation of zinc as a function of time in the borderline region between slip and creep. In all these cases, the curves are characterized by a rapid rise at short times for the virgin material and a steady flow at long times. This suggests the division shown in Fig. 83, in which the strain versus time curve is resolved as the sum

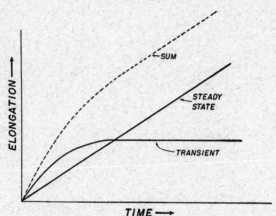

Fig. 83.—Hypothetical division of a creep curve into a transient and a steady-state component.

of a linear curve passing through the origin and a curve that starts linearly at the origin and asymptotically approaches a constant value. From the standpoint of velocity of flow, the second curve is analogous to a transient, since its contribution to the velocity is negligible at long times. The existence of this transient is recognized in practical work by reference to the "short-time" creep and to the steady, or "long-time," creep. We shall refer to the two components as the "transient" and "steady-state" parts.

It should be added that some investigators have obtained creep curves with single crystals that cannot readily be resolved in the simple fashion shown in Fig. 83. A curve of this type for

[1] W. Boas and E. Schmid, *Z. Physik*, **100**, 463 (1936).

zinc, obtained by R. F. Miller,[1] is shown in Fig. 84. The stress used in obtaining this curve was 8.0 g per mm[2], whereas that used in obtaining the curves of Fig. 82 was 176 g per mm[2]. Thus, the first is much smaller than the second. It may be seen that in Miller's case the elongation obeyed the usual relation for the first 40 hr, for the rate of flow decreased with increasing

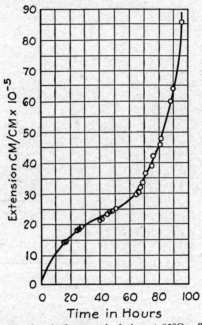

FIG. 84.—The creep of a single crystal of zinc at 25°C. The load employed was 8.0 g per mm[2]. It may be observed that a tertiary range of creep appears in this case. The time of observation is much longer in this case than in the cases shown in Fig. 82. (*After Miller.*)

time. However, it then exhibited a strong deviation. A similar "tertiary" range of creep has been observed[2] in single crystals of iron and of α brass. This tertiary range is probably caused by necking of the specimen.

Figure 85 shows an elongation versus time curve of brass for a shearing stress comparable with the critical shearing stress for slip in a well-annealed specimen. It should be observed that the

[1] R. F. MILLER, *Trans. A.I.M.E.*, **122**, 176 (1936).
[2] H. BURGHOFF and C. MATHEWSON, *A.I.M.E. Tech. Pub.* 1288 (1941).

scale of unit of creep is much coarser than in the previous curves in this chapter.   In this case, the creep cannot be resolved into transient and steady-state parts of the type shown in Fig. 83, for the rate increases during the first 600 hr.   There is a well-defined steady-state range, however, for the creep becomes zero for sufficiently long times on this scale of measurement.

The steady-state creep is strongly dependent upon temperature, being more rapid at high temperatures than at low.   It has been

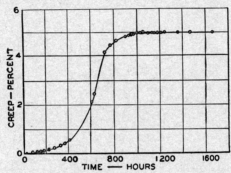

Fig. 85.—A creep curve for 70-30 brass at 25°C.   The resolved shearing stress in the slip plane was 1,100 g per mm². (*After Burghoff and Mathewson.*)

analyzed in several metals and seems generally to obey the equation

$$\text{Rate} = Ae^{-\frac{\epsilon}{kT}} \tag{1}$$

in which A and ϵ are constants.   Experimental values of ϵ are given in Table XIII.

Chalmers[1] has made a careful study of the transient creep of tin for very low stresses.   Creep for two specimens of tin of different purity is shown in Fig. 86.   The applied shearing stress was identical in the two cases; the specimens behaved somewhat differently, however.   This shows that the creep characteristics are strongly dependent upon the impurity content.   In the two cases shown in the figure, the creep vanished for long times.   It was found, however, that the steady-state creep was different from zero in cases in which the stress appreciably exceeded the value of 120 g per mm² for which the illustrated curves were

[1] B. CHALMERS, *Proc. Roy. Soc.*, **156**, 427 (1936); *J. Inst. Metals*, **61**, 103 (1937).

TABLE XIII.—VALUE OF THE ACTIVATION ENERGY ε FOR THE STEADY-STATE
CREEP RATE
(In kg cal/mol)

Metal	ε
Zinc	16.8
Cadmium	15.2
Bismuth	20.0
Tin	17.3

obtained.   Figure 87 illustrates the initial slope of the elongation versus time curve as a function of stress for the two types of tin.

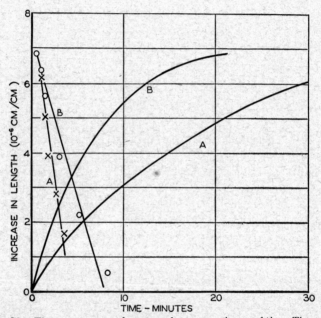

FIG. 86.—The creep curve at low stress for two specimens of tin.   The applied shearing stress was 120 g per mm² in both cases.   The heavier curves represent elongation versus time, whereas the other curves represent the logarithmic derivatives of these on a relative scale.   Curve A was obtained from Chempure tin, whereas curve B was obtained from Williams-Harvey tin.   (*After Chalmers.*)

This slope varies linearly with stress for both specimens in the range in which the steady-state rate vanishes.   Moreover, the lines for both specimens coincide in this range.   The curves break sharply upward at the stresses for which the steady-state rate becomes different from zero and continue to rise with continuously increasing slope.   It may be noted that the curves differ for the two specimens in the range where the steady-state rate is different from zero.

It was noted in Sec. 18 that, if it can be shown that the initial creep and stress curves generally obey the relation shown in Fig. 87, the critical shearing stress for slip can be defined unambiguously as the stress corresponding to the knee of the curve.

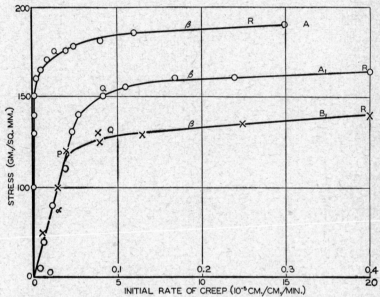

Fig. 87.—The relationship between stress and creep rate for two specimens of tin (see Fig. 86). The upper scale of creep rate applies to curves A_1 and B_1, whereas the lower one applies to curve A. A_1 and A were obtained from single crystals of Chempure tin, whereas curve B_1 was obtained from Williams-Harvey tin.

It is interesting to note that Gensamer and Mehl[1] have observed a type of creep which eventually stops in single crystals of α iron. The magnitude of the creep measured in this case is much larger than that with which Chalmers was concerned. Moreover, the elongation versus time curve does not start out linearly in this case, as it does in Chalmers's results. Consequently, it is probably safe to say that the type of creep observed by Gensamer and Mehl is not simply the transient component.

[1] M. GENSAMER and R. F. MEHL, *Metals Tech. Pub.* 893 (1938).

The interpretation of creep on the basis of the theory of dislocations is not difficult as long as we are interested only in obtaining a qualitative correspondence between the two. However, the theory has not yet advanced to a point where a quantitative treatment of creep can be expected. If the theory of dislocations developed previously is correct, we may expect any specimen of metal to possess a number of dislocations, even when thoroughly annealed, simply because obstructions such as impurity atoms prevent all dislocations from diffusing out during an annealing operation. If we grant this, the transient part of the creep can be explained as the strain resulting from the migration of these "trapped" dislocations under the combined influence of the externally applied stresses and temperature fluctuations. The fact that such flow eventually ceases would then imply that these residual dislocations eventually become stuck at regions where they meet opposing stresses. When the applied stress becomes sufficiently high to allow new dislocations to be generated, flow can occur even after the trapped dislocations have become stuck and the specimen exhibits a constant creep. If Chalmers's results for tin are found to be generally applicable, true slip may be said to occur as soon as the applied stresses are of sufficient magnitude to generate new dislocations.

It is found that creep occurs discontinuously in many metals for stresses near the value commonly designated as the critical shearing stress for slip. Generally speaking, the jumps decrease in size with decreasing temperature and increase in frequency with increasing temperature, so that they are not observable for a given specimen at all temperatures. The effect has been studied[1] with particular care in aluminum, zinc, and brass. In the case of zinc, in which the effect is observable in the vicinity of room temperature, Schmid and Valouch have shown conclusively that the discontinuities are associated with slip and not with twinning, which, as we saw in Chap. VI, also causes a discontinuous type of flow.

[1] A. F. JOFFÉ, *The Physics of Crystals* (McGraw-Hill Book Company, Inc., New York, 1928): M. CLASSEN-NEKLUDOWA, *Z. Physik*, **55**, 555 (1929); E. SCHMID and N. A. VALOUCH, *Z. Physik*, **75**, 531 (1932); Much as yet unpublished work on this effect has also been carried out by S. Dushman at the General Electric Research Laboratories.

It seems possible that this effect is related to the heating effects accompanying cold-work; that is, that the heat generated during the motion of one dislocation furnishes part of the thermal energy required for the next, and so forth. Since the energy required to produce cold-work is about ten times higher than the stored energy, it follows that the moving dislocation is the source of

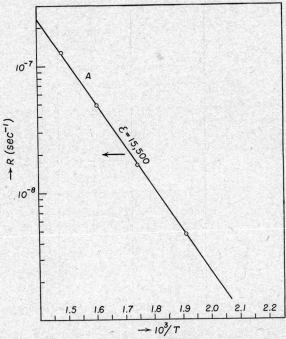

FIG. 88.—Relation between the creep rate and the reciprocal of the absolute temperature for aluminum. ϵ is expressed in units of calories per mol. (*After Dushman.*)

considerable thermal energy. This interpretation is in qualitative agreement with the fact that the effect is not observable at sufficiently low temperatures.

33. Creep in Polycrystals.[1]—The general facts concerning creep in polycrystals appear to be about the same as those for single crystals. In other words, creep can usually be analyzed into a transient and a steady-state part, the second of which is very sensitive to temperature and obeys Eq. (1) of the preceding sec-

[1] Tapsell, *op. cit.*; Kanter, *op. cit.*; Kauzmann, *op. cit.*

tion closely. Figure 88 shows,[1] for example, the linear relation that is valid between the reciprocal of the absolute temperature and the logarithm of the rate of creep in the case of aluminum.

It should be added that a tertiary range of creep in which the rate of flow increases rapidly with time in a manner similar to that shown in Fig. 84 is commonly observed in polycrystalline materi-

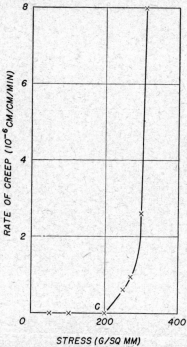

Fig. 89.—The rate of creep as a function of stress for a bicrystal of tin. (*After Chalmers.*)

als. The effect is of considerable commercial interest since it implies a breakdown in the serviceability of the material when it is placed under stress for a sufficiently long time. As in the case of single crystals, the onset of the tertiary range of creep is probably associated with a change in the nature of the flow. However,

[1] S. DUSHMAN, *op. cit.* The writer is indebted to Dr. Dushman for the use of Figs. 88 and 90 and for discussion of this topic prior to publication. The measurements were made on 10-mil wires composed of a few single crystals.

whereas the change is probably always the onset of necking in single crystals, it may be another process in the case of a polycrystalline specimen. For example, it could be caused by the separation of the material at grain boundaries.

Figure 89 shows the rate of creep as a function of stress for a bicrystal of tin, as determined by Chalmers.[1] It may be seen

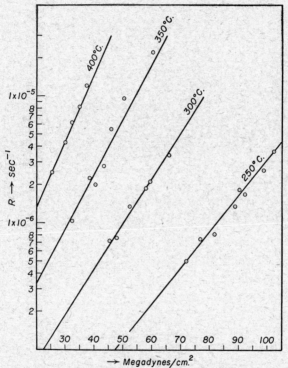

Fig. 90.—Relation between the rate of creep and the applied stress for aluminum at several temperatures. (*After Dushman.*)

that the creep becomes negligibly small for finite values of the stress in this case, which shows that the linear dependence found for single crystals of tin (Fig. 87) does not carry over to polycrystals. It is not known whether the difference between polycrystals and single crystals found in the case of tin occurs

---

[1] B. Chalmers, *J. Inst. Metals*, **61**, 103 (1937).

generally, since rates of creep as small as those measured by Chalmers have not yet been widely studied.

Dushman[1] has made an extensive study of the dependence on stress of creep in many metals for rates of the order of 10^{-5} per

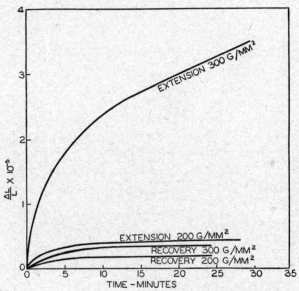

Fig. 91.—The upper two curves show the extension versus time for specimens of tin stressed at 300 g per mm² and 200 g per mm², respectively. The lower two curves show the subsequent contraction when the stress is released. (*After Chalmers.*)

sec. His results show that, at a given temperature, the dependence on stress is usually given by the equation

$$\text{Rate} = Ae^{aS}$$

where S is the stress and A and a are temperature-dependent constants. The extent to which this law is obeyed is shown in Fig. 90.

34. Creep Recovery.—Let us consider a specimen of metal that has been elongated as a result of plastic flow under tension. Immediately after the stresses are released, the specimen undergoes an *elastic* contraction, corresponding to the displacement from the point A to the point O' in Fig. 46 (page 72). It is

[1] DUSHMAN, *op. cit.*

found in the case of polycrystalline specimens that the material is not in complete equilibrium after this initial contraction, for it continues to contract for a subsequent period of time. This contraction is generally larger the larger the initial extension, but it can be observed even in cases in which the extension has been produced by the process of creep. Figure 91 shows, for example, the creep recovery that occurs[1] in tin after creep. The upper pair of curves represent the elongations obtained for different loads, whereas the lower pair represent the subsequent contractions of the two specimens. It may be seen that one of the specimens was extended for stresses so low that the steady-state creep was zero, whereas the other was stressed in a range where the steady-state creep was finite. The recovery curves are nearly the same, although the total recovery is larger for the specimen that was elongated farthest. It is evident that the recovery bears a strong resemblance to creep.

Creep recovery apparently can be given a satisfactory explanation on the basis of a principle proposed by Masing.[2] He pointed out that individual grains in a polycrystal deform differently during plastic flow because of differences in orientation and the anisotropy of crystals. As a result, the stresses resulting from both the applied load and the degree of work-hardening in each grain are different. When the externally applied stresses are released, those grains in which the stresses are highest have a natural tendency to undergo the highest elastic contraction. They are not able to contract to a point where the stress is entirely relieved, however, for in so doing they would necessarily compress neighboring crystals to a point where the stresses in the latter would reverse sign. Actually, they contract until the average compressive stress in the specimen is zero, in which state some of the grains possess residual compressive stresses and others residual extensive stresses. If the temperature is sufficiently high for creep to occur, these residual stresses are dissipated as a result of a gradual flow. It is easy to see that the crystals under compression should yield most, for they have been work-hardened least and hence should be in the most favorable condition for

---

[1] B. CHALMERS, *J. Inst. Metals*, **61**, 103 (1937).

[2] G. MASING, *Wiss. Siemens Konzern*, **3**, 231 (1924); **4**, 74, 244 (1925); **5**, 135, 142 (1926).

further plastic flow. As a result, the specimen should contract as the residual stresses are released.

It is clear that the picture would be completely reversed if the specimen were placed initially under compression instead of tension. In this case, the crystals in which the highest compressive stresses have occurred place their neighbors under tension when the external forces are released and, as a result, produce a slow elongation of the specimen if the temperature is sufficiently high for creep to occur.

35. The Bauschinger Effect.[1]—If the previous interpretation of creep recovery is correct, we might expect that just after a polycrystalline specimen has been unloaded, following plastic flow, it would contain residual stresses which would aid in producing a deformation of opposite sign. Thus we might expect the critical shearing stress required to produce plastic compression following an elongation to be lower than the critical shearing stress required to produce further elongation. An effect of this type was first observed by Bauschinger[2] and was explained qualitatively on the basis of Masing's principle, discussed in the preceding section. Figure 92 shows[3] the Bauschinger effect in fine-grained brass. Figure 92a is the stress-strain curve obtained during an extension of a virgin specimen of the material by a few percent. The critical shearing stress is about 10 kg per mm². Essentially the same value would have been obtained if the specimen had been compressed instead of extended. Figure 92b shows the stress-strain curve for further extension after an initial extension such as that which yielded Fig. 92a. Figure 92c shows the stress-strain curve similar to Fig. 92a for extension following compression. It may be seen that the critical shearing stress for this deformation is very small for the range of compression corresponding to the initial extension. In fact, the initial yield stress for compression is lower than the yield stress of the virgin material. The last figure of the set shows the stress-strain curve obtained in compression after the originally extended specimen has been annealed at 150°C for several hours. The Bauschinger effect has disappeared, but the hardness remains, which shows that the factors

[1] See Schmid and Boas, *op. cit.*
[2] J. Bauschinger, *Ziviling.*, **27**, 289 (1881).
[3] G. Sachs and H. Shoji, *Z. Physik*, **45**, 776 (1927).

contributing to the Bauschinger effect are not immediately connected with the hardening. We may, in fact, conclude that creep recovery occurred during the annealing operation carried out before Fig. 92d was obtained.

A quantitative treatment of the Bauschinger effect on the basis of the concepts used to explain creep recovery has been carried out by Heyn.[1] He found that curves of the type of Fig. 92c

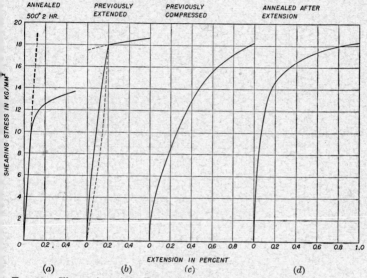

Fig. 92.—Illustration of the Bauschinger effect in fine-grained polycrystalline brass. (a) shows the extension-versus-time curve for the virgin material. (b) is the stress-extension diagram obtained after previous extension. (c) is the same curve obtained after previous compression. (d) is the stress-strain curve similar to (c) obtained when the specimen is annealed at relatively low temperature after compression; this anneal does not affect the hardness but removes the Bauschinger effect. (*After Sachs and Shoji.*)

could be obtained for polycrystals in a reasonable manner. Heyn's explanation of the Bauschinger effect actually antedates the explanation of creep recovery given above. For this reason, the residual stresses between grains that appear after release of load are commonly called *Heyn stresses*.

We should not expect Heyn stresses to appear in a homogeneously strained single crystal since both the stress and the degree of work-hardening should be the same throughout the specimen.

[1] E. HEYN, *Festband Kaiser Wilhelm Gesellschaft* (1921), p. 131; *J. Inst. Metals*, **12**, 3 (1914).

As a result, we should not expect to observe the Bauschinger effect or creep recovery in a good single crystal. Although single crystals usually obey this rule, Sachs and Shoji[1] actually have observed a well-developed Bauschinger effect in single crystals of brass. This metal is highly anisotropic, and it is probable that

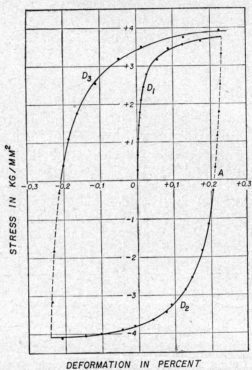

FIG. 93.—The stress-strain diagram for a single crystal of brass obtained during a cyclical deformation process. The negative strains correspond to compressions, the positive ones to elongations. The branch D_1 corresponds to the virgin material.

small inhomogeneities in plastic flow, when coupled with this anisotropy, are sufficient to account for the observation. Figure 93 shows a complete hysteresis type of stress-strain curve for one of the single crystals used in this work. The branches D_1 and D_3 of the curve were obtained in tension, whereas D_2 was obtained in compression. The Bauschinger effect is clearly indicated by

[1] SACHS and SHOJI, op. cit.

the difference in slopes of the D_1 and D_2 branches at corresponding points relative to the axis of zero stress.

36. The Elastic Aftereffect.—Another interesting secondary effect that is observed commonly in polycrystals and occasionally in single crystals, such as the specimens of brass in which Sachs and Shoji observed the Bauschinger effect, is the *elastic aftereffect*. This is illustrated in Fig. 94 for a single crystal of brass. It is found that the stress-strain curve obtained when the specimen is unloaded and then reloaded is not a single-valued function but has the form shown in the figure.

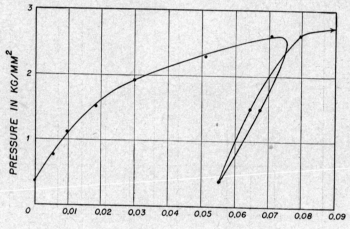

FIG. 94.—The elastic aftereffect in a compressed single crystal of brass.

This effect is obviously closely connected with creep recovery and may readily be explained on the basis of Heyn stresses. We may suppose that the contraction is entirely elastic when the specimen is first unloaded. As soon as the elastic forces in the regions that have undergone the most extensive plastic deformation are released, the remaining regions exert stresses on them of such sign as to reverse the original deformation. These stresses increase as the unloading proceeds and cause a small amount of irreversible plastic flow.

37. The Dependence of the Stress-Strain Curve on the Rate of Flow.—The fact that the rate of plastic flow depends upon stress suggests, conversely, that the stress-strain curve for a material is dependent upon the rate at which it is deformed. This effect[1] has been observed in several solids and has been the object of extensive research during recent years. The effect is apparently a comparatively small one for most metals in the range of strain above the creep range that is of customary interest. This range extends from values of the order of 0.01 per sec to values of the order of 100 per sec. The existing evidence indicates that the

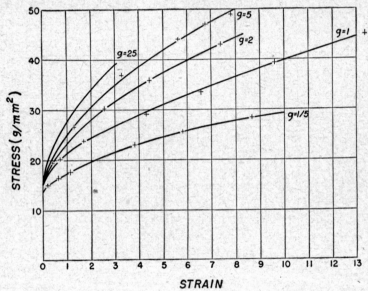

Fig. 95.—Stress-strain curves of naphthalene for various velocities of flow. These curves are averages of somewhat less regular experimental curves. The unit of velocity of flow corresponding to $g = 1$ is 3.1 per hour. (*After Kochendörfer.*)

critical shearing stress varies approximately logarithmically with the strain rate, that is,

$$S = A \log R + B \qquad (1)$$

in which R is the strain rate, S is the critical shearing stress for plastic flow at the rate R, and A and B are constants. If this

[1] A recent summary of experiments on the deformation of metals at high rates of speed has been given by M. Manjoine and A. Nadai, *Proc. A.S.T.M.*, **40**, 822 (1941). See also the paper by D. S. Clark and G. Daetwyler, *Proc. A.S.T.M.*, **38**, 98 (1938).

relation is inverted, it yields the equation

$$R = Ce^{\frac{S}{A}}$$

in which $C = e^{-\frac{A}{B}}$. Thus the logarithmic law for the influence of strain rate implies that the strain rate varies exponentially with stress. This result agrees with that shown in Fig. 90 for creep.

In the case of copper,[1] the magnitude of A in Eq. (1) is such that a thousand-fold variation in strain rate has the effect of increasing the critical stress by about 25 percent. This variation of speed covers the range extending from ordinary "static" tensile tests to those encountered during high-speed rolling operations. Measurements at high strain rates have not yet progressed to a point at which it can be said whether or not the speed effect is of the same order of magnitude in all metals.

There is evidence that the influence of speed may be much greater in some nonmetals than in metals. Figure 95 shows,[2] for example, the stress-strain curves of naphthalene in a range of strain rate near that of interest for creep. The strain rates employed in each of the tests differed by a factor five, the basic unit being $g = 3.1$ per hr. It may be seen that the increase in stress is about 25 percent for each fivefold increase in strain rate.

[1] See MANJOINE and NADAI, *op. cit.*
[2] A. KOCHENDÖRFER, *Z. Kryst.*, **97**, 263 (1937); *Z. Physik*, **108**, 244 (1938).

CHAPTER X

INTERNAL FRICTION[1]

38. Introduction.—If any solid is set into oscillation, it eventually dissipates its vibrational energy even though it is so completely isolated from its surroundings that sound loss and similar effects are negligible. This dissipative effect is called *internal friction*. It is convenient to express the magnitude of the internal friction in terms of the *decrement* Δ, defined by the relation

$$\Delta = \frac{\Delta W}{W}$$

where ΔW is the energy dissipated per cycle and W is the total vibrational energy. Materials in which the internal friction is small are characterized by values of Δ of the order of magnitude 10^{-7}, whereas those in which it is large may be characterized by values of the order of 0.1.

There are two important sources of internal friction in solids that are not ferromagnetic, namely, plastic flow and intergranular thermal currents. The first, which usually is independent of frequency in the range of frequency investigated at present, may be regarded as arising from the oscillatory motion of dislocations, whereas the second, which has a characteristic frequency dependence, arises from intercrystalline temperature differences that originate in the thermoelastic effect. The second type has been observed only in polycrystalline materials, so that the first type may be isolated by investigating single crystals. It should be added that ferromagnetic metals, such as iron, cobalt, and nickel, exhibit an additional type of internal damping that originates in their ferromagnetism. Although this type is of interest, we shall defer a discussion of it until Sec. 83.

Historically, the internal friction of ferromagnetic origin was investigated first. However, the first systematic interpretive

[1] This chapter is not essential for the continuity of the book and may be omitted in a first reading.

work is that of Zener[1] and his associates, who studied and explained the internal friction of thermoelastic origin found in polycrystals. The internal friction of plastic origin was subsequently investigated by Read, Lawson, and Zener, although some investigations had been carried out earlier by Wegel and Walther.

In recent years, internal friction has been studied over a frequency range extending from about one hundred cycles to about one hundred kilocycles.

39. Internal Friction in Single Crystals.—As was mentioned above, the internal friction of plastic origin may be isolated by studying single crystals.[2] Let us begin by considering the internal friction of single crystals of copper. The decrement Δ in such a crystal is independent of frequency in the kilocycle range; however, it varies with the amplitude of oscillation in the manner shown in Fig. 96. The first striking fact is that the internal friction decreases very much as a result of anneal. In addition, the decrement increases with increasing strain amplitude. The change of decrement with amplitude is completely reversible for the range of amplitude shown in the figure; however, it is not reversible when the amplitude is increased by a factor one hundred or more. In this case, the internal friction at small amplitudes is larger after the specimen has been subject to the large-amplitude oscillation than it was previously. That is, the effect of the large stress is the reverse of that of the annealing operation.

The experimental results for copper may be explained simply in a qualitative manner on the following assumptions:

a. The internal friction shown in Fig. 96 arises from the motion of dislocations already present in the crystal under the action of

[1] The leading papers by Zener and his associates are as follows: C. ZENER, *Phys. Rev.*, **52**, 230 (1937), **53**, 90 (1938); W. OTIS and R. NUCKOLLS, *Phys. Rev.*, **53**, 100 (1938); R. H. RANDALL, F. C. ROSE, and C. ZENER, *Phys. Rev.*, **56**, 343 (1939); C. ZENER, *Proc. Phys. Soc.*, **52**, 152 (1940), *Phys. Rev.*, **60**, 455 (1941); C. ZENER and R. H. RANDALL, *Trans. A.I.M.E.*, **137**, 41 (1940); C. ZENER, H. CLARKE, and C. S. SMITH, *Trans. A.I.M.E.*, **147** (1942); C. ZENER, D. VAN WINKLE, and H. NIELSEN, *Trans. A.I.M.E.*, **147** (1942); C. ZENER, *Trans. A.I.M.E.*, **147** (1942).

[2] The most extensive investigation of the internal friction of single crystals has been carried out by T. A. Read. His principal publications on the subject are as follows: *Phys. Rev.*, **58**, 371 (1940); *J. Applied Phys.*, **12**, 100 (1941); *Trans. A.I.M.E.*, **143**, 30 (1941).

the stresses that give rise to the oscillation. These stresses do irreversible work on the dislocations and hence dissipate energy, just as during plastic flow of the type discussed in Chap. VI. It is reasonable to suppose that the decrement would increase with increasing number of dislocations, as long as they do not interact, for the number of dissipating centers would then increase.

b. The number of dislocations in the annealed specimen is smaller than in the unannealed one because some of the disloca-

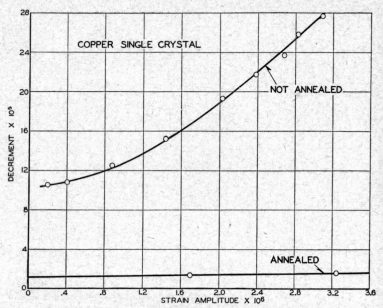

Fig. 96.—The internal friction of a single crystal of copper before and after being annealed. It may be seen that the internal friction increases with increasing strain amplitude and decreases during annealing. (*After Read.*)

tions present before annealing diffuse out of the crystals during the heat-treatment. If this is true, we should expect the internal friction of an annealed single crystal to increase when it is strained by an amount sufficient to introduce new dislocations. As we saw above, this is the case.

c. In order to explain the reversible rise of internal friction with amplitude of strain, we must assume that not all dislocations can be moved with the same ease in the range of stress employed. In other words, a higher stress is required to move some than to move others.   This postulate is entirely reasonable; for as we saw in Chap. VI, dislocations of the type introduced by Prandtl, Orowan, and Taylor interact with one another.   Thus those which are situated in regions where the density of dislocations is high should have more difficulty in moving than those in places where it is low.

The fact that the decrement of an unannealed single crystal of copper does not automatically decrease at room temperature is in agreement with the fact that this metal does not resoften at room

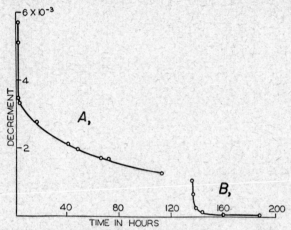

Fig. 97.—The variation with time of a single crystal of zinc.   The amplitude of oscillation employed during these measurements was constant and very small. During the period of time *A*, the crystal was maintained at room temperature. It may be seen that the internal friction gradually decreases.   At the end of this period, it was annealed for the time indicated.   Measurements *B* were made during the subsequent period of time.   (*After Read.*)

temperature.   Conversely, we should expect the internal friction of an unannealed single crystal of zinc to decrease with time at room temperature, if our assumption concerning the outward diffusion of dislocations is correct, for this metal does resoften at room temperature.   Figure 97 furnishes actual support of this expectation.   It shows the decrease in decrement that takes place in zinc for low amplitudes of oscillation at room temperature. The crystal was initially unannealed.   Curve *A* shows the decrease that occurs during a period of 120 hr.   At the end of this time the crystal was annealed; curve *B* shows the subsequent behavior of the internal friction.   It is to be noted that the internal friction is nearly as high after the annealing operation as before; however, the decrease is much more rapid. The relatively high value observed just after annealing was probably caused by the handling the crystal received while being mounted for measurement. Evidently the dislocations introduced during

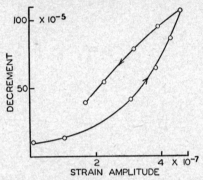

FIG. 98.—Irreversible dependence of the internal friction of a single crystal of zinc on the amplitude. The arrows indicate the course of the experiment. (*After Read.*)

the mounting are more easily freed than those present at the end of run *A*.

Dislocations can be introduced into zinc with comparative ease at room temperature. Figure 98 shows the irreversible dependence on strain amplitude of the internal friction of a single crystal of zinc for a range of amplitude comparable with that

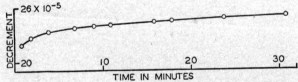

FIG. 99.—The manner in which the internal friction of a single crystal of zinc increases after the amplitude of vibration has been increased.

shown in Fig. 96 for copper. It may be seen that the internal friction at a given amplitude is higher just after the specimen has been vibrated at a greater amplitude than it was previously. Figure 99 shows the manner in which the internal friction increases with time as the result of an increase in vibrational amplitude.

It should be added that the internal friction of zinc, unlike that of copper, depends on frequency in the kilocycle range. This dependence, which is as yet unexplained, has not been analyzed carefully; however, it appears to vary inversely as the first power of the frequency. It is also interesting to note that in zinc, for a given amplitude of oscillation, the decrement increases as the component of shearing stress in the basal, or shearing-stress, plane increases. This fact illustrates further the close correlation between the type of internal friction considered here and the slip properties.

It will be seen in the next section that experiments on poly-crystals show that the dislocations which are principally responsi-ble for the internal friction are not the same as those responsible for hardness. The experimental facts that compel us to draw this conclusion are as follows:

a. The internal friction of a hardened specimen of copper or brass may be decreased by a low-temperature annealing operation that does not decrease the hardness. This shows that the mild annealing process causes the dislocations responsible for internal friction to diffuse out of the specimen but does not affect those responsible for hardness.

b. The internal friction of both copper and brass passes through a maximum and then decreases as the amount of cold-work increases. This shows that not all dislocations contribute to the internal friction, for the number of dislocations introduced into a specimen by cold-work should not decrease with extended work-ing if the picture suggested in Chap. VI is correct.

A reasonable interpretation of (*a*) is as follows: Only the newly formed pairs of dislocations which extend over a few atomic dis-tances can contribute to the internal friction at the relatively high frequencies at which it ordinarily is measured. The longer dislocations, which grow from the smaller ones during extensive plastic flow and which are responsible for the hardness of the material, do not react to frequencies as high as this. It may readily be shown that the cooperative action of many atoms that is needed for the motion of a long dislocation requires much more time than does the similar motion of a short dislocation. The short dislocations diffuse from the crystal more readily than the longer ones, since they are at an earlier stage of formation.

Hence they may be removed by an anneal that does not affect the bulk hardness.

A possible interpretation of (*b*) along the same lines is as follows: As the density of dislocations grows during extensive cold-working of a metal, the stresses opposing the motion of any dislocation becomes larger. Hence, the material hardens and the internal friction decreases. This decrease is not observed during the early stages of cold-work because the rate at which dislocations increase, and hence the rate at which new dissipating centers occur, more than counterbalances the increase in difficulty of motion.

40. The Internal Friction of Polycrystals.[1]—It was mentioned in Sec. 38 that two types of internal friction occur in polycrystals, namely, that having plastic origin and that originating in the thermoelastic effect. We shall first consider the second of these.

When a crystal is stressed suddenly, its temperature changes. The change in temperature is proportional to the stress and reverses its sign if the sign of the stress is reversed. Since the stresses in polycrystals are not uniform but vary from grain to grain, it follows that in these the temperature resulting from the thermoelastic effect also varies from grain to grain. Now if the stresses vary slowly compared with the time required for heat to flow between regions having different temperatures, the temperature remains constant and the transfer of mechanical energy into heat, and vice versa, takes place reversibly. In this case, the net amount of heat generated during a complete cycle is zero, and there is no contribution to the internal friction. Similarly, if the variations in stress take place so rapidly that no heat flows during a stress cycle, the process is said to occur "adiabatically," for every grain of the specimen behaves as if it were thermally isolated. It follows that the net conversion of elastic energy into heat during a complete cycle is also zero in this case. However, if the frequency or the thermal conductivity is such that the process is neither isothermal nor adiabatic, the conversion of

---

[1] Papers other than those of Zener and his associates that deal with the internal friction of polycrystals are as follows: K. BENNEWITZ and H. RÖTGER, *Physik. Z.*, **37**, 578 (1936), **19**, 521 (1938); R. L. WEGEL and H. WALTHER, *Physics*, **6**, 141 (1935); A. W. LAWSON, *Phys. Rev.*, **60**, 330 (1941).

mechanical energy into heat is not reversible and there is a finite contribution to the internal friction from the thermoelastic effect.

Zener has pointed out that, if the average applied stress is uniform throughout the specimen, the critical distance for thermal diffusion in a polycrystal should be the average linear dimension of the grains, for stresses should vary abruptly from one grain to another. Reasoning from this on the basis of dimensional analysis, he suggested that the internal friction should depend on the dimensionless quantity fd^2/D. Here d is the grain diameter,

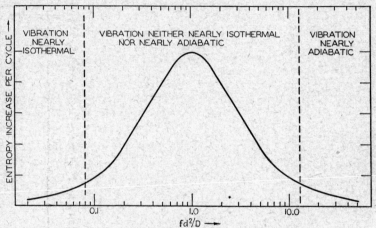

Fig. 100.—The variation of the internal friction of thermoelastic origin with the dimensionless variable fd^2/D. (*After Zener.*)

f is the frequency, and D is the thermal-diffusion constant defined by the equation

$$D = \frac{\text{thermal conductivity}}{(\text{specific heat})(\text{density})}.$$

In other words, for a given material the relative value of the internal friction should be a universal function $g(fd^2/D)$. Figure 100 shows schematically the manner in which this function should depend on its argument. It has a peak near the value unity and decreases to zero on either side. This type of dependence of internal friction has been observed in brass.

The factors contributing to the absolute value of the thermoelastic internal friction have been investigated by Zener but will not be discussed here since they would lead us too far afield. His work shows that in general we should expect the internal friction arising from variations of stress between grains to be smaller the more nearly elastically isotropic the material is.

If the average stress is not uniform throughout a specimen, as during the transverse vibration of a reed, there will be an additional contribution to the thermoelastic internal friction resulting from the variations in temperature across the specimen. This contribution is determined by a function similar to that shown in Fig. 100. In this case, the argument is fL^2/D where L is the distance between the points of maximum temperature difference, which is the thickness of the specimen in the case of the vibrating reed. The thermoelastic internal friction was first discovered and studied systematically in inhomogeneously stressed systems of this type.

It should be noted that the thermoelastic internal friction should be independent of amplitude, whereas that of plastic origin may not, as we have seen in the preceding section.

The separation of the internal friction of plastic origin from the thermoelastic contribution can be carried out in several ways. For example, if measurements are carried out for frequencies extending into the adiabatic or isothermal regions, the plastic component will appear as an additive constant on a function of the form shown in Fig. 100. Thus, in the case of three specimens of brass of different grain size, a residual plastic decrement of $0.15 \cdot 10^{-5}$ was determined by extrapolating the internal friction to the region of low frequencies.

Barnes and Zener carried out a similar separation at fixed frequency in zinc possessing about 0.5 percent impurities. Measurements were made on specimens possessing four grain sizes for various temperatures in the range from 0 to 100°C. The values of fd^2/D at the frequency used were 0.008, 0.008, 0.02, and 0.8 for the four specimens. In the first three cases, the internal friction varied with temperature in the manner

$$\Delta = Ae^{-\frac{\epsilon}{kT}} \tag{1}$$

the constant ϵ being the same in all cases and the constant A varying inversely as the linear dimensions of the grains. In the fourth case, in which the thermoelastic internal friction should be near its maximum value, the internal friction could be expressed in the form

$$\Delta = C + A_4 e^{-\frac{\epsilon}{kT}} \tag{2}$$

in which C is independent of temperature and is equal to $44 \cdot 10^{-5}$, ϵ is the same as in the other three cases, and A_4 is such that its ratio to the values of A occurring in other cases varies inversely as the grain sizes. The investigators conclude that the temperature-dependent term has its origin in the plasticity of the material whereas the constant in Eq. (2) corresponds to the thermoelastic dissipation. They also conclude from the dependence of the constant A in Eq. (1) upon grain size that the internal friction is proportional to the area of the grains rather than to the volume of the material.

The plastic internal friction of polycrystalline brass has been studied as a function of temperature, frequency, and cold-work. Above 200°C, that is, above the recrystallization temperature, this internal friction is similar to that described above for zinc. In other words, it is independent of frequency, varies inversely as the grain size, and depends upon temperature in the manner expressed by Eq. (2). Since the magnitude of this internal friction depends upon the area of the grains, Zener has suggested that it is caused either by flow along the boundaries of grains or by the motion of twinned areas. It is to be noted that present evidence indicates that this component is important only above the recrystallization temperature. Below 200°C, the internal friction of polycrystalline brass changes its character and is principally of thermoelastic origin in the specimens on which the measurements were made.

Presumably the type of internal friction of plastic origin found in single crystals of copper should also occur in polycrystals. This has apparently been observed at room temperature in polycrystalline copper and brass although the work has not yet been carried out with sufficient care to establish the identity with certainty. In both cases, the specimens on which measurements were made were chosen so that the internal friction of thermoelastic origin could be easily separated. A residual component was found that was independent of frequency and that was

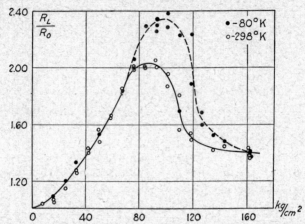

Fig. 101.—The relative increase in the internal friction of polycrystalline copper with stress. The solid circles refer to measurements made at 80°K, whereas the open circles refer to measurements made at room temperature. (*After Lawson.*)

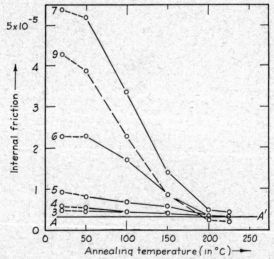

Fig. 102.—Curves showing the decrease in internal friction of six work-hardened specimens of 70-30 brass as a result of anneals which did *not* decrease the hardness of the specimens. The initial variations in internal friction were obtained by varying the degree of cold-work. Line *AA'* represents the internal friction of the annealed stock from which the specimens were made. (*After Zener, Clarke, and Smith.*)

affected both by cold-work and by the annealing temperature, as in the single crystals. Figure 101 shows the variation of the internal friction of polycrystalline copper in the adiabatic range of frequency, as a function of the amount of previous stress to which the specimens have been subject. It may be seen that the internal friction passes through a maximum and falls. A similar maximum was observed in brass. As mentioned at the end of the preceding section, this type of maximum suggests that not all the dislocations contribute to the internal friction.

Figure 102 shows the decrease of internal friction observed in brass when the specimens are annealed without reduction in hardness. An explanation of this effect was given at the end of the preceding section.

CHAPTER XI

RUPTURE AND FATIGUE

41. Rupture in Single Crystals.[1]—Any crystalline material ruptures when placed under sufficiently high tensile stress. Careful work indicates that associated with each crystallographic plane of a single crystal there is a characteristic normal stress under which the crystal will rupture on this plane. Since this normal stress is usually widely different for differently oriented planes, it can be measured for only one or two of the weakest planes. This stress is very sensitive to the previous history of the specimen in the case of nonmetallic substances, such as salts; however, it is much less sensitive in the ductile metals.

It is probably well to point out here that a material may fail as a result of shear as well as of tensile rupture. Thus under appropriate conditions a single crystal may shear in two along a slip plane. Similarly, a section of a sheet of metal may be sheared from the sheet by a punching operation. During such processes the stresses that produce the separation are shearing stresses of the type considered in the previous chapters. The process of rupture treated in this chapter is essentially different in nature.

The true critical tensile stress for metals appears to be almost independent of the amount of plastic flow that has occurred in the crystal. For example, Figure 103 shows[2] the dependence on the previous shearing strain of the rupture stress of a number of specimens of zinc at liquid air temperature. In all these cases, the specimens broke on the basal plane. It may be seen that the spread in values is of the order of 3 and that any dependence on shearing strain lies nearly within this spread. It should be added that the critical rupture stress appears to be practically

[1] Summaries of experimental material are given in the books by E. Schmid and W. Boas, *Kristallplastizität* (Verlag Julius Springer, Berlin, 1936) and by C. F. Elam, *The Distortion of Metal Crystals* (Oxford University Press, New York, 1936).

[2] W. Fahrenhorst and E. Schmid, *Z. Physik.*, **64,** 845 (1930).

independent of temperature in the range from room temperature to liquid-hydrogen temperature in both zinc and bismuth, the only metals for which extensive temperature tests have been made thus far. This conclusion is not to be confused with the common observation that the energy required to fracture a notched specimen in a Charpy or Izod test is frequently dependent upon temperature. The system of stresses occurring in a notched specimen

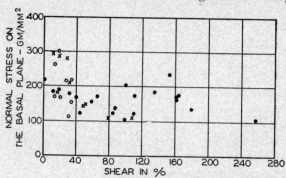

Fig. 103.—Dependence of the critical rupture stress on the amount of previous extension for a number of zinc crystals. The experiments were carried out at −185°C and indicate a slight downward trend. The crystals ruptured on the basal planes. (*After Fahrenhorst and Schmid.*)

is far more complicated than that in a simple tension test, and the impact energy required for rupture in the former is a function of the ductility of the material as well as of its inherent tensile stress.

TABLE XIV.—THE RUPTURE STRENGTHS OF SINGLE CRYSTALS
(In kg/mm²)

Crystal	Plane	Temperature, °C	S_b
Bismuth............................	(111)	20	0.32
	....	−185	0.32
Antimony...........................	(111)	20	0.66
Zinc...............................	Basal	20	0.18
	....	−185	0.18
	....	−255	0.18
	(0$\bar{1}$0)	−185	1.80
Silver chloride.....................	(100)	20	∼10
Sodium chloride....................	(100)	20	∼10

Values of the rupture stresses for the single crystals of several substances are given in Table XIV. Measurements for different crystallographic planes and for different temperatures are given if available.

It may be noted that the two salts appear to be much stronger than the simpler metals which are listed. Actually, this fact is somewhat deceptive, for the high values of the rupture stress of most salts usually can be achieved only under very special conditions, such as when the salts are moistened with water. The effect of moisture on the alkali halides has been studied extensively. It has been found in rock salt, for example, that the values of the rupture stress may be raised by wetting from about 0.5 kg per mm² to the reproducible value given in the table. The accepted explanation of this effect is that the unmoistened specimens contain many fine surface cracks which act as sources of stress magnification and weaken the crystals. Such regions are commonly called *stress raisers* in practice. The solvent action of water operates to remove or smooth these cracks in such a way that the stress magnification arising from them is lowered to a negligible value. The influence of surface cracks has also been studied in mica and in glass, and similar conclusions concerning their weakening action have been drawn for these materials. It should be added that some salts, such as silver chloride, whose rupture stress is listed in the table, resemble metals more closely than the alkali halides in being nearly insensitive to previous history.

A theoretical estimate of the rupture stress of an ideal crystal may be made in the following way, suggested by Polanyi:[1] A part of the work expended in breaking a crystal reappears as the energy of the newly formed surface. Thus, if we assume that the major part of the attractive forces between the two halves of a breaking specimen operates for distances of the same order of magnitude as the spacing d between neighboring planes, a lower limit to the theoretical breaking stress S_b may be obtained from the equation

$$S_b d = 2F \tag{1}$$

where F is the energy required to form one square centimeter of surface and the factor two enters in the right-hand side because

[1] M. POLANYI, *Z. Physik*, **7**, 323 (1921)

two surfaces are formed during breaking. Now F cannot be readily measured for solids, but it can be measured for liquids, since it is just the surface tension, as we saw in Sec. 13. The values of S_b computed from the measured values of F for molten metals and salts by the use of Eq. (1) appear in Table XV. It may be seen that in the metals the computed lower limit to S_b is about a thousand times larger than the observed values. Zwicky[1] has made a more careful estimate of the value for sodium chloride on the basis of the ionic theory of salts and has obtained a theoretical value of 200 kg per mm² in place of the value of 84 kg per mm² estimated by the use of Eq. (1).

TABLE XV.—THEORETICAL VALUE OF THE RUPTURE STRESS
(In kg/mm²)

Substance	Min. Eq. (7)	Max. (0.5E)	S_b (obs.)
Al	372	3,000	
Ag	656	4,000	
Au	782	4,000	
Bi	247	......	0.32
Cd	416	3,500	
Fe	~1,200	10,000	
Cu	885	6,000	
Ga	267		
Hg	320		
K	165		
Na	122		
Pb	261	800	
Pt	125	8,000	
Sb	249	......	0.66
Se	63		
Sn	357	2,000	
Zn	580	5,000	0.18
AgCl	93	......	~10
NaCl	84	......	~10

An upper limit for the critical breaking stress of any ideal crystal may be obtained through reasoning analogous to that used in evaluating the critical shearing stress of a perfect crystal (Sec.

[1] F. ZWICKY, *Physik. Z.*, **24**, 131 (1923).

22).   If we assume that a tension strain of about 0.5 is required to produce a deviation from Hooke's law for the forces between atoms in a perfect lattice, the stress at which rupture should be observed is of the order of magnitude $0.5E$ where E is Young's modulus.   Values of this quantity are also given in Table XV. It may be seen that they are somewhat higher than those derived by the use of Eq. (1).

As in the case of the critical shearing stress for slip, we may conclude from this discrepancy between the observed and calculated values of S_b that lattice imperfections have a weakening influence on the tensile strength of crystals.

Among the suggestions[1] that have been offered to account for the source of weakness, the most plausible is based on the assumption that all crystals contain cracks at block boundaries which are produced during growth.   If this viewpoint is adopted, it would appear necessary to assume that the weak spots occur in a fairly regular fashion, for Fig. 103 shows that in some cases the rupture stress in different crystals depends upon previous history to within a factor as small as 3.   Since the total stress magnification factor is of the order 1,000 this seems to imply that the weak spots differ from specimen to specimen of the same material by no more than 1 percent.   It is difficult to imagine that weak spots having this degree of regularity could arise as a result of accidents in growth.   It is possible, however, that measurements such as those shown in Fig. 103 were made on crystals prepared so nearly in the same way that the accidents of growth are nearly the same in all specimens and that a much wider range of values would have been obtained if the crystals had been made under different conditions and from different starting materials.

One of the great advantages of this picture is that it readily explains the fact that breakdown is practically insensitive to temperature, at least in the range well below the melting point.   If the imperfections occur during growth, they should be completely frozen in the specimen at a temperature near or lower than room temperature in metals such as zinc and bismuth.

It has frequently been suggested that the weakness of crystals is related to temperature fluctuations and that the stresses produced

[1] The relation between weakness and cracks was first stressed by A. A. Griffiths, *Phil. Trans. Roy. Soc.*, **221**, 163 (1920).

during such fluctuations aid the applied stress in rupturing the lattice. A quantitative estimate of the probability that a fluctuation of sufficient magnitude to have an appreciable effect of this kind would occur shows that the possibility is undoubtedly out of the range of reason.

It is interesting to note that the theory of dislocations would have to be appreciably modified if not entirely discarded if the observed values of the rupture stress were characteristic of the truly perfect crystal. As was pointed out in the last chapter, a dislocation is the center of a stress field whose amplitude dies off inversely as the first power of the distance. The actual values of the stresses are very large in the immediate vicinity of the dislocation but are comparable with the rupture stress calculated from Eq. (1) only for the atoms near the center. On the other hand, tensile stresses comparable with the observed breaking stress occur within a sphere having a radius of about fifty atom diameters, so that this region would be badly cracked if the true rupture stress were as low as the observed value. There is no doubt that such cracking would completely alter the properties for which dislocations are introduced into the theory of plastic flow. We may conclude that the theory of dislocations requires that the intrinsic rupture stress of the material should be sufficiently high for the material to sustain the high tensile stresses near the center, that is, for the theoretical values given in Table XV to be representative of the material inside the blocks.

42. Rupture in Polycrystals.—It was pointed out in the previous chapter that rupture in polycrystals is transcrystalline except at temperatures near the melting point. This indicates that grain boundaries are not sources of great weakness, so that we might expect to correlate the rupture strengths of polycrystals with those of single crystals.

A correlation of this type is difficult for two reasons. (1) Stresses within grains are not necessarily the same as the average applied stress because of the influence of grain boundaries. (2) Specimens of the same material prepared in different ways extend differently during a rupture test and hence usually have different orientations when fracture occurs. Fortunately, the second factor may be eliminated to an appreciable extent by comparing specimens that already possess the maximum degree of preferred orientation of the type that would be produced during the rupture test.

We saw in the previous section that each crystallographic plane of a single crystal appears to possess a characteristic tension stress at which it will rupture. Moreover, evidence was cited which indicates that this stress is independent of previous deformation.

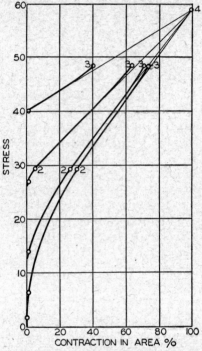

Fig. 104.—The stress-strain curves for variously worked specimens of polycrystalline copper. It may be seen that the rupture stresses are closely the same in each of the cases. The strain is measured in terms of the contraction in cross-sectional area.

Reasoning from this, we should expect the rupture stress of a polycrystalline metal to be independent of deformation as long as the deformation does not produce widely different orientations. This expectation seems to be borne out in the case of copper. Figure 104 shows[1] stress-strain curves for specimens of copper wire

[1] J. v. MOLLENDORF and J. CZOCHRALSKI, Z. *Verein. deut. Ing.*, **54**. 931 (1931).

prepared from the same material. Prior to the test the wires were drawn to different diameters. During this process, comparable degrees of preferred orientation presumably were attained. The specimens were then subjected to tension, and the strain was measured in terms of the contraction in cross section. The specimens began to neck at the stress corresponding to the points 2, and fracture occurred at the points 3. It may be seen that the rupture stresses are nearly the same in all four cases. This indicates that the previous strain had little effect on the breaking stress.

Just as in the case of slip, there seems to be evidence that the grain size has an important influence on the rupture strength even when the crystal size is small compared with the dimensions of the specimen. As was pointed out in the previous chapter, this type of result is inexplicable unless it is assumed that the different treatments required to produce various grain sizes result in different distributions of impurities at grain boundaries. This interpretation of the effect is supported by the experiments of Corson, discussed in the previous chapter.

A comparison of experimental rupture strengths and those computed from Polanyi's equation by the use of experimental values of the surface tension is given in Table XVI. It may be seen that

TABLE XVI.—TENSILE STRENGTHS OF ANNEALED PURE POLYCRYSTALS
(In kg/mm²)

Metal	Tensile strength	
	Obs.	Calc.
Al	9.2	372
Au	12.0	782
Ca	6.4	
Cu	22.6	885
Mg	9.2	
Ni	32	
Pb	1.1	261
Pd	14	
Pt	12	125
Sn	1.4	357
Zn	13	580

the experimental values are smaller than the theoretical ones by a factor of the order of 100 or more, just as in the case of single crystals. There is a slight indication that polycrystals are somewhat stronger than single crystals, but this effect may be related to the redistribution of stresses resulting from the influence of grain boundaries.

43. Fatigue.[1]—Solids break under oscillating stresses whose maximum value is smaller than the critical tensile stress for rup-

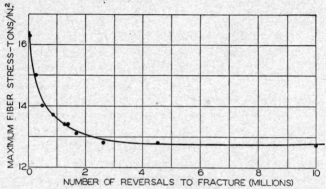

Fig. 105.—A typical fatigue curve. This shows the relationship between the maximum applied stress during a cyclic load and the number of cycles required to produce rupture. It may be seen that there is a safe range of stress below about 12.8 tons per in.[2] (1 ton per in.[2] is equal to 1.55 kg per mm[2]). The original experiments were by Stanton and Pannell. The logarithm of the number of oscillations is also commonly plotted along the horizontal axis.

ture determined in static tests. This effect, known as *fatigue*, has been studied primarily in polycrystalline specimens since it has had greater practical than scientific interest. However, there appears to be little qualitative difference in the facts covering fatigue in single and polycrystals.

Figure 105 shows[2] the relation between the maximum stress and the number of cycles required to produce fracture in a typical polycrystalline case. It may be seen that there is a stress below which the specimen does not break, regardless of the number of cycles. Above this limiting *safe stress*, or *endurance limit*, the number of cycles required to cause failure decreases with increasing load and approaches unity for the static tensile stress for rup-

[1] The practical aspects of fatigue are presented in the book by H. J. Gough, *Fatigue of Metals* (Scott. Greenwood and Son. 1924).

[2] *Ibid.*

ture. It seems to be a general rule, at least in the case of poly-crystals, that the safe stress is about half the limiting static value.

Work on fatigue in single crystals has been carried out princi-pally by Gough[1] and his collaborators. These investigators have shown that fatigue is usually accompanied by evidence of slip and work-hardening. This deformation stops early in the history of a specimen in the safe range but continues to the rupture point in the unsafe range. Polycrystals and single crystals do not seem to differ in any essential way in this respect.

Orowan[2] has proposed the following picture of the mechanism of fatigue failure: The specimen contains weak spots, which act as sources of stress magnification. These may be assumed to be the same as the spots that are responsible for the weakness toward rupture in static tests. During the earlier stress cycles, the stress near one or more of these weak spots would rise above the value required for rupture even for stresses somewhat below the safe limit if the material were not plastic. Actually, slip occurs in the regions of high stress during the early stages of the fatigue test; and, as a result, the stress becomes distributed in such a way that the value for rupture is not exceeded. Work-hardening accom-panies the plastic flow, however, so that the strain produced by the stress decreases monotonically during successive cycles. Thus the maximum stress near the weak spot rises with the num-ber of cycles since it is less effectively distributed by plastic flow. In the safe range, the limiting value of the peak stress is less than the critical stress for rupture, whereas it is larger in the unsafe range. According to this picture, the ability of the material to flow raises the static value of the rupture stress. The specimen breaks after successive stress cycles for stresses lower than the static value because its ability to flow is lost as a result of work-hardening.

Using this concept of the fatigue process, Orowan has given an excellent semiquantitative account of the facts surrounding fatigue. For example, he has been able to account satisfactorily for the shape of fatigue curves of the type shown in Fig. 105.

---

[1] H. J. GOUGH, D. HANSON and S. J. WRIGHT, *Phil. Trans. Roy. Soc.*, **226,** 1 (1925); H. J. GOUGH, *Proc. Roy. Soc.*, **118,** 498 (1928); H. J. GOUGH and H. L. COX, *Proc. Roy. Soc.*, **123,** 143 (1928), **127,** 453 (1930); *J. Inst. Metals*, **45,** 71 (1931), **28,** 227 (1932).

[2] E. OROWAN, *Proc. Roy. Soc.*, **171,** 79 (1939).

CHAPTER XII

DIFFUSION IN METALS

44. Introduction.[1]—Reactions in solid phases take place by means of migration of atoms through the solid, that is, by diffusion. The rate of migration, or diffusion, is expressed in terms of the diffusion constant D, which is defined in the following way: Let us consider the diffusion of a substance B in a substance A and designate the amount of B per unit volume at any point of the solid by c, which we shall call the *concentration*. If the concentration varies from point to point, the effect of diffusion is to smooth the distribution and ultimately to make it uniform throughout the solid. Let us consider a bar of A in which the concentration varies along the axis of the bar, but not across it. If dc is the difference in concentration at two points separated by a distance dx along the axis of the bar, the diffusion coefficient D is defined in terms of dc, dx, by the equation

$$dm = AD \frac{dc}{dx} dt$$

Here dm is the amount of substance B that diffuses in time dt across a surface of area A that lies between the two points and is normal to the axis of the bar. Although D is often called a constant, it actually depends upon both the concentration and the temperature.

It should be noted that D is independent of direction in cubic crystals; however, it usually depends upon direction in noncubic materials.

[1] The topic of diffusion is reviewed in the following publications: R. F. MEHL, *Trans. A.I.M.E.*, **122**, 11 (1936), *J. Applied Phys.*, **8**, 174 (1937); R. M. BARRER, *Diffusion in and through Solids* (The Macmillan Company, New York, 1941); W. JOST, *Diffusion und Chemische Reaction in Festen Stoffen* (T. Steinkopf, Leipzig, 1937); W. SEITH, *Diffusion in Metallen* (Verlag Julius Springer, Berlin, 1939).

The following three methods are commonly used to study diffusion:

a. The Direct Method.—Two specimens of the substances *A* and *B* are placed in contact and are maintained at constant temperature until appreciable diffusion has occurred. The specimens are then cut into sections, and the concentration of the constituents at various distances from the junction is determined by chemical analysis.[1] From the distribution of concentration the diffusion constant may be determined as a function of composition for the given temperature. The procedure may be carried through at various temperatures to determine the dependence of the diffusion coefficient upon temperature. It is evident that this method is not restricted to cases in which both substances *A* and *B* are solids, for it may be employed to determine the rate of diffusion of a gas into a solid. In this case, the concentration of the gaseous element at various depths below the surface of the solid may be determined by chemical means, and the diffusion coefficient as in the solid-solid case.

Figure 106 shows the variation in the composition near the interface between specimens of copper and nickel in cases in which the diffusion has been allowed to occur for various lengths of time at 1000°C. The composition was measured in this case by chemical means.[2] It may be seen that the distance over which the composition varies is readily determined.

b. The Radioactive Tracer Method.[3]—In this method the substance *B* is obtained in radioactive form, and radioactive rather than chemical methods are used to determine the concentration at various regions in the specimen. When first introduced, this method was restricted to the study of diffusion of the naturally radioactive elements in other metals. This was a great restric-

---

[1] The chemical method has been applied most extensively. Typical examples of the method are to be found in the papers of A. Bramley and his associates. See, for example, *Iron Steel Inst. (London) Carnegie Schol. Mem.*, **15**, 155 *ff.* (1926).

[2] G. GRUBE and A. JEDELE, *Z. Elektrochem.*, **38**, 799 (1932).

[3] The radioactive tracer method was first used by G. von Hevesy, W. Seith, and A. Keil [see *Z. physik. Chem.*, **37**, 528 (1931); *Z. Physik*, **79**, 197 (1932)]. It has been used extensively in more recent times. See, for example, F. Banks and H. Day, *Phys. Rev.*, **57**, 1067, (1940); W. A. JOHNSON, *Metals Tech. Pub.* 1281 (1941).

tion, for lead and bismuth are the only useful elements possessing naturally radioactive isotopes. The discovery of artificial radio-activity has removed this obstacle and has opened a wide field of application to the method.

Among other features, the radioactive tracer method has the advantage that it can be used to determine the rate at which

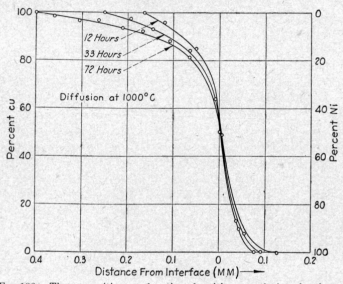

FIG. 106.—The composition as a function of position near the interface between specimens of copper and nickel after diffusion has been allowed to proceed for various periods of time at 1000°C. The horizontal axis represents the distance in millimeters. (*After Grube and Jedele.*)

the atoms of a pure metal diffuse in that metal. This diffusion coefficient is known as that of *self-diffusion*.

c. Thermionic-emission Method.[1]—The ability of a given metal to emit electrons when heated may be greatly affected by the presence of a coating of another metal on its surface. For example, the thermionic emissivity of tungsten is greatly increased by thorium. As a result, it is possible to determine the rate of diffusion of thorium in tungsten by studying the changes in thermionic emission accompanying such diffusion.

[1] See, for example, S. DUSHMAN and I. LANGMUIR, *Phys. Rev.*, **20**, 113 (1922); G. R. FONDA, A. H. YOUNG, and A. WALKER, *Physics*, **4**, 1 (1933).

This method evidently is more restricted than the others, for not all metals can be placed in a form suitable for studies of thermionic properties; moreover, not all metals affect the thermionic properties of a given metal appreciably.

We shall now survey the principal rules and facts derived from studies of diffusion in solids.

45. Principal Facts Concerning Diffusion.—*a.* The measurement of diffusion is sometimes critically dependent upon the crystalline texture of the specimen. The basic reasons for this are as follows: (1) Diffusion may take place along grain boundaries as well as through the grains, so that the nature of the grain structure affects the rate of migration. (2) In a case in which the diffusing constituent is present in high concentration, the lattice structure of the specimen may be different in different regions. For example, in a case in which the rate of diffusion of zinc in copper is being studied by placing the two pure metals in contact, the portion of the copper specimen near the boundary possesses the face-centered cubic structure initially and retains this structure until the concentration of zinc exceeds the solubility limits of the α phase. When the concentration increases, this region transforms to the β phase. It is to be noted that the concentration is discontinuous at the interface of the α and β phases; moreover, the interface moves into the copper as diffusion proceeds. The structure near the original boundary retains the β phase until the concentration of zinc reaches the saturation limit of that phase, whereupon the γ phase appears. It is evident that under proper conditions the transition region between pure copper and pure zinc will contain all the phases of the alloy system which are stable at the temperature at which the diffusion is occurring (see Fig. 107). This evidently is not an equilibrium state of affairs. It is easy to see that the boundaries between the regions possessing different phase structures gradually move from the original interface of the two metals to the surfaces of the specimens. The final structure contains one or two phases, depending upon the amounts of metal present.

One of the disadvantages of the chemical method of determining the diffusion coefficient is that the concentration of the diffusing element generally must be so high that phase transformation is often inevitable. Since the manner in which these phases occur depends upon the physical condition of the specimen, it is clear that their formation can only lead to complexities.

In practice, diffusion along grain boundaries may be avoided by using either single crystals or very coarsely crystalline material. Similarly, the difficulties accompanying formation of new phases at the boundary may be avoided by using a low concentration of one of the diffusing metals.

b. Diffusion along grain boundaries is rapid in comparison with inner-crystalline diffusion in some materials, although it is not

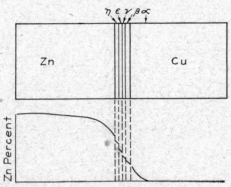

Fig. 107.—Hypothetical distribution of layers of intermediate phases during the diffusion of two pure metals into one another. The situation shown is for brass. The lower curve represents the concentration of zinc schematically.

invariably more rapid. This is most easily demonstrated by studying the rate of diffusion in fine-grained and coarse-grained materials. In this way, it has been shown that (1) in tungsten the rate of diffusion of thorium along grain boundaries is much higher than in the crystals; (2) the rate of grain-boundary diffusion of zinc in copper is slightly higher than the rate within crystals. The fact that diffusion is sometimes more rapid along grain boundaries than within grains is not surprising if we recall the evidence summarized in Sec. 25, which shows that the transition layer between grains is thermodynamically less stable than the material within grains. As a consequence of this, we might expect diffusion to be more rapid in this layer.

c. The precipitation of one phase from another under conditions such as those occurring during the age-hardening of aluminum-copper alloys (see Sec. 31) occurs in part by the mechanism of diffusion. We shall see in subsequent sections that this is also true of the precipitation processes occurring in steel. For this reason, the topic of diffusion plays a fundamental role in determining the manner in which alloying agents affect the hardenability of steel.

d. The rate of diffusion is strongly dependent upon temperature. It is found that the law governing the temperature depend-

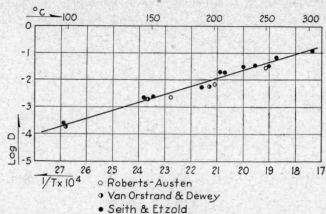

Fig. 108.—The diffusion coefficient of lead in gold as a function of temperature. (*After Mehl.*)

ence of any one type of diffusion, such as diffusion along grain boundaries or diffusion within grains, is expressed by the equation

$$D = Ae^{-\frac{Q}{RT}} \tag{1}$$

where A and Q are practically independent of temperature but may be dependent upon composition, R is the gas constant ($R = 2.0$ cal/deg), and T is the absolute temperature. Q evidently provides a measure of the activation energy that must be supplied by thermal fluctuations before an atom may jump from one position in the lattice to another. According to this equation the logarithm of D when plotted as a function of $1/T$ should be represented by a straight line. From this we may conclude that comparatively small changes in temperature may have a very large effect upon the rate of diffusion. Figure 108 shows[1] the

[1] Taken from the review article by Mehl, *op. cit.*

TABLE XVII.—VALUES OF A AND Q FOR THE INTERDIFFUSION OF METALS
(Values of A are given in square centimeters per second, and those of Q are
given in units of calories per mol.   After Barrer.)

System	A	Q	Eq. (2) Q
Pb in Pb	5.1	27,900	24,400
Sn in Pb	$3.4 \cdot 10^{-2}$	24.000	23,200
Au in Pb	$4.9 \cdot 10^{-1}$	13,000	13,300
Bi in Pb	$7.7 \cdot 10^{-3}$	18,600	21,900
Hg in Pb	$3.6 \cdot 10^{-1}$	19,000	
Au in Au	$1.26 \cdot 10^{2}$	51,000	
Pd in Au	$1.11 \cdot 10^{-3}$	37,400	
Cu in Au	$5.8 \ \cdot 10^{-4}$	27,400	
Th in W	1.0	120,000	
U in W	1.0	100,000	100,500
Mo in W	$6.3 \cdot 10^{-4}$	80,500	
N in Fe	$1.07 \cdot 10^{-1}$	34,000	38,100
C in Fe	$4.9 \cdot 10^{-1}$	36,600	36,700
Zn in Cu (4 percent Zn)	$1.57 \cdot 10^{-3}$	34,100	
Al in Cu (4 percent Al)	$6.34 \cdot 10^{-2}$	40,200	
Si in Cu (4 percent Si)	$1.0 \cdot 10^{4}$	64,200	
Sn in Cu (4 percent Cu)	$6.7 \cdot 10^{2}$	54,000	
Cu in Ag	$5.9 \cdot 10^{-5}$	24,800	
Sb in Ag	$5.3 \cdot 10^{-5}$	21,500	
Sn in Ag	$7.9 \cdot 10^{-5}$	21,400	
Cd in Ag	$4.9 \cdot 10^{-5}$	22,350	
Au in Ag	$5.3 \cdot 10^{-5}$	29,800	
Bi in Bi ($\perp c$ axis)	$(1.3 - 16) \cdot 10^{45}$	137,000	
Bi in Bi ($\parallel c$ axis)	$(2.2 - 6.5) \cdot 10^{4}$	30,000	
Cu in Al	2.3	34,900	31,400
Mg in Al	$1.5 \cdot 10^{2}$	38,500	29,000
Cu in Cu	$1.1 \cdot 10^{1}$	57,200	
Zn in Cu	$8 \cdot 10^{-1}$	38,000	44,000
Si in Cu	$5.2 \cdot 10^{-2}$	39,950	
Be in Cu	$4.5 \cdot 10^{-5}$	27,900	

high degree of accuracy with which Eq. (1) is obeyed during the diffusion of gold in lead.

Table XVII contains values of the constants A and Q for a number of metals. Values of A are more difficult to measure accurately than are those of Q because D is far less sensitive to variations in the former. As a rule, it turns out that the observed values of A are given quite accurately by the equation

$$A = Qd^2C \tag{2}$$

in which C is a universal constant and d is the interatomic distance. Equation (2) is commonly known as the Dushman-Langmuir equation. If Eq. (2) is substituted in (1), it is possible to evaluate Q with the use of one value of D. Values of Q obtained in this way are given in the last column of Table XVII.

Several rules similar to that expressed by Eq. (2) have been discovered. For example, it seems to be generally true that the value of Q for self-diffusion is larger than the values for diffusion of foreign atoms.

Another rule states that the values of Q for diffusion of various metals in a given metal are proportional to the melting temperatures of the metals. Thus, in the case of the diffusion of copper, palladium, and platinum in gold, Q is equal to $20T_m$, if Q is expressed in calories and T_m is taken as the melting temperature in degrees absolute.

e. The diffusion coefficient depends markedly upon composition in many alloys. For example, Fig. 109 shows[1] the type of variation that is observed in a number of copper alloys at 800°C. Although D is very sensitive to changes in Q, the variation with composition of A in Eq. (1) appears to be as important as that of Q in determining this effect.

f. It is frequently observed that the composition of an alloy which is conducting a direct electric current changes from one end of the specimen to the other, during the course of time. This effect is most pronounced at elevated temperatures. For example, it has been found[2] that carbon migrates electrolytically in γ iron, as does gold in lead and palladium. Similarly, it has been

[1] F. N. RHINES and R. F. MEHL, *Trans. A.I.M.E.*, **128**, 185 (1938).
[2] W. SEITH and O. KUBASCHEWSKI, *Z. Elektrochem.*, **41**, 551 (1935).

found[1] that the thorium on a thorium-coated tungsten wire migrates to the cathode if the wire is heated by direct current. This type of electrolysis is easy to understand on the basis of diffusion. The atoms in an alloy are not neutral, for the constituents lie at different places in the electromotive series. In general, we may expect the atoms of a given element to become positively charged when alloyed with an element that lies below it in the electromotive series. For example, we may expect

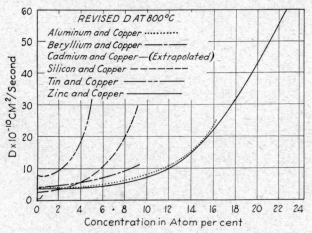

FIG. 109.—The dependence of the diffusion coefficient upon temperature for a number of copper alloys. (*After Rhines and Mehl.*)

thorium to become positively charged relative to tungsten. When the alloy is placed in an electrostatic field, the force resulting from the action of the field on the charge of a given diffusing atom causes the atom to migrate in the direction of the force. The fact that such electrolysis occurs is, in fact, excellent evidence for diffusion. It is interesting to note that the carbon in γ iron does not electrolyze in the manner one would anticipate, for it behaves as if positively charged.

It is evident that the migration of the charged atoms under the action of an electric field results in an electrolytic current. It may be shown[2] that the contribution to the conductivity of the

[1] R. P. JOHNSON, *Phys. Rev.*, **53**, 766 (1938).

[2] See, for example, F. SEITZ, *The Modern Theory of Solids*, p. 557, (McGraw-Hill Book Company, Inc., New York, 1940).

material arising from the electrolytic migration of a given atom is given by the equation, first derived by Einstein,

$$\sigma = N \frac{e^2}{kT} D \tag{3}$$

in which e is the charge on the ion, k is Boltzmann's constant, N is the number of diffusing atoms per cubic centimeter, and D is the diffusion coefficient for the migrating atoms in the *absence* of the field.

g. The rate of diffusion in a given metal has been observed to depend markedly on the degree of cold-work the specimen has received. For example, Fonda, Walker, and Young have observed that the rate of diffusion of thorium in thoriated tungsten wire is greatly increased by cold-work. Similarly, Smith and Derge have found evidence that hydrogen diffuses preferentially along slip bands in palladium.

46. The Mechanism of Diffusion in Metals.—There are three reasonable mechanisms by which a given atom of type B may diffuse relative to atoms of type A in a given lattice, namely: (1) The atoms A and B may interchange places, (2) B atoms may diffuse through the interstices of the lattice, (3) B atoms may diffuse as the secondary result of the diffusion of *vacancies* through the lattice. Vacancies are normal lattice sites from which atoms are absent. They are generated at the surface of the specimen when atoms jump from the outermost completed layer of atoms to the surface of this layer (Fig. 110); they then migrate or diffuse into the interior of the crystal.

The three mechanisms for diffusion are illustrated schematically in Fig. 111.

There has been considerable speculation[1] concerning the actual mechanism of diffusion in particular cases. It seems almost beyond doubt that the first mechanism does not occur because the force required to squeeze two atoms by one another in a closely packed lattice is too large. It also seems beyond question that the diffusion of the interstitial component in interstitial alloys, such as carbon in steel, takes place by means of the interstitial diffusion mechanism. The mechanism by which diffusion

[1] See, for example, *ibid.;* also N. F. Mott and R. W. Gurney, *Electronic Processes in Ionic Crystals* (Oxford University Press, New York, 1940).

occurs in substitutional alloys is still open to question. Estimates[1] of the relative magnitudes of the forces incurred in the interstitial and vacancy diffusion processes, however, indicate that the vacancy mechanism is definitely more likely.

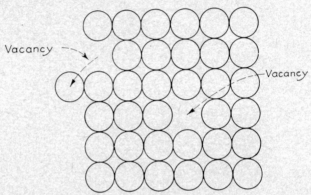

Fig. 110.—Vacancies in a crystal lattice.

The fact that the activation energy for self-diffusion is usually larger than the activation energy for diffusion of a foreign substitutional atom in a given metal has been made the object of a theoretical investigation by Johnson.[2] He has drawn the

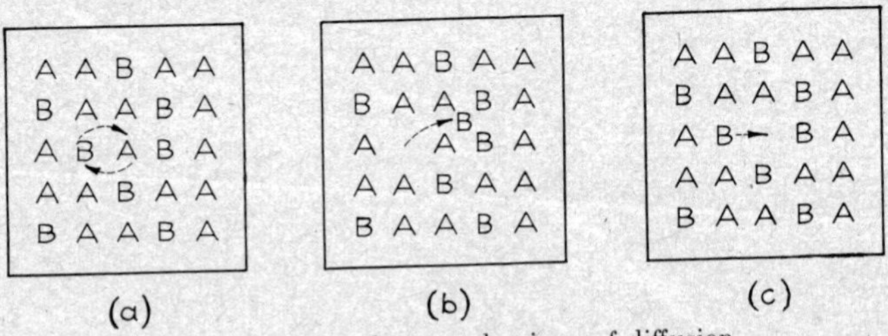

Fig. 111.—The three mechanisms of diffusion.

conclusion that in most dilute solid solutions the vacancies cluster preferentially about the foreign atoms and that diffusion of these atoms takes place as the result of the simultaneous migration of the bound vacancy and the foreign atom.

[1] See, for example, H. B. Huntington and F. Seitz, *Phys. Rev.*, **61**, 315 (1942); H. B. Huntington, *Phys. Rev.*, **61**, 325 (1942).

[2] R. P. Johnson, *Phys. Rev.* **56**, 814 (1939).

47. Diffusion in Nonmetals.[1]—The diffusion of atoms in nonmetallic substances has nearly as much interest as diffusion in metals because of its importance for understanding processes such

TABLE XVIII.—VALUES OF THE RADII OF IONS
(In Å)

Metals	Radii	Nonmetals	Radii
Li^+	0.78	H^-	1.27
Na^+	0.98	F^-	1.33
K^+	1.33	Cl^-	1.81
Rb^+	1.49	Br^-	1.96
Cs^+	1.65	I^-	2.2
Cu^+	0.53	$O^=$	1.32
Ag^+	1.03	$S^=$	1.74
Tl^+	1.49	$Se^=$	1.91
		$Te^=$	2.03
Mg^{++}	0.78		
Ca^{++}	1.06		
Sr^{++}	1.27		
Ba^{++}	1.43		
Be^{++}	0.34		
Zn^{++}	0.83		
Cd^{++}	1.03		
Hg^{++}	1.12		
Al^{+++}	0.57		
Sc^{+++}	0.83		
Yt^{+++}	1.06		
Ga^{+++}	0.62		
In^{+++}	0.92		
Tl^{+++}	1.05		
Mn^{++}	0.91		
Fe^{++}	0.83		
Co^{++}	0.82		
Ni^{++}	0.78		
Pb^{++}	1.32		

as the oxidation or tarnishing of metals that occur in everyday metallurgy.

[1] See BARRER, *op. cit.;* JOST, *op. cit.* Much basic research with ionic crystals has been carried out by C. Wagner, *Z. physik. Chem.,* **22,** 181 *ff.* (1933).

Salts contain at least two types of ion; one of the important problems is that of determining the relative ease with which each type of ion diffuses. This question can be answered most readily by an investigation of the ionic conductivity of the substance; for, as was mentioned in Sec. 45 in connection with the electrolytic effects that are observed in certain alloys, there is an intimate connection between diffusion and ionic conductivity. The connection is, in fact, expressed by Eq. (3) (Sec. 45). Thus the relative ease with which different ions move may sometimes be measured by measuring the relative amounts of electrolytic current carried by the different ions in the crystal. The fraction of the electrolytic current carried by a given ion is called its *transport number*. There are many important cases in which the use of the electrolytic method is made complicated by the fact that the material possesses a large electronic conductivity which tends to mask the electrolytic conductivity. Alloys represent extreme cases of this type, for the current in these is so largely electronic that the ionic component makes itself evident only under unusual circumstances.

The general rules concerning diffusion in ionic crystals are as follows:

a. Metallic ions in salts usually move more readily than nonmetallic ions. This now well-established fact seemed surprising when first discovered; however, the reason for it is not hard to find. Metallic ions usually are small compared with the ions of nonmetals. Table XVIII contains the sizes[1] of many important ions and demonstrates this fact.

As a consequence of their small size, metallic ions experience less difficulty in diffusing. Table XIX contains a listing[2] of a number of common salts on the basis of the type of ion that carries the current. It may be seen that the ions are of comparable size in those salts such as $PbCl_2$ in which the negative ion carries part or most of the current.

b. Diffusion in salts has the same type of temperature dependence as diffusion in metals. This has been proved both by direct means and by investigation of ionic conductivity (Fig. 112).[3]

---

[1] See, for example, SEITZ, *op. cit.*, p. 92.

[2] C. TUBANDT, *Handbuch der Experimentalphysik*, vol. XII.

[3] W. LEHFELD, *Z. Physik*, **85**, 717 (1933).

TABLE XIX.—CARRIERS IN SEVERAL COMMON SALTS

Positive ion	Negative ion	Both
CuI	$PbCl_2$	NaCl
Cu_2O	$BaCl_2$	PbI_2
Cu_2S		
ZnO		
ZnS		
Al_2O_3		
FeO		
AgCl		
Ag_2S		

c. Salts are commonly produced at the surface of a metal by direct interaction of the metal with a nonmetal in solid, liquid,

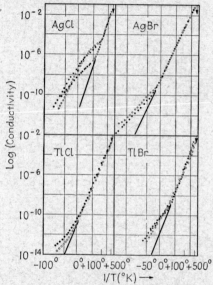

FIG. 112.—The relationship between ionic conductivity and temperature in several salts. It may be seen that at sufficiently high temperatures the relation between the logarithm of conductivity and the reciprocal of the absolute temperature is linear. The same relation is obeyed between the diffusion coefficient and the temperature.

or gaseous form. In such cases, the reaction takes place primarily as a result of the diffusion of the metal if the salt is one in which only the metallic ion diffuses readily. This situation occurs, for example, in the oxidation of many metals and is an important difference between the oxidation process and such processes as nitriding, or carburizing, in which the nonmetal diffuses directly into the metal. A case of this type which has been investigated[1] very carefully is that of the reaction between silver and sulphur.

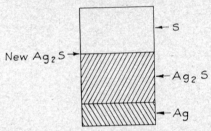

Fig. 113.—Schematic arrangement of the cell used by Wagner to establish the mechanism of formation of silver sulfide from the elements (see text).

It has been shown conclusively that in this case silver ions diffuse through the layer of silver sulphide that separates the pure metal and the sulphur and form a new layer of sulphide near the sulphur (Fig. 113). If the salt layer that is formed on the surface of the metal possesses a number of macroscopic pores that is sufficient to allow the electronegative reactant, such as oxygen or

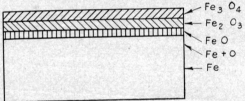

Fig. 114.—Schematic diagram showing the disposition of layers of oxide in a coating of iron oxide. The thicknesses of the layers are not shown in true proportion. Actually, the thicknesses of FeO, Fe_2O_3, and Fe_3O_4 are in the ratio $100:10:1$.

sulphur, to seep through it, it obviously will not be necessary for the metallic ions to diffuse to the surface of the salt even though the transport number of the electronegative ion is zero. Apparently silver sulphide is not sufficiently porous to permit this alternative process.

There does not seem to be any basic difference between the case of the formation of silver sulphide from metallic silver and sulphur and that of the oxidation of iron. Actually, the oxida-

[1] C. Wagner, *Z. physik. Chem.*, **B21**, 42 (1933); **23**, 469 (1933).

tion of iron is made somewhat more complicated by the fact that there are several stable forms of iron oxide, so that the coating of iron oxide may contain layers of Fe_2O_3, Fe_3O_4, and FeO in the transition from the metallic iron to the surface exposed to oxygen. The transition layers are shown schematically in Fig. 114.

TABLE XX.—THE RATIO OF THE VOLUME OF OXIDE TO THAT OF METAL FOR METALS WHICH DO AND DO NOT FORM PROTECTIVE COATINGS

Protective coating		No protective coating	
Metal	Ratio	Metal	Ratio
Al	1.38	Li	0.57
Cr	1.97	Na	0.58
Mn	1.25	Mg	0.58
Fe	2.23	K	0.65
Ni	1.64	Ca	0.69
Co	1.78	Rb	0.46
Cu	1.71	Si	0.73
Zn	1.44	Mo	3.01
Pd	1.60	Cs	0.86
Cd	1.19	Ba	0.71
Sn	1.31		
La	1.11		
Ce	1.24		
W	3.50		
Tl	2.38		
Pb	1.40		
Bi	1.29		
Be	1.71		
Zr	1.56		

d. The coatings of oxide that form on metals during oxidation differ widely in their ability to inhibit further oxidation. Generally speaking, such oxides may be divided into three main types: (1) those in which the coating has essentially no protective effect and in which the coating grows linearly with time, (2) those in which the coating has an intermediate protective effect in the sense that the rate of formation of the oxide decreases with time, (3) and those in which the coating entirely protects the metal after it has grown to a definite thickness of the order of 50 Å. It has been suggested that in the first case the oxide is porous. This would be the case, for example, if the oxide formed from a given

volume of metal has a smaller volume than the metal.   Table XX
shows the ratio of the volume of oxide to that of metal for a
number of metals.   The metals in the first column are those in
which the oxide forms an intermediate or a complete protective
coating; it may be seen that the ratio is invariably greater than
unity in these cases.   The second column contains metals for
which the oxide does not form a protective coating; it may be seen
that the ratio is usually less than unity, although there are
exceptions.

Most of the oxides that have intermediate protective effect
obey the following parabolic relation between thickness and time:

$$x^2 = at \tag{1}$$

in which x is the thickness and t is the time.   It may readily
be shown that this equation is exactly[1] what is to be expected
if the oxidation takes place by diffusion of one or both of the
reacting constituents through the oxide coating.   In fact, the
constant a in Eq. (1) may be related to the diffusion coefficient by
means of the equation

$$a = 2VDn.$$

Here D is the diffusion coefficient, V is the mean volume per
diffusing ion in the oxide, and n is the concentration of diffusing
ions at the oxide-metal boundary.   Careful investigation leaves
little doubt that in cases in which Eq. (1) is obeyed the diffusion
of at least one of the reacting constituents through the oxide coating is uninhibited.

It is commonly found that in cases in which the oxide forms a
complete protective coating, as is the case for aluminum and
zinc at room temperature, the coating first grows with time in
accordance with Eq. (1) and then abruptly ceases to grow,[2]
or grows at a vastly slower rate, when the coating achieves a
thickness of about 50 Å, as mentioned above.   Following work
of Wagner and Grünewald,[3] Mott has suggested that in cases of
this type the oxide layer grows by migration of metal ions and

[1] N. F. MOTT, *Trans. Faraday Soc.*, **35**, 1175 (1939); **36**, 472 (1940).

[2] Measurements of this thickness have been made by W. H. J. Vernon,
Trans. Faraday Soc., **23**, 152 (1927) and A. Steinheil, *Ann. Physik*, **10**, 465
(1934).

[3] C. WAGNER and K. GRÜNEWALD, *Z. physik. Chem.*, **B40**, 455 (1938).

electrons from the metal to the oxygen-oxide interface. As long as the oxide film is less than about 50 Å, the electrons are able to pass through the oxide film; however, their diffusion coefficient decreases very rapidly when the thickness exceeds this. This peculiar variation of the mobility of the electron can be understood in terms of the wave theory of electrons, which is discussed in Chap. XV. The electronic mobility may be raised to a value comparable with or larger than that of the ions by raising the temperature of the system sufficiently. Thus it may be expected that the parabolic law (1) will be valid at sufficiently high temperatures in materials which form a thoroughly protective coating at room temperature.

48. The Mechanism of Diffusion in Salts.—The three basic mechanisms for diffusion discussed in connection with metals also apply to salts. It is generally agreed that the interchange mechanism involves too high an activation energy and can be excluded from consideration. A detailed investigation reveals that both the other two types of mechanism, namely, diffusion by vacancies and diffusion by interstitial atoms, occur frequently. The former occurs commonly in cases such as sodium chloride in which the ions have nearly equal size and in which the interstitial spaces are small in comparison with the ionic sizes. Not all salts in which the interstitial spaces are small prefer the vacancy mechanism, however; there is definite evidence that diffusion in silver halides, which have the sodium chloride lattice, takes place by interstitial migration. Diffusion in salts such as zinc oxide and alumina, in which the metallic ion is very small and the interstitial spaces are very large, undoubtedly occurs by the interstitial mechanism.

CHAPTER XIII

THE SOLUBILITY OF GASES IN METALS

49. Introduction.[1]—When processed, most metals are heated or melted in the presence of gases. For this reason as well as for the purpose of understanding fundamental concepts, there is considerable interest in knowing the extent to which these gases enter into combination with the metals. In some instances, as we shall see, the influence of dissolved gas is negligible whereas in others the influence either is desirable, as in the case of carburized or nitrided metals, or is deleterious. Among the deleterious cases are those, for example, in which gas dissolved in the molten state is rejected during solidification and thus forms blowholes or pipes.

There are two important ways in which metals can take up gases, namely, by *adsorption* and by *absorption*. In the first case, the gas atoms become attached to the surface and do not permeate the lattice. Thus the amount of material attached is proportional to the area of the specimen. The adsorption of oxygen and other gases by carbon and platinum are perfect examples of this type of bonding between gases and solids. Although the subject of adsorption is very important in certain fields of solid chemistry, we shall not consider it further here, for purposes of simplicity.

The absorption of a gas by a solid is exemplified by the manner in which palladium may absorb hydrogen in arbitrary quantities ranging from zero to 100 molar percent and by the manner in which iron at elevated temperatures absorbs nitrogen from ammonia to form a solid solution or iron nitride.

Before proceeding with a discussion of the rules concerning the absorption of gases by metals that have been discovered as the result of extensive research, it is convenient to consider several

---

[1] This topic is surveyed in the following books: C. J. SMITHELLS, *Gases in Metals* (John Wiley & Sons, Inc., New York, 1937); R. M. BARRER, *Diffusion in and Through Solids* (The Macmillan Company, New York, 1941).

facts. In treating the combination of a gas and a metal, it must be borne in mind that the possible modes of combination may be expressed in terms of a conventional phase diagram. At temperatures in the vicinity of room temperature, the concentration limits of the phases are usually quite small, unlike the situation met with in the case of ideal alloys. On the other hand, the concentration limits may be expected to broaden with increasing temperature in the manner indicated schematically in Fig. 115.

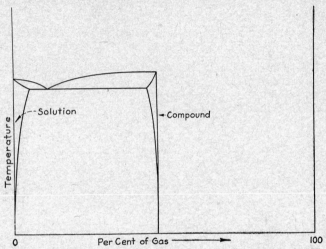

Fig. 115.—Hypothetical phase diagram for a gas and a metal. The gas may possess a finite solubility in the metal; in addition the two may form compounds.

The fact that the compounds usually have sharply specified compositions at low temperatures is in agreement with the ordinary rules of valence. It is interesting to note that the concentration limits of compounds are not always negligibly small at ordinary temperatures. For example, galena (PbS) and Wustite (FeO) form for ranges of composition that extend over about 1 percent of that of the ideal compounds. Other examples of this type are discussed in Sec. 76, which deals with semi-conductors.

We see from Fig. 115 that a metal may absorb a gas, such as oxygen, either by forming a compound or by dissolving it in the manner corresponding to the terminal solid solution shown in the diagram. We shall refer to the first process as *compound forma-tion* and the second as *solution*. If there are no intermediate compounds, the only mechanism for absorption is solution. It is evident that, in general, larger amounts of gas are absorbed during compound formation than during solution. Moreover, since compounds are usually stable at room temperature whereas the concentration limits for solution may decrease with decreas-ing temperature, it follows that the gas absorbed at elevated temperatures in compound formation is more likely to be retained during subsequent cooling than is that absorbed by solution.

It is important to realize that at any given temperature the gaseous constituent of a given solution or compound possesses a definite vapor pressure which is, in general, dependent upon the precise composition. It is evident that, if the gas pressure is higher than that required for solution but is not sufficiently high for the formation of a compound, solution will occur whereas compound formation will not. In such cases, the compound may be formed by raising the pressure to a value above its equilibrium vapor pressure. It also follows that, if the equi-librium vapor pressure of a solution increases with increasing concentration of the dissolved gas, the concentration of dissolved gas may be altered by varying the pressure within the range below the maximum vapor pressure. The fact that the solu-bility obtained at a given temperature depends upon the applied pressure greatly complicates the problem of determining the phase diagram of a given metal-gas system, for pressure as well as temperature must always be kept in mind as a variable.

The principles that apply when gases combine with metals also apply to any case in which an alloy is raised to such a tem-perature that one of the constituents possesses an appreciable vapor pressure. For example, at temperatures above 500°C, the compositions of the phases of brass that may be kept at equilibrium depend upon the vapor pressure of zinc that is maintained. Thus, from one point of view, the problem of solubility of gases in metals is a particular part of the more general problem of the pressure-temperature equilibrium of solids.

The results of extensive studies of the absorption of gases may be summarized in the following manner:

a. The process of absorption of a gas by solid or molten metal usually requires a finite time (see Fig. 116). This undoubtedly is associated with the fact that the atoms of the gas must diffuse into the solid; for as we have seen in the previous chapter, diffusion requires time.

b. Hydrogen is the most generally soluble gas. Oxygen and nitrogen are frequently absorbed in appreciable quantities, particularly at high temperatures. Oxygen, however, has a tendency to form a separate oxide compound with the metals in

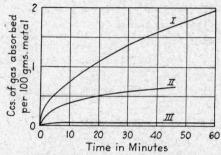

Fig. 116.—The relation between the quantity of dissolved gas and the time allowed for solution. Curve I represents the rate of solution of nitrogen in aluminum at 800°C (760 mm); curve II represents the rate of solution of oxygen in silver at 280°C (336 mm); curve III represents the rate of solution of hydrogen in silver at 700°C (100 mm). It may be seen that a finite time is required to attain saturation. (*After Smithells.*)

which it is absorbed strongly, a fact indicating that its solubility limits are usually small in the solid phases of the metal. The solubility of oxygen in copper has been studied with particular care because of the embrittlement induced in copper that contains oxygen when the metal is exposed to hydrogen during heating. Figure 117 shows the phase diagram[1] for the copper–copper oxide system and illustrates the fact that the maximum solubility decreases with decreasing temperature. It is believed that the oxygen dissolved in copper at elevated temperatures forms precipitates of cuprous oxide during subsequent cooling and that this oxide is reduced in the presence of hydrogen. The steam generated as a result of the reaction opens grain boundaries by expansion, thus embrittling the metal.

[1] F. RHINES and C. MATHEWSON, *Trans. A.I.M.E.*, **111**, 337 (1934).

 c. Polyatomic gases dissociate at the surface of a metal and
diffuse into the metal as single atoms. This principle appears
plausible; for, except in the case of hydrogen, it is difficult to
imagine polyatomic molecules diffusing through a crystal lattice
with ease. Convincing proof of this principle is obtained by
studying the dependence of solubility of a diatomic gas upon

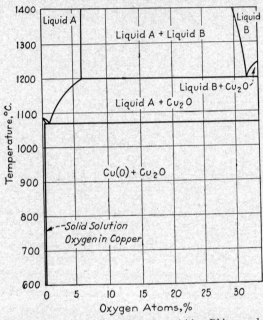

Fig. 117.—The copper-oxygen phase diagram. (*After Rhines and Mathewson.*)

pressure of the gas. If the molecules dissolve without dissocia-
tion in accordance with the usual rules of mass action, we should
expect the solubility to vary as the first power of the pressure,
whereas, if the molecules dissociate during solution, we should
expect the solubility to vary as the square root of the pressure.
It is found[1] that the second law, which is commonly known as
Sievert's law, is valid almost without exception (see Fig. 118).
The exceptional cases usually are those in which the dissolved
gas forms a compound with the metal.

[1] See SMITHELLS, *op. cit.*

d. The solubility of hydrogen at constant pressure usually
increases with temperature in simple systems in which hydrides

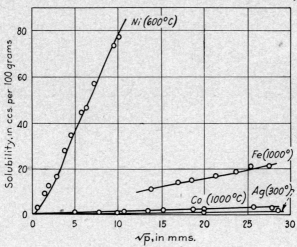

FIG. 118.—The relation between the solubility of hydrogen and pressure for several metals that do not form hydrides.

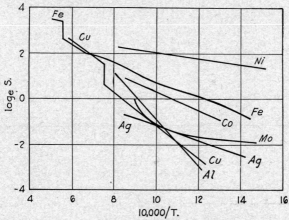

FIG. 119.—The relation between temperature and solubility of hydrogen for a number of metals that do not form hydrides.

are not formed. In addition, it is found that the solubility
when considered as a function of temperature frequently obeys
the simple equation

$$S = Ae^{-\frac{Q}{RT}}$$

in which Q and A are constants, as usual, T is the absolute temperature, and R is the gas constant   There are, however, many exceptions to this rule.   Figure 119 shows that the rule is closely obeyed in the case of solution of hydrogen in solids which do not form hydrides.

e. The absorption of nitrogen by iron has been studied extensively.   The iron-nitrogen phase diagram, shown in Fig. 120,

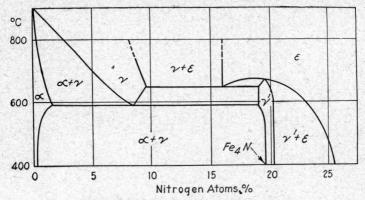

Fig. 120.—The iron-nitrogen phase diagram.

resembles somewhat the iron-carbon phase diagram, as may be seen by comparing Fig. 120 and Fig. 122 (page 203).   The solubility of nitrogen evidently is much larger in the γ phase than in the α and δ phases.   Moreover, it is much larger in liquid iron than in any of the solid phases, as is shown in Table XXI.

TABLE XXI.—SOLUBILITY OF NITROGEN IN IRON AT ATMOSPHERIC PRESSURE

Phase	Temperature, °C	Solubility, cc/100 g
α.................	750	0.32
	890	1.6
γ.................	900	20
	1390	16.6
δ.................	1420	7.9
	1500	9.5
Liquid.................	1540	24.5

f. Oxygen usually forms compounds with solid phases of the metals and has only small solubility. On the other hand, the solubility in molten metals is often very high. An interesting case in which this solubility has practical interest occurs in connection with silver. This metal does not form a solid oxide that is stable near the melting point of the metal at atmospheric pressure; however, the liquid can dissolve about twenty times

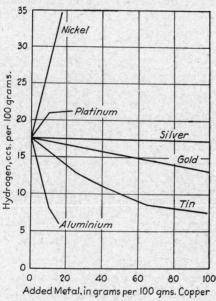

Fig. 121.—The influence of alloying elements on the solubility of hydrogen in copper.

its own volume of oxygen. This oxygen is dismissed as gas during solidification, thus forming blowholes. Thus, in casting silver, it is necessary either to melt the metal under conditions in which the surface of the metal is insulated from the air or to alloy the metal with another which forms a stable solid oxide. In the second case, the oxide formed in solidification may be retained in the casting as an inclusion.

Molten iron and steel also dissolve appreciable oxygen. This is rejected as carbon monoxide in steel during solidification unless a substance that forms a stable solid oxide is present in the melt. A steel to which such substances have been added is said to be *killed* since it does not effervesce during solidification. Silicon and aluminum are two of the most commonly used killing agents. They combine with the oxygen to form silica and alumina, respectively, which tend to float to the top of the melt.

g. The solubility of a gas in a metal may be altered by adding alloying agents. Examples of cases in which an effect of this type is observed are shown in Fig. 121.

50. The Mechanism of Diffusion of Gases in Metals.—The mechanism by which gases diffuse in metals has not been studied so extensively as the mechanisms of diffusion of ions in salts or of metal atoms in alloys. There seems no doubt, however, that the atoms of gases such as hydrogen and nitrogen, which commonly form interstitial alloys with the transition metals, diffuse interstitially. On the other hand, it is still an open question whether the larger atoms of gases such as oxygen can diffuse interstitially or whether they enter the vacancies of the metal lattice (see Fig. 111, page 184) and diffuse like the atoms of the metal.

CHAPTER XIV

THE PROPERTIES OF IRON-CARBON ALLOYS

51. Introduction.[1]—In this chapter, we shall discuss the properties of steel and attempt to understand these properties on the basis of the principles presented in preceding chapters.

Steel derives its most interesting properties from four sources, namely, from the iron atoms that constitute the bulk of the material, from the carbon atoms that enter the interstices of the lattice of the iron atoms, from various additional alloying agents that are frequently present and that substitute for the iron atoms, and especially from the allotropic change from the γ to the α phase. There are several important alloying agents of the substitutional type; each imparts to the steel special properties, which will be discussed in detail later.

52. Pure Iron.—Pure iron is a noteworthy metal in several respects. (1) It is strongly ferromagnetic at room temperature. (2) It has a high melting point (1528°C). (3) It possesses several allotropic modifications. The phase that is stable at room temperature possesses the body-centered cubic lattice and is ferromagnetic. This ferromagnetism gradually decreases as the temperature is raised and disappears at about 769°C. Since the crystal structure does not alter during this transition, both the ferromagnetic and the nonferromagnetic body-centered structures are commonly called the α phase. Above 910°C, the body-centered structure becomes unstable relative to a face-centered cubic structure and the α phase transforms to the latter

[1] Surveys of the material discussed here may be found in the following sources: M. GROSSMANN, *The Principles of Heat Treatment* (American Society for Metals, Cleveland, Ohio, 1937); E. C. BAIN, *Alloying Elements in Steel* (American Society for Metals, Cleveland, Ohio, 1939); S. EPSTEIN, *The Alloys of Iron and Carbon*, vol. I (McGraw-Hill Book Company, Inc., New York, 1936); F. T. SISCO, *The Alloys of Iron and Carbon*, vol. II (McGraw-Hill Book Company, Inc., New York, 1937); *The Hardenability of Alloy Steels* (American Society for Metals, Cleveland, Ohio, 1938).

or, as it is commonly called, γ phase. The γ phase, however, becomes unstable relative to the body-centered cubic structure above 1401°C and transforms to the latter, which is then stable to the melting point at 1528°C. The body-centered lattice that is stable in this range is termed the δ phase. As we shall see later, there is definite evidence for regarding the δ phase as an extension of the α phase and not as a "new" body-centered cubic phase. This intrusion of the face-centered phase within the domain of the body-centered phase for a range of temperature is a type of allotropy that is not entirely unique for iron, for it is also observed in cobalt. It is not found, however, among the metals outside the transition series and for this reason may be regarded as a property of metals with unfilled d shells. We shall investigate the source of the effect more closely in a later chapter devoted to the behavior of electrons in metals. The source of the ferromagnetism of iron will also be considered at that time.

53. The Influence of Carbon on the Equilibrium Properties of Iron.—The iron-rich end of the iron-carbon equilibrium phase diagram is shown[1] in Fig. 122. It may be seen that carbon has very small solubility in the body-centered phases (α and δ iron) and is considerably more soluble in the γ phase. In fact, the maximum solubility in the former is about 0.04 weight percent and in the latter is 1.7 weight percent. As we saw in Chap. III, this difference in solubility of carbon in the two types of phases can be explained, at least qualitatively, on the basis of the fact that the interstitial spaces in the face-centered lattice can accommodate larger spheres than those in the body-centered. The γ phase containing carbon is commonly called *austenite*, whereas the body-centered phase containing carbon is termed *ferrite*.

The intermediate compound of iron and carbon shown at the right-hand side of the diagram is called *cementite* and corresponds to the composition Fe_3C. Careful thermodynamical analysis[2] has shown that cementite is not stable below 710°C and has a tendency to decompose into ferrite and carbon. The phase boundaries of Fig. 122 are determined, however, by comparing

[1] See *Metals Progress*, 511 (1941).

[2] H. SELTZ, H. J. McDONALD, and C. WELLS, *Trans. A.I.M.E.*, **140**, 263 (1940).

the stability of each solid solution of carbon in iron relative to cementite. For this reason, it is commonly called the iron-cementite phase diagram instead of the iron-carbon phase diagram. This procedure of regarding cementite as stable is of practical value because cementite does not decompose rapidly and is readily observed during reactions in steels.

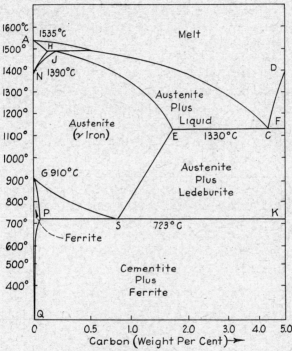

FIG. 122.—The phase diagram of the iron-carbon system. It is to be noted that the abscissa is weight percent. (*After Epstein.*)

It may be seen that the presence of a small amount of carbon broadens the range of temperature in which γ iron is stable, increasing the high-temperature limit and decreasing the low-temperature one. This effect ceases at about 0.1 weight percent of carbon on the high-temperature side and at about 0.80 weight percent on the low-temperature side. It may also be noted that the limiting curve of the γ phase at low temperature possesses a cusp at 0.80 weight percent, the lowest point of the cusp occurring at 723°C. This cusped junction of two parts of the solubility curve is reminiscent of the cusp in the liquidus curve occurring at a eutectic point (Sec. 8). For this reason, the corresponding point in the γ range is said to be the *eutectoid point* of the solubility curve. A plain iron-carbon steel possessing 0.80 weight percent of carbon is said to be a *eutectoid steel*.

When a specimen of iron containing less than 1.7 percent of carbon is heated above GSE (Fig. 122), the iron transforms to the γ structure and the carbon goes into solution. If the carbon content is higher than 1.7 percent, not all of it dissolves in the γ iron. The remainder forms cementite. In such a case the austenite is saturated with carbon to the limit of solubility at the corresponding temperature.

54. The Transformation of Austenite in Plain Carbon Steel.— When Austenite is cooled below the solubility-limit curve GSE of Fig. 122, it becomes unstable and has an inherent tendency to decompose into ferrite and cementite. Should it be quenched to room temperature very quickly, there is not sufficient time for the transition to take place to completion and a homogeneous metastable structure (martensite) not unlike ferrite in lattice structure is obtained. On the other hand, if it is cooled more slowly and in accordance with one of several types of procedures, other structures that are more stable than martensite are obtained. In certain of the alloy steels to be discussed later in the chapter, austenite itself may be retained by cooling to room temperature sufficiently rapidly. We shall now discuss the structures obtained by cooling austenite that has nearly eutectoid composition.

If the steel is cooled at an approximately constant rate that is less than about 15°C per sec, the transformation occurs within about 150° of the equilibrium temperature, that is, above about 550°C, and the steel has a *pearlitic* structure. This structure, which is formed by a process of nucleation and growth,[1] derives its name from the fact that it contains pearlite, a nodular formation that consists of alternate bands, or lamellae, of ferrite and cementite. If the composition is exactly eutectoid, or if it is nearly eutectoid and is cooled sufficiently rapidly, the steel is composed entirely of pearlite. If, however, the steel is *hyper-*

[1] R. F. MEHL, *Trans. A.S.M.*, **29**, 813 (1941).

eutectoid, that is, if its composition lies to the right of point S in Fig. 122, and it is cooled sufficiently slowly, it contains grains of cementite in addition to those appearing in the pearlite. Similarly, if the steel is *hypoeutectoid*, that is, if its composition lies to the left of point S in Fig. 122, and it is cooled sufficiently slowly, it contains additional grains of ferrite. The factors that influence the formation of pearlite will be discussed later.

When the cooling rate is approximately constant and is more rapid than about 200°C per sec, which rate can be achieved only in very thin sections in a plain carbon steel, the resulting structure does not contain pearlite. In fact, the steel does not transform until the temperature is in the vicinity of room temperature and then is converted to a form that is hard and brittle. The microscopic structure of this transformed steel is not homogeneous but consists of platelike grains of martensite embedded in a matrix of the parent austenite. X-ray examination shows that martensite is not one of the true equilibrium lattice arrangements of iron and carbon and must be regarded as a metastable structure which represents a stopping point during the transition from austenite to ferrite. In fact, martensite has an inherent tendency to transform to the more stable structures. This transformation proceeds at a measurable rate if the martensite is heated above 200°C. We shall discuss the properties of martensite further in another section.

Careful investigation shows that the plates of martensite are formed at a high rate of speed, each plate requiring less than 0.002 sec.[1] This fact suggests that the mechanism of formation of this structure is not nucleation and growth but a shearing process resembling closely the process of mechanical twinning.

When the austenite is cooled so rapidly in the range of temperature above 550°C that the formation of pearlite is avoided and is then held at a temperature between 250 and 550°, a new structure termed *bainite* is obtained. This does not appear homogeneous under the microscope and consists of platelike grains of ferrite somewhat like the plates of martensite in which grains of carbide may be seen. The form of bainite differs somewhat, depending upon the temperature at which the quenched austenite is held. The different structures are sometimes distin-

[1] F. Forster and E. Scheil, *Z. Metallkunde*, **28**, 245 (1936).

guished by the names *upper bainite* and *lower bainite*, respectively, when formed in the upper and lower parts of the temperature range from 250 to 550°C. The bainites may be preserved at room temperature by quenching from the temperature at which they are formed. The plates of bainite are too fine to resolve completely in an optical microscope. The recent development of the electron microscope[1] offers the possibility of extending the resolution. Bainite, like pearlite, is formed by a process of nucleation and growth.

The connection between the structure developed during the quenching of austenite and the cooling conditions is conveniently illustrated[2] in Fig. 123. This shows the time required at a given temperature partly to transform eutectoid austenite to one of the structures discussed above. The logarithmic scale of time should be noted. The austenite is quenched to the given temperature from a temperature at which it is stable. The individual curves correspond, respectively, to start of conversion, 25 percent, 50 percent, 75 percent, and 100 percent conversion. These curves, which were first determined by Bain and Davenport[3] and were later modified by other investigators, have a characteristic S shape and hence are commonly called *S curves*. The region between 723 and about 550°C is that in which pearlite is formed. It may be seen that the time required to start or complete the conversion from austenite decreases as the temperature decreases below the transformation temperature. As we shall see later, the spacing between the lamellae in the pearlite also decreases with decreasing temperature. It is clear that, in order to prevent the formation of pearlite during cooling of austenite, it is necessary that the cooling rate between 721 and 550° be sufficiently rapid that the time required to reach the upper knee of the S curve be less than that required to initiate the formation of pearlite.

The bainites are produced isothermally in the range of temperature between the upper and lower knees of the S curve. It

---

[1] MEHL, *op. cit.*

[2] The upper part of this curve is taken from Bain, *op. cit.* The lower part is taken from the suggestion by M. Cohen, *Trans. A.S.M.*, **28**, 563 (1940).

[3] E. S. DAVENPORT and E. C. BAIN, *Trans. A.I.M.E.*, **90**, 117 (1930); **100**, 13 (1932).

may be seen that the time required to initiate or complete the transformation increases as the temperature is lowered.

The reentrant domain below about 200°C is that in which martensite is formed. Extensive work[1] by Greninger and Troi-

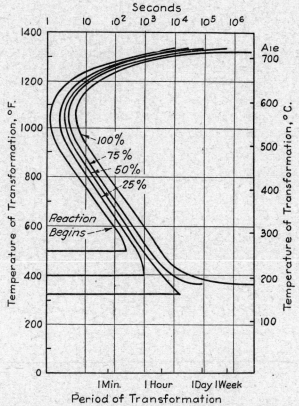

Fig. 123.—The time interval required for 25, 50, 75, and 100 percent transformation of austenite at constant temperature in a eutectoid steel. Note the logarithmic time scale at the top of the diagram.

ano and Wever and Engel has shown that only a limited amount of martensite is produced by holding the steel at any given tem-

[1] See A. B. GRENINGER and A. R. TROIANO, *Trans. A.S.M.*, 537 (1940); F. WEVER and N. ENGEL, *Mitt. Kaiser Wilhelm Inst. Eisenforsch.*, **12,** 93 (1930); H. CARPENTER and J. M. ROBERTSON, *Metals* (Oxford University Press, New York, 1939).

perature. The fraction of martensite may be increased, however, by lowering the temperature, as is indicated schematically in the figure.

From the standpoint of the principles concerning phase transformations that take place by nucleation, which were discussed in Chap. IV (Sec. 12), the acceleration of the transformation to pearlite as the temperature is lowered from 721 to 550°C is not surprising. If this transformation occurs by nucleation and growth of nuclei, as is now known to be the case,[1] we should expect the rate of nucleation to increase initially below the transformation temperature because more numerous nuclei become stable with decreasing temperature. Moreover, if pearlite could occur at temperatures below 550°C, we should expect the rate to decrease eventually because both the rate of formation of nuclei of a given size and the rate of growth of stable nuclei probably decrease with temperature. Actually, this effect is not observed because the transformation to pearlite is replaced by that to bainite at the temperature corresponding to the knee of the curve. Moreover, the fact that the rate of formation of bainite decreases with decreasing temperature in the range below the knee is not surprising, for we may suppose that in this domain of temperature even small nuclei of bainite are stable and that the factor determining the rate of the reaction is the rate of growth of the stable nuclei, which decreases with decreasing temperature. The transition to martensite, however, is remarkable, for the amount of martensite formed is practically independent of time and depends principally on the temperature at which the steel is held. In general, martensite is formed by a decrease in temperature; in fact, the processes take place even at liquid-air temperatures. As was remarked earlier, this suggests that the transformation from austenite to martensite is not an ordinary type of phase change but one involving a process, such as slip or twinning, that can occur even at the absolute zero of temperature.

Let us now consider the changes that take place in pearlite, bainite, and martensite when they are subject to prolonged heating. We should expect them to approach more nearly a state of minimum surface energy. This is found to be the case. In

[1] MEHL, *op. cit.*

pearlite, for example, the cementite lamellae draw together into more nearly spherical units, thus decreasing the surface energy. Ultimately, the cementite decomposes into graphite and ferrite; for, as was remarked in the previous section, cementite is unstable below 710°C. The changes that take place in bainite and martensite are more subtle and are detected most directly by means of X-ray analysis, the results of which will be discussed in the next section. There is little doubt, however, that the essential effect of prolonged heating is the coagulation of carbon into larger and larger units. This process is always accompanied by a decrease in hardness, which indicates that microscopic strains are relieved, much as when precipitation-hardened Duraluminum is annealed.

55. The Properties of the Products of Transformation of Austenite.—We shall now summarize briefly the properties of the principal structures occurring in steel before, during, and after transformation.

a. Austenite.—This phase may be retained in small proportion during vigorous quenching in plain carbon steels containing more than 0.60 percent carbon. Moreover, as we shall see in the next section, very large amounts may be retained in steels containing certain alloying elements. As a result, the properties of this phase may be investigated in a reasonably satisfactory manner at room temperature. It is found that austenite is soft relative to some of the phases obtained from it by transformation. For example, the Rockwell C hardness number of a high-carbon alloy steel composed almost entirely of retained austenite is about 35, whereas the hardness number of the corresponding martensitic steel is about 70. Retained austenite may be converted to martensite by quenching the specimen from room temperature to liquid-air temperature. Such a transformation naturally increases the hardness of the steel.

If a relatively soft specimen of steel containing a large amount of retained austenite is heated to an elevated temperature and then cooled, its hardness is altered as a result of the heating. Figure 124 shows the hardness of such steel after tempering at various temperatures. It may be observed that the hardness increases at the lower temperatures and then decreases. The product of the transformation during tempering is not martensite,

but a structure resembling closely the bainite that would have
been produced during an initial quenching to the temperature
at which the conversion takes place during the tempering.   The
curve of Fig. 124 resembles closely the type of curve that would
be obtained in a fully quenched specimen of copper-beryllium
alloy if it were subject to a similar tempering operation that
allowed the dissolved beryllium to precipitate.   In other words,
the transformation from austenite to bainite appears to resemble

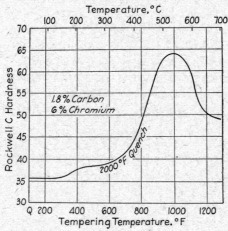

Fig. 124.—The hardness of reheated steel that originally is almost wholly
austenitic.   The steel was first quenched from 2000°F, which left it in the
austenitic state, and was then heated to successively higher temperatures.   During this heating, iron carbide precipitated from the homogeneous solution, and
the hardness varied very much as in a precipitation-hardened alloy of the
Duraluminum type.   (*After Bain.*)

the precipitation processes observed during precipitation hardening of nonferrous metals.   It seems reasonable to assume that
the carbon is practically atomically dispersed in the austenite
and that bainite is formed during a process in which the carbon
coagulates into carbides.   During this precipitation process, the
lattice is strained as a result of the changes in volume that occur
in the formation of the precipitate.

The density of austenite is of the order of 1 percent larger than
that of the transformed products, so that the transformation is
generally accompanied by a decrease in volume, as may readily
be determined by dilatometric studies.

Retained austenite is not ferromagnetic. As a result, steels containing a large amount of austenite are not so strongly attracted to a magnet as ordinary steels are.

b. Martensite.—The crystallographic structure of martensite has been the object of extensive investigation. It now seems to be established beyond reasonable doubt that the iron atoms in martensite which has been newly formed in the vicinity of room temperature are arranged in a tetragonal body-centered structure (Fig. 126b). The body-centered lattice of ferrite may be viewed as if derived from the lattice of martensite by contracting the latter in the tetragonal direction and expanding it in the other two. The ratio of the length of the tetragonal axis to the contracted axis of martensite varies from 1.00 in a hypothetical carbon-free martensite to 1.08 in tetragonal martensite containing 1.8 percent carbon. When the tetragonal phase is heated above 100°C, it actually undergoes a crystallographic change to a body-centered cubic lattice. As far as the position of the iron atoms is concerned, this change is equivalent to the contraction along the tetragonal axis and the expansion along the other pair described above. The change is, however, accompanied by a net decrease in volume that is of the order of 0.1 percent in a 1 percent carbon steel.

The great hardness of martensite relative to that of the other common steel structures is shown clearly in Fig. 125, which compares this hardness with that of pearlite and a steel in which the carbide is spheroidized.

It has been suggested that the change from tetragonal martensite to cubic martensite represents a conglomeration of carbon in a manner analogous to the conglomeration occurring during the formation of bainite. Since martensite is unquestionably unstable relative to ferrite and cementite, this general view of the transition probably is correct. However, the actual details of the transition merit further discussion.

There are two principal bases upon which the great hardness of martensitic steel could be explained, namely, the following:

1. The hardness is of the precipitation type, the plates of martensite representing the precipitate that hardens the *entire matrix* of austenite plus martensite by introducing residual stresses.

2. The hardness resides entirely in the grains of martensite, which are intrinsically hard because of their structure or because carbides have precipitated within them on a submicroscopic scale.

It does not seem possible to give preference to either of these explanations at the present time; in fact, it seems most likely

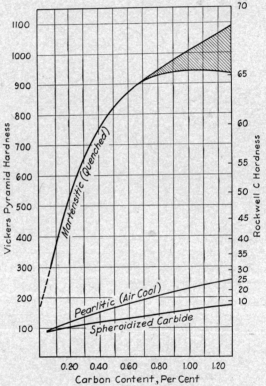

Fig. 125.—The relative hardness of martensite, pearlite, and spheroidized steel as a function of the carbon content. (*After Bain.*)

that both factors play a role.   That is, it is likely both that the grains of martensite are very hard and that the entire matrix is hardened as a result of the formation of the plates of martensite. Unfortunately, it is not possible to examine the extent to which the carbon atoms in martensite have agglomerated, for carbon is a very poor scatterer of X rays.   For this reason, it is not possible to say whether the individual plates of martensite are hard because of precipitation or because of structure, as is true, for example, of the grains of γ brass (see Sec. 30).

The mechanism of the transition from austenite to martensite has been a topic of widespread interest.[1] In this case, X-ray methods have been of great service and appear to provide a picture of the mechanism that is correct in principle, if not in detail. It is found that the grains of martensite possess a

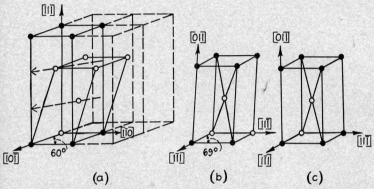

Fig. 126.—The mode of transformation of austenite into martensite proposed by Kurdjumow and Sachs. Figure (a) shows the face-centered cubic lattice of austenite, and the arrow in the second plane of atoms indicates the displacement that carries the lattice to a tetragonal body-centered one. Figure (b) shows the arrangement of iron atoms in tetragonal body-centered martensite. Figure (c) shows the arrangement in cubic martensite.

definite orientation relative to the parent austenite. This orientation is dependent upon the carbon content in a complicated way, which we shall not discuss in detail here. However, in low-carbon steels, the grains or plates of martensite, when formed above room temperature, are invariably oriented so that the plane of the plate is parallel to the (111) plane of the grain of austenite in which it was formed. Moreover, the [110] direction of the martensite is always parallel to the [111] direction of the austenite. On the basis of these facts and knowledge of

[1] The most recent paper dealing with this subject is that by G. V. Smith and R. F. Mehl, *Metals Tech. Pub.* 1459 (1942). Important earlier papers are those by G. Kurdjumow and G. Sachs, *Z. Physik*, **64**, 325 (1930); Z. Nishiyami, *Science Rept. Tohoku Imp. Univ.*, **22**, 637 (1934).

the structures of the two phases, Kurdjumow and Sachs proposed that the transformation takes place as the result of a shearing action, analogous to twinning. Successive (111) planes of the austenite lattice are supposed to become displaced relative to one another by an amount not equal to a translational distance (see Fig. 126). In addition, the (111) planes become distorted from ideal hexagonal form. Presumably, a similar mechanism operates in eutectoid and high-carbon steels even though the details of the transformation are doubtless more complicated. It is not known, of course, whether large groups of planes become displaced simultaneously or whether the process takes place as a result of the passage of an avalanche of dislocations, as was suggested in the case of twinning (Sec. 23). In either case, it is possible that the resulting lattice is far from perfect, either because the shearing does not occur homogeneously or because many dislocations become trapped during the avalanche. In this event, the hardness of martensite could arise from the residual distortion. Figure 126 shows the difference between the arrangement of iron atoms in cubic and tetragonal martensite and indicates the small amount of strain required to pass from one structure to the other.

Martensitic steel softens gradually on being heated above 200°C, presumably because the tempering process results in continued precipitation and agglomeration of iron carbide from the solution. These softer products obtained by tempering do not possess the brittleness characteristic of martensite and, as a result, are found very useful in practice since toughness rather than full hardness usually is desired. There is evidence that the X-ray diffraction pattern of cementite does not appear in measurable time unless martensite is tempered above 300°C. This indicates that the conglomeration of carbon occurring below 300°C takes place on a very small scale.

Martensite is ferromagnetic. Its Curie point does not appear to be known, however, for measurement of this would involve heating the phase to a point where the transformation to carbide and ferrite would proceed very rapidly.

c. Cementite.—The lattice structure of cementite[1] is shown in Fig. 127. This material possesses no well-defined slip planes

---

[1] H. Lipson and N. J. Petch, *J. Iron and Steel Inst.*, **142**, 95 (1941).

and is, presumably as a result, very hard and brittle. Its presence in large amounts is undoubtedly responsible for the hardness of cast iron.

When a steel containing cementite is tempered sufficiently long, the grains of cementite become spherical in form as a result of the forces of surface tension that act upon them. This process is known as *spheroidizing*.

Cementite is ferromagnetic and possesses a Curie point in the neighborhood of 200°C. Aside from this, little appears to be known about its magnetic properties.

As we noted previously, cementite is unstable below 710°C and will decompose to graphite and ferrite if kept for a sufficiently long time at elevated temperatures.

d. Pearlite.—Although pearlite is not a homogeneous phase, being composed of lammellae of ferrite and cementite, it possesses a number of the properties of a distinct phase.

We have seen above that this structure is characteristic of the eutectoid composition and, as a result, forms in separate nodules as if it were a single phase. It has

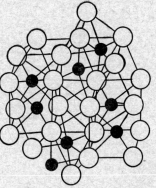

Fig. 127.—The positions of the iron and carbon atoms in cementite. The iron atoms are represented by large circles and the carbon atoms by small ones. (*After Lipson and Petch.*)

been definitely established by Mehl[1] and his coworkers that the formation of these nodules occurs as the result of a nucleation process. The nuclei occur most commonly at the boundaries of the parent austenite but do occur infrequently within the grains. The most effective nuclei, or *inoculators*, are undissolved carbides and free cementite. The formation of pearlite may be appreciably delayed by maintaining the austenite at elevated temperatures for a period of time sufficient to allow all carbides to dissolve. It is reasonable to assume that the presence of undissolved carbides furnishes surfaces at which the cementite nuclei in pearlite may form with lower activation energy than is required in completely homogeneous austenite.

[1] MEHL, *op. cit.*

Since chemical analysis has established that the alternate lamellae appearing in pearlite are composed of ferrite and cementite, it is natural to suppose that the separation of carbon that occurs in their formation is the result of a diffusion process. Figure 128 shows[1] in fact that the rate of diffusion of carbon in iron actually is sufficiently rapid above 550°C for this to be a reasonable process. It is not known, however, why the lamellar spacing decreases as the temperature at which pearlite is formed

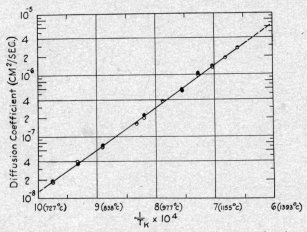

Fig. 128.—The relation between the diffusion coefficient of carbon in eutectoid steel and the reciprocal of the absolute temperature. (*After Wells and Mehl.*)

decreases. As the result of analysis of this spacing, Mehl[2] has pointed out the beautiful relationship shown in Fig. 129, in which the logarithm of the interlamellar spacing is plotted as a function of the reciprocal of the absolute temperature at which the pearlite was formed. It may be seen that the resulting curve is linear, as if the spacing were determined by a process requiring thermal fluctuations. Although the nature of this process is not clearly understood, Mehl has shown that the temperature dependence of the rate of formation of pearlite can be deduced from the curve of Fig. 129 on the assumption that the formation of the lamellae

[1] C. WELLS and R. F. MEHL, *Trans. A.I.M.E.*, **140**, 279 (1940).

[2] R. F. MEHL in *The Hardenability of Alloy Steels* (American Society for Metals, Cleveland, Ohio, 1938).

occurs as a result of diffusion of carbon through a distance equal to the lamellar spacing.

It is also interesting to note that the lamellar spacing becomes of the order of atomic dimensions at the lower edge of the interval of temperature in which this structure occurs. This fact indicates that the separation of carbide occurs on an atomic scale, if at all, at the knee of the *S* curve. Moreover, it probably

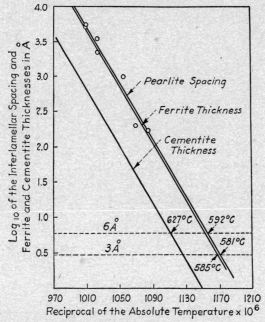

Fig. 129.—Relation between the dimensions of the constituents of pearlite and the reciprocal of the absolute temperature. (*After Mehl.*)

explains why structures are very difficult to resolve microscopically in the bainite range: the carbides that are formed in this region are very small.

e. Bainite.—The amount of experimental information that is available concerning the properties of bainite is much less than that concerning martensite. However, there is evidence which shows that the phases possess common properties. For example, both appear as needles that have formed directly from austenite. Moreover, X-ray evidence obtained by Smith and Mehl[1] indicates that the orientation relationships between the plates of bainite and the parent crystals of austenite are similar to those found between the needles of martensite and the parent crystals of austenite. This suggests that the nuclei of bainite may be formed from austenite by a shear process in much the same way as martensite.

56. The Influence of Alloying Elements.—Elements are added to steel in amounts of the order of 5 percent or less, for a number of reasons. In general, these elements may be placed in two separate classifications: one group is added primarily to alloy with the iron and carbon in the steel and another is added to combine with and possibly remove other constituents such as oxygen or sulphur.

The most important of the reasons for adding purely alloying agents are as follows:

a. To decrease the rate at which the transformation of austenite takes place at a given temperature. This decrease promotes the formation of martensite in specimens so large that if made of plain carbon steel they could not be cooled with sufficient speed to avoid the knee of the *S* curve. The elements that are most commonly used for this purpose are chromium, nickel (usually in combination with chromium), manganese, molybdenum and vanadium.

b. To form a hard abrasive carbide, such as is needed in a high-speed cutting tool. The most common agents of this type are vanadium, molybdenum, chromium, and tungsten. The last is often added in amounts well in excess of 5 percent.

c. To induce secondary hardness in a steel to be used in a high-speed tool. When properly tempered, a tool of such a steel will not soften during its period of serviceability even though it operates at an elevated temperature at which plain carbon steel would become very soft. The principal elements employed for this service are molybdenum, chromium, vanadium, and tungsten.

d. To inhibit the growth of grains in austenite during heat-treatment. Vanadium is an element that is very effective in this respect.

e. To increase strength, particularly at high temperatures, in steels of particular compositions or to inhibit creep. Manganese,

[1] SMITH and MEHL, *op. cit.*

nickel, silicon, phosphorus, cobalt, chromium, and molybdenum are added to steel to render particular services of this type.

f. To inhibit corrosion resistance under particular conditions. Chromium and nickel in combination are frequently used to perform this service.

Reasons for adding elements that combine with constituents other than iron and carbon are as follows:

a. To combine with dissolved oxygen in molten steel and thereby prevent the formation of blowholes in ingots. The elements most serviceable as deoxidizers are silicon, aluminum, and titanium.

b. To combine with elements such as sulphur and phosphorus that would otherwise induce brittleness. Manganese is added, for example, to combine with sulphur.

It is interesting to note that some of the constituents added for a specific purpose may play a dual role. Thus the aluminum oxide formed when aluminum is added as a deoxidizing agent also retards the growth of grains in austenite.

It obviously is not the purpose of this book to undertake a detailed discussion of these topics for the numerous steels of commercial interest. Instead, we shall consider briefly the underlying principles that determine the influences best understood at present.

a. Retardation of the Transformation of Austenite.—This is probably the most interesting and most important effect that may be produced by alloying agents. Without it, steel could be transformed into martensite or bainite only in very thin sections and the field in which the metal could be used would be greatly restricted.

Figure 130 shows the *S* curve for an alloy steel containing about 4 percent of nickel and 2 percent of chromium as the essential alloying elements. When this is compared with Fig. 123, it is seen that the knee of the *S* curve of the alloy steel is shifted along the time axis by a factor of about 1000. This example illustrates the extent to which the transformation process may be decelerated by moderate addition of alloying elements. The steel corresponding to Fig. 130 can be fully hardened in sections as thick as 5 in., whereas a plain carbon steel cannot be fully hardened in sections thicker than about $\frac{1}{2}$ in.

There are several mechanisms that might be proposed to explain the retardation of the formation of pearlite in these alloy steels. We shall examine these and discuss the supporting and contradicting evidence for each.

1. Since the formation of pearlite requires the diffusion of carbon, it is natural to suggest, as a first proposal, that the alloying agents inhibit the rate of diffusion of carbon. This picture is not tenable, however, for investigation by Wells and Mehl[1]

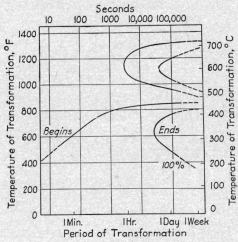

Fig. 130.—The *S* curve for a nickel-chromium steel. (Taken from the book by Bain. The experimental work was carried out by Davenport, Kelley, Grange, and Rutherford.)

shows that at a given temperature the rate of diffusion of carbon is not appreciably different in plain carbon steel and in most of the steels in which the rate of transformation has been decreased by the addition of alloying elements.

2. As a second hypothesis, we might suppose that the addition of the alloying elements lowers the temperature at which austenite transforms so that the rate of diffusion of carbon is slower during the transition because the thermal fluctuations necessary for diffusion are rarer. Figures 131 and 132 show that this cannot be the case for manganese and chromium alloys, for the γ range is scarcely affected by the amount of these agents ordinarily added to produce retardation. In fact, if any of the

[1] C. Wells and R. F. Mehl, *op. cit.*

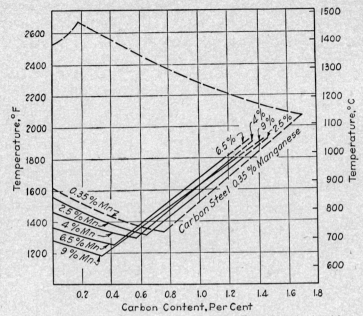

FIG. 131.—The variation of the γ range of several manganese steels with manganese content. (*After Bain.*)

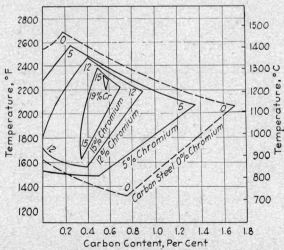

FIG. 132.—The variation of the γ range of several chromium steels with chromium composition. (*After Bain.*)

cases in which appreciable temperature differences actually do occur are examined, it is found that in general the differences are not nearly sufficient to account for the decrease in rate of transformation in the alloy steel.

3. A third hypothesis, which is most commonly accepted at present, is based on the supposition that the transformation rate is slower in the alloy steels because it is necessary to wait for the alloying element to diffuse before the nuclei may form and grow. Since the rate of diffusion of the alloying elements, such as manganese and chromium, which substitute for iron, is much slower than the rate of diffusion of carbon at any given temperature, it follows that, according to this hypothesis, the diffusion of the former is the factor that determines the rate of formation of carbide.

In order to appreciate the significance of this mechanism, it is necessary to summarize a few facts concerning the affinities of the various alloying elements with carbon. If the elements are plotted in a sequence of increasing affinity, the order is as follows:

Cobalt
Nickel
Silicon
Aluminum
Iron
Manganese
Chromium
Tungsten
Molybdenum
Vanadium
Titanium

Thus cobalt, nickel, silicon, and aluminum prefer being in the ferrite phase to being in the carbide, whereas manganese, chromium, tungsten, molybdenum, vanadium, and titanium prefer being in the carbide phase. Manganese is only a slightly better carbide former than iron, which, we have seen previously, forms a moderately unstable carbide, whereas chromium, tungsten, molybdenum, vanadium, and titanium form very stable carbides. According to the third viewpoint of the retarding influence of the alloying elements, the reaction

$$\text{austenite} \rightarrow \text{ferrite} + \text{cementite} \tag{1}$$

can proceed only when the alloying elements are distributed between ferrite and cementite in such a manner that the ratio of the percentages in each phase is different from unity. When the reaction occurs, the strong carbide formers are preferentially in the carbide, whereas the weaker ones are preferentially in the ferrite. For example, nickel should diffuse away from the carbide toward the ferrite, whereas manganese, chromium, tungsten, and so forth, should diffuse into the carbide.

This viewpoint has been justified experimentally inasmuch as chemical analysis of the carbide in pearlitic alloy steels shows that the alloying elements actually diffuse. However, the rudiments of the process have not yet been investigated sufficiently extensively to allow us to understand the basic reason why diffusion is necessary.

To make this point clearer let us consider a steel containing only an infinitesimally small amount of one of the retarding elements, such as manganese. In such a case, the alloying element presumably has negligible influence, for experience shows that the rate of transformation is independent of alloy content in plain carbon steels containing mere traces of these elements. Conversely, since the transformation is rapid, it follows that the alloying elements have not had sufficient time to diffuse between the ferrite and the carbide and hence must be practically homogeneously distributed when the transformation is complete. In other words, it would appear that reaction (1) can proceed without regard to the distribution of the special alloys as long as their concentration is small. As the concentration of these elements is increased, however, there must come a point at which the reaction can proceed only when the special alloying elements no longer are distributed homogeneously. At this point, the alloying elements must have an influence on the stability of one of the constituents of the reaction. Evidently austenite must remain stable relative to ferrite and cementite at the usual transition temperature (723°C) when the alloying elements are homogeneously distributed but must again become unstable when these elements diffuse in such a way as to be inhomogeneously distributed between carbide and ferrite.

Careful thermodynamical analysis should allow us to determine the changes in stability that actually do occur when the alloying elements are present in effective amounts and are homogeneously distributed. It is possible, for example, that the free energy of the carbide and cementite are not greatly affected, whereas the free energy of austenite is lowered. Conversely, it is possible that the free energy of austenite is almost unaffected by the alloying elements, whereas the free energy of either one or both of the constituents on the right-hand side of Eq. (1) is raised. Until such work has been done, the detailed explanation of the retarding influence of alloying elements is impossible.

There are additional points of interest to be raised in this connection. As was mentioned above, when the amount of retarding alloy is raised from infinitesimal values, a point is reached at which austenite can transform only when the alloying elements diffuse. How does this effect vary with composition? It is possible that for one sharply defined range of composition the reaction is limited only by the rate at which carbon diffuses and that for another sharply defined range the reaction is limited mainly by the rate at which the alloying elements diffuse. Conversely, it is possible that the two regions gradually blend into one another. Further experimental work is needed to throw light on this matter.

A possible explanation of the retardation effect may be provided by considering the problem in the following way: There are two reactions that may, at least in principle, occur in an alloy steel. In the first, austenite decomposes into ferrite and cementite without diffusion of the alloying elements. We shall call this reaction (I).

$$\text{austenite} \rightarrow \text{cementite} + \text{ferrite (homogeneous)} \qquad (I)$$

In the other, the alloys diffuse during the transformation, and the concentration of alloying elements is different in the carbide and cementite. We shall call this reaction (II)

$$\text{austenite} \rightarrow \text{cementite} + \text{ferrite (inhomogeneous).} \qquad (II)$$

A phase diagram may be constructed for each of these reactions by the use of the principles of thermodynamics. In general, these diagrams should involve more than two dimensions since there should be one dimension for each of the constituents of the steel, including iron and carbon. In determining the equilibrium state at given temperature and composition, we should use that diagram in which the reaction can proceed most rapidly. Presumably in the range of low-alloy compositions corresponding to plain carbon steels, the diagram associated with reaction (I) should be employed, since this reaction is the more rapid, whereas the diagram associated with reaction (II) should be used when the alloying elements actually separate.

There is no adequate experimental basis on which to construct these diagrams at the present time; hence, it is not possible to discuss the mode of transition between the two diagrams in a rigorous manner. The following, however, would seem to be a reasonable qualitative method of regarding the problem: Let us restrict our attention to a steel of given carbon content, for example, that corresponding to the eutectoid composition, and let us vary the amount of only one of the retarding alloying agents, such as chromium. It is possible that as the amount of chromium is increased from zero the temperature at which austenite becomes unstable relative to pearlite decreases very rapidly if the chromium remains homogeneously dispersed in both carbide and ferrite. The variation of the equilibrium temperature with chromium for reaction (I) would then correspond to curve I of Fig. 133. On the other hand, it is possible that the equilibrium temperature decreases much more slowly with increasing amounts of chromium if the chromium diffuses and becomes preferentially located in the cementite. Thus it is possible that the variation of the equilibrium temperature with composition for reaction (II) corresponds to curve II of Fig. 133. The two curves must meet at the left-hand end of the diagram since the position of an infinitesimal amount of alloying agent cannot affect the diagrams. As was suggested in the preceding paragraph, the actual course of the reaction will be determined by the relative rates at which the two reactions may proceed. In the chromium-poor end of the diagram, the equilibrium temperature for reaction (I) is high and carbon is sufficiently mobile at this temperature for the homogeneous process to be preferred. Conversely, the opposite should be true in the chromium-rich portion of the diagram at which the equilibrium temperature for the homogeneous reaction is very low. In the intermediate range of composition, the reaction proceeds by means of mechanism (I) if the temperature is sufficiently low, that is, if the temperature-composition point is below curve I in the figure, whereas the opposite is valid if the temperature is maintained between curves I and II. According to this view-

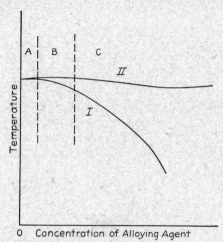

Fig. 133.—Hypothetical variation of the equilibrium temperature for reactions (I) and (II) (see text) with changing alloy content. It is suggested that this temperature drops for reaction (I). In the region *A*, the transformation occurs by means of the homogeneous reaction because the equilibrium temperatures for the two reactions are nearly the same, and reaction (I) requires only the diffusion of carbon. In the region *B*, the reaction proceeds by mechanism (I) at temperatures below the lower curve and by mechanism (II) at temperatures between the two curves. In region *C*, the reaction proceeds by mechanism (II).

point, there should be a range of composition (see Fig. 133) in which the reaction proceeds by reaction (I) below a certain temperature and proceeds more slowly by mechanism (II) above this temperature. Naturally, if the steel of this composition were cooled at a uniform rate, the range of temperature in which the transformation occurs would depend upon this rate. If the rate is more rapid than the critical value for which reaction (II) would occur in the high-temperature range, the transformation will occur by means of reaction (I) at the lower temperature.

On the other hand, the reaction will occur at the higher temperature by means of mechanism (II) if the rate is slower.

b. Formation of a Hard Abrasive Carbide.—The carbides of the various alloying elements differ greatly in hardness and strength. In particular, chromium, vanadium, molybdenum, and tungsten form very hard carbides. For this reason, these elements are added to tools required for abrasive purposes. The structure desired in such cases is not pearlite, since this does not possess the requisite toughness. Instead, tempered martensites or

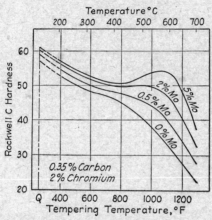

Fig. 134.—The influence of tempering temperature on the hardness of chrome-molybdenum steels. The carbon content is 0.35 percent, the chromium content is 2 percent, and the molybdenum content is as shown. (*After Bain.*)

bainites, in which the carbide is formed in much finer aggregates than occur in pearlites, prove more serviceable.

c. Secondary Hardness.—Figure 134 shows the variation of hardness with tempering temperature of martensitic steels containing various amounts of molybdenum between 0 and 5 percent. It may be seen that the 2 and 5 percent molybdenum steels show a secondary range of hardness that is related to the presence of the alloy. Steel containing comparable amounts of vanadium or tungsten exhibit a similar secondary hardness. As was pointed out earlier, this effect is desirable in steels for high-speed tools, since they do not soften so rapidly as plain carbon steels when heated as a result of use.

Since secondary hardness is not observed in plain carbon steels, it follows that it cannot be due to the mere aggregation of carbon. As Bain[1] has suggested, it seems more reasonable to suppose that the secondary hardness is related to the formation of a secondary carbide phase which is rich in the alloying elements. This phase forms after carbon has first precipitated in the form of cementite containing the same proportion of alloying element as is present in the martensite. Since the carbide rich in alloy is much more stable than this cementite, it follows that the carbide will form in the course of sufficient time. This time is determined by the rate of diffusion of the alloying element and the rate at which the cementite decomposes.

Even if we grant, however, that a secondary carbide can form, it is not immediately obvious why such precipitation should result in secondary hardness. Presumably this phenomenon is closely similar to the type of precipitation hardening observed in Duraluminum. That is, it is possible that the aggregates of secondary carbide are initially very small and in this state produce a large amount of submicroscopic residual strain which inhibits the motion of dislocations. Given sufficient time, the secondary-carbide particles increase in size and break away from the surrounding matrix, thus relieving the residual strains and producing the decrease in hardness that is observed after a sufficient amount of tempering.

If this interpretation of secondary hardness is correct, it follows that cementite and ferrite in which the alloying elements are homogeneously distributed are stable relative to martensite of the same alloy composition, for the structure that shows secondary hardness on tempering may be obtained by tempering martensite and hence is more stable than the latter. Moreover, since martensite is stable relative to austenite, it follows further that cementite plus ferrite of homogeneous alloy composition should be stable relative to austenite at the tempering temperatures below 300°C. This result seems to support the suggestion given in connection with the discussion of the retarding influence of alloying agents (Sec. 56a, page 224) that the homogeneous transformation of austenite [reaction (I)] could occur at sufficiently low temperatures in alloy steels which possess a slow

[1] BAIN, *op. cit.*

transformation rate. It is possible that the reaction does not occur in this way during ordinary quenching of alloy steels and prefers the inhomogeneous route because this route is more rapid at elevated temperatures.

d. Inhibition of Grain Growth.—The reason certain alloying elements, such as vanadium, inhibit the growth of grains in austenite is not yet clearly understood. Since such growth probably takes place by the motion of atoms near the boundary in such a manner that they transfer their positions from the sites of one lattice to the other, it is possible that the alloying elements exert their influence by retarding the rate at which such motion occurs.

e. Killing Agents.—The influence of killing agents was discussed in connection with the general problem of gases in metals.

f. Contribution to Strength.—The explanation of the fact that particular alloying agents contribute to strength and toughness is not entirely beyond the range of present knowledge. It is known, for example, that nickel and silicon dissolve in ferrite which is formed in the transformation from austenite to ferrite and cementite and thus harden the grains of that phase. On the other hand, it cannot be claimed that all the manifold effects imparted by alloying agents are understood.

g. Corrosion Resistance.—The influence of alloying elements on resistance to corrosion is probably connected with the effect they produce in the coatings that are formed during the early stages of corrosion. As we saw in dealing with the oxidation of metals in Sec. 47, the oxide layer formed on aluminum and similar metals during the initial stage of oxidation is sufficiently impermeable to prevent further oxidation. It is likely that in some cases the alloying elements assist in forming similar impermeable coatings on the metals which contain them. In most cases, however, the effect of the alloy is connected with changes in electrolytic potentials of the surface that they induce during the early stages of corrosion. This topic merits a more detailed discussion than is possible in this book.

CHAPTER XV

INTRODUCTION TO THE CONCEPTS OF MODERN PHYSICS

57. Introduction.[1]—Up to this point in the development of the physics of solids, we have used only those concepts of the atom which may be gained from an examination of the structures of crystals. With these simple ideas alone we are able to correlate many of the interesting facts surrounding metals, such as the fact that some metals alloy and others do not and the fact that there are slip planes within grains, and so forth. It is evident, however, that many questions cannot be answered satisfactorily without more complete knowledge of atomic structure. Consider, for example, the following: Why are some substances metals and others insulators? Evidently we cannot answer this question if we know only that atoms have a definite size and arrange themselves in lattice array, for the atoms in metals and insulators have this in common. A number of other questions of the same type are as follows:

1. Why are some metals good conductors and others poor conductors?

2. Why are iron, cobalt, and nickel ferromagnetic and other metals not ferromagnetic?

3. Why is carbon a good conductor when in the form of graphite and a poor one when in the form of diamond?

4. Why does iron change from a body-centered to a face-centered structure and then back to a body-centered one when it is heated from room temperature to the melting point?

5. Why are some salts, such as copper oxide or galena, better conductors at high temperatures than at low, and why do metals show the reverse behavior?

---

[1] A survey of this subject may be found in the book by F. K. Richtmyer and E. H. Kennard, *Introduction to Modern Physics* (McGraw-Hill Book Company, Inc., New York, 1942).

This list could be extended indefinitely, but even these few questions serve to show that many data would be better understood if there were a more complete knowledge of the atomic structure of solids.

Fortunately, knowledge of atomic structure has grown to a point where many questions of this type can be answered in a clear manner. The following chapters will be devoted to this topic. Before we proceed, however, it is necessary that we survey briefly the concepts of modern atomic physics, since these concepts form the basis for the presentation.

The advance of atomic physics rests primarily upon knowledge of the properties of two entities, namely, the electron, the fundamental unit of negative electricity, and the photon, the fundamental unit of which light is composed. As a result of ingenious experimental research extending over a period of fifty years, it is now felt that all the basic facts concerning these units which are necessary for understanding the properties of solids are known. At the present time, it seems as unlikely that the present picture of electricity and light will be altered as that Newton's laws of motion will be found to be in error when applied to ordinary ballistics or mechanical engineering.

58. The Electron.—The concept of the electron was originated by Lorentz about sixty years ago. He decided that the optical properties of transparent materials could be explained only if they possess bound electrical charges that are free to vibrate about fixed positions of equilibrium. He termed this hypothetical charge the electron.

The laws of electrolysis furnish good indirect support for Lorentz's assumption. Faraday found that a fixed amount of electricity (about 96,500 coulombs) is required to electroplate a chemical equivalent of an electrolyte from solution. It will be recalled that an equivalent weight of an element is its atomic weight divided by its valence. Since there are equal numbers of atoms in atomic weights of all elements, Faraday's law suggests that atoms in electrolytic solutions are charged by amounts equal to their respective valences times a fundamental unit of electricity. It is reasonable to suppose, as has actually been proved, that the charge of the electron is equal to this fundamental unit.

If F is the charge required to electroplate an equivalent weight of an element, N_a is the number of atoms per atomic weight (Avogadro's number), and e is the electronic charge, we may anticipate the relation

$$F = N_a e. \tag{1}$$

Since F is known, this relation could be employed to determine N_a if e were known, and vice versa. Actually, the first attempts to determine e were based on prior determinations of N_a. We shall not take the space to describe the early methods of determining N_a, since this would carry us far afield. It may be

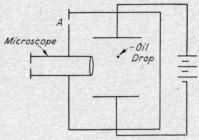

Fig. 135.—Schematic diagram showing Millikan's method for measuring the charge of an electron. The charged oil drop moves under the combined action of the electric field and gravity. From its motion, which may be observed under the microscope, the charge may be determined.

mentioned, however, that they were relatively crude and were generally in error by about 10 percent.

A notable advance in the determination of the atomic constants came about as a result of Millikan's direct measurement of e. His method, known as the "oil-drop method," is shown schematically in Fig. 135. A fine spray of oil is formed by an atomizer in the chamber A. One of these drops settles through the hole into a second chamber and is subsequently kept under observation as the following sequence of measurements is made: First its rate of fall is determined. From this and known laws of viscosity, it is possible to determine the mass of the drop. A vertical electric field is then applied. If the droplet is uncharged, no appreciable change in the rate of fall is observed. If, however, the particle has a charge, which it presumably gained as a result of friction during the atomizing process, the rate of fall is changed because of the additional electric force. The magnitude of the charge on the drop may be determined from the change in velocity. Millikan found in this way that

    a. All charges are integer multiples of a fixed amount.

    b. The magnitude of the fundamental unit is $1.6 \cdot 10^{-19}$ coulomb (or $4.80 \cdot 10^{-10}$ esu).

A number of additional methods for determining *e* have been devised since Millikan's earliest work, and these agree with the value given above to within a comparatively small experimental error.

It follows that N_a may be determined as accurately as *e* by use of Eq. (1), which relates the two. In this way it is found that $N_a = 6.03 \cdot 10^{23}$. Once N_a is known, the mass of any atom, such as hydrogen, may be computed by dividing its atomic weight by N_a. It is found in this way that the mass of the hydrogen atom is $1.66 \cdot 10^{-24}$ g.

The ratio of the charge of the electron to its mass may be measured in the following way: A beam of electrons may be obtained from a hot metal filament by a simple evaporation procedure, which we shall consider in detail in another chapter. A beam of this type is commonly called a *cathode-ray* beam, since it emanates from the cathode, or negatively charged electrode, of an electrical discharge. That it is composed of electrons was first deduced by J. J. Thomson from the fact that it may be deflected by either an electric or a magnetic field. Now the amount by which it is deflected by given fields depends both on the velocity of the electrons and on the ratio of the charge to mass. By suitably observing the deflection in a combination of electric and magnetic fields, it is possible to measure both these quantities. The first depends upon the particular way in which the electron beam is generated, whereas the second is a universal constant having the value $e/m = 5.3 \cdot 10^{17}$ esu per g. When this is combined with the accurate value of *e*, it is found that $m = 9.0 \cdot 10^{-28}$ g. This is about 1/1,840 times the mass of the hydrogen atom. Thus we see that the electron is much lighter than the atom.

The size of the electron cannot be determined by direct measurement at the present time, for it is extremely small compared with the dimensions of the atom. Guided by theoretical work, however, Lorentz has suggested that the electronic radius is of the order of magnitude of 10^{-13} cm.

We shall see below that the electron has a magnetic field associated with it; that is, it behaves like a small magnet. This fact is of fundamental significance for understanding the magnetic properties of metals.

59. Other Types of Charged Radiation.—The naturally radioactive substances such as radium and its decomposition products emit three characteristic types of radiation, which have been identified as beams of very fast electrons (beta rays), fast positively charged helium atoms (alpha particles), and light waves of very high frequency or very short wave lengths (gamma rays). The latter are not charged. These three types of radiation have proved to be very valuable in determining the internal structure of atoms, for they penetrate through appreciable thicknesses of matter.

It may be added that it is now possible to produce comparable beams of these types of particles and waves by artificial means, such as cyclotrons and electrostatic generators. These means have the advantage that other particles such as the nuclei of hydrogen (protons and deuterons), can be accelerated and used in the same manner as the natural radioactive radiations.

60. Composition of the Atoms.—Thomson was the first person to suggest that matter is entirely electrical in origin. Early in the history of modern physics, he suggested that the atoms are made of the negatively charged electrons described in the previous section, which are embedded in a comparatively large sphere of positively charged electricity. Since experiments had shown that all electrons are the same, he concluded that the difference between different elements arose as a result of differences in the nature of the positively charged unit. A typical Thomson atom is shown in Fig. 136. Subsequent experiments showed that Thomson's model is incorrect.

The first insight into the true nature of the atom was given by Rutherford in 1911. He bombarded gold foil with alpha particles and studied the angles through which the particles are bent as a result of collision with the gold atoms. He found that many of the particles are deflected through angles much larger than could be explained on the basis of Thomson's atomic model and was compelled to conclude that the positive charge in atoms is very strongly localized so that there is a region of very intense electrostatic field. Careful work showed that the combined sizes of the nucleus and the alpha particle could be placed at about 10^{-13} cm, which is about 1/100,000 times the size of an atom. Present evidence shows that only a small part of this combined radius can be associated with the alpha particle. Thus Rutherford was led to picture the atom as being composed of electrons and a small positively charged nucleus in which practically all the mass resides. It may be added that much subsequent work has shown that all the positive charge in the atom resides in this nucleus.

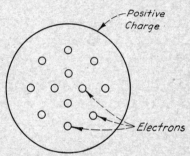

FIG. 136.—The Thomson atom. In it the electrons were assumed to be embedded in a large unit of positive charge.

Soon after Rutherford's research, Bohr (1913) developed a dynamical theory of the atom that formed a steppingstone to our present picture of the atom. Bohr suggested that the electrons move about the positively charged nucleus in a manner resembling closely the motion of the planets about the sun. The analogy with the solar system is a good one, but it is not precise; Bohr introduced special stipulations on the motion that will be better understood after we have discussed the modern picture.

61. The Theory of Light.—The earliest theory of light is the corpuscular theory developed by Newton (1665). Newton argued that light must consist of a stream of corpuscles, for otherwise it would be diffracted by edges and slits, just as any wave is diffracted. However, he had overlooked the possibility that the waves might have such short wave lengths that the diffraction effects would be very small unless one uses very narrow slits. The question was subsequently reopened by Fresnel and Young (1800–1825), who showed conclusively that light is a wave form of extremely short wave length.

The next stage in the development of the wave theory of light is due to Maxwell (1860), who suggested that light is an electromagnetic phenomenon and that light waves are generated by oscillating electric charges. In support of this, he showed that the velocity of light is intimately related to certain electromagnetic quantities. Maxwell's theory passed out of the purely theoretical stage in 1890, when Hertz proved the existence of electromagnetic waves in a way that subsequently led to the development of wireless transmission and radio. Thus by 1900 the wave theory was so thoroughly entrenched that it would not have seemed likely to need modification or extension. There were, however, one or two outstanding difficulties that ultimately led to a fundamental change in the concept of light.

In the first place, it was found that the frequency distribution of radiation in a hot enclosure could not be explained by classical theory. Planck, however, showed that the observed distribution could be explained if it were assumed that a minimum energy is required to stimulate a light wave of given frequency. In particular, he concluded that the energy, or *quantum*, associated with the wave of frequency ν is $h\nu$, where h is a constant independent of frequency (Planck's constant). The exact implications of Planck's discovery were not clearly understood at the time, but they seemed to imply that light radiation traveled in bundles, the energy per bundle in a wave of frequency ν being $h\nu$. This implication clearly was at variance with the wave theory in the form developed by Maxwell.

A second difficulty arose in connection with the photoelectric effect. It was observed by Lenard that light of suitable wave length ejects electrons from metals. This effect is extensively used at present in the commercial cesium photocell (the magic eye), which responds to visible and infrared radiation. Experiment shows that the current produced by illumination is proportional to the intensity of light. These facts in themselves are not surprising, for it is easy to imagine that the electrons in a metal resonate to particular wave lengths and gain such a large amplitude of vibration that they are ejected from the specimen. On the other hand, one would expect the electrons to require a longer time to gain the critical amplitude when the light is weak than when it is strong. Experiments with very weak light showed that electrons are ejected as soon as the light is turned on, even in cases in which it would take hours for sufficient radiation to pass through a single atom if the radiation were uniformly distributed. This fact again forced physicists to the conclusion that a light beam is composed of bundles of energy. In particular, Einstein suggested in 1905 that the energy absorbed by an electron when irradiated with light of frequency ν must be one quantum of magnitude $h\nu$. In this connection, he suggested the equation

$$h\nu = \frac{mv^2}{2} + W$$

governing the quantum energy. Here $mv^2/2$ is the final kinetic energy of the electron and W is the energy expended by the electron in getting out of the metal. This energy is known as the *work function*. Experiments on the velocity of ejected electrons verified this equation and led to the value

$$h = 6.60 \cdot 10^{-27} \text{ erg sec}$$

for Planck's constant. This verification covers frequencies ranging over those from gamma rays and X rays to infrared radiation and high-frequency radio waves.

If it were not for the indisputable facts explained by the wave theory of light, one would have been led to conclude that a corpuscular theory such as Newton's was the correct one. Thus physics faced the following serious dilemma: Light possesses both wave and corpuscular properties. It is extremely difficult to conceive of a stream of corpuscles behaving like a wave. It required about twenty years for physicists to clear up this mystery. The solution will be discussed below.

62. Influence of the Quantum Theory of Light on Atomic Ideas.—The photoelectric effect compels us to conclude that a beam of light when absorbed by electrons behaves like a stream of corpuscles of energy $h\nu$. It is natural to attempt to generalize this by saying that, when electronic systems, such as atoms, emit radiation, the emitted frequency is related to the change in energy of the atom by the relation

$$\Delta E = h\nu$$

where ΔE is the change in energy.

Now the absorption spectra of gaseous atoms, such as those in mercury vapor, consist of individual separated lines, or, in the accepted terminology, are *discrete*. That is, only particular wave lengths are absorbed. This fact was first pointed out by Frauenhofer over a hundred years ago on the basis of observations of the sun's spectrum and has been thoroughly confirmed by laboratory experiments on particular gases. Since atoms are electronic systems, it is necessary to conclude that the spacing between atomic energy states is discrete. To be more specific, let us represent the energy states of an atom by a set of horizontal lines on a vertical energy scale— this scheme is known as an energy-level diagram. Now in most ordinary mechanical systems, the energy may take all values from a certain lowest minimum to infinity. For example, we may make a pendulum vibrate with any specified amount of energy by raising its bob to a definite height and letting it go, or by giving it a preassigned push. Thus, in this case, the energy-level diagram is represented by a continuum above the value for which the system is at complete rest (Fig. 137). If atomic systems had the same type of spectrum, they would normally occupy the lowest energy state but presumably could be excited to higher states by absorption of light. Since there would be states lying arbitrarily near to the lowest one, the system could presumably absorb radiation of arbitrarily small frequency, unlike actual atoms. Since atoms actually absorb discrete frequencies, we are led to conclude that the lowest levels of atoms are separated by a finite amount. This same fact is supported by the observation that emission spectra of atoms consist of discrete frequencies.

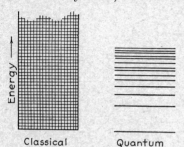

Energy →

Classical   Quantum

Fig. 137.—Difference in the energy-level diagram of a classical and an atomic system. In these diagrams the various energies a system can have are represented by horizontal lines. In the classical system, which obeys Newton's laws of motion, the allowed energy levels are continuous, whereas in the atomic system, which does not obey Newton's laws, they are discrete.

An experiment having considerable bearing on these ideas was performed by Franck and Hertz in 1913. They arranged a source of electrons in a nearly evacuated tube containing a small amount of neon vapor and placed a set of accelerating electrodes having a potential difference V before the cathode. The electrons are emitted from the cathode with nearly zero velocity and gain an amount of kinetic energy eV as a result of the attraction of the electrode, which is perforated in order to allow them to pass. Franck and Hertz found that, as long as the applied potential is below about 21.5 volts, no change is observed in the tube. However, as soon as the potential is greater than this amount, the gas becomes conducting. Presumably the electrons strike the gas atoms but have not sufficient energy to disrupt them unless their kinetic energy exceeds a certain amount. This experiment furnishes direct evidence that atomic changes can be induced only when a definite amount of energy is available.

As a result of extensive accurate spectroscopic work, the energy states of many atoms are now known and tabulated. Since units of wave length are more accurately known than units of energy, these levels are usually expressed in terms of reciprocal wave lengths, or *wave numbers*.

63. Bohr's Theory of the Hydrogen Atom.—A planetary theory of the hydrogen atom based on Newton's equations meets with two outstanding difficulties. (1) It should possess no discrete levels, since all orbits having energy ranging from minus infinity to plus infinity should be allowed. (2) One would expect such an atom to radiate all its energy and the electron to fall into the nucleus. Thus the planetary hypothesis needs appropriate modification. The first successful attempt to supply restrictive conditions was made by Bohr in 1913. Bohr noted that the dimensions of Planck's constant, namely, erg-seconds, are the same as those of angular momentum and postulated that the angular momentum L of an atom possesses only discrete values corresponding to integer multiples of $h/2\pi$, thus,

$$L = \frac{lh}{2\pi} \qquad (l = 1, 2, 3, \cdots)$$

This evidently restricts the allowed electronic orbits to discrete values, at least as far as the bound electronic states are concerned. In his original work, Bohr considered only the circular orbits that have values of l ranging by integer steps from zero upward.

It may be shown that the energies of these states are given by the
equation

$$E = -\frac{R}{n^2}$$

where R is expressible only in terms of known atomic constants
e, h, m, and, in the present case, $n = l$. Moreover, the energy
levels computed from this equation agree with the observed
values within measured accuracy.

Subsequently Sommerfeld pointed out that there also are
elliptical orbits satisfying Bohr's condition and computed their
energies. These energies also satisfy Bohr's equation, and so
their inclusion affects Bohr's picture only by altering the number
of states of given n. Experimental work ultimately justified
the inclusion of these elliptical orbits.

Although Bohr's theory was highly successful when applied
to the hydrogen atom, it met with considerable difficulties else-
where. In the first place, it could not be made to work for the
next most simple atom, namely, helium, or for the simple molecular ion H_2^+. As time passed, the theory came to be looked
on as a makeshift affair that happened to give the right answer to
a particular problem in a special case. It should be emphasized
that all the difficulties with Bohr's model did not become appar-
ent at once but came to light only after ten years of work. By
1923 it was universally admitted that the model was inadequate.

64. Electron Spin.—During the period in which the Bohr-
Sommerfeld theory was being tested, two great discoveries were
made, namely, the existence of electron spin and the Pauli
exclusion principle.

The first of these was brought to light by Goudsmit and
Uhlenbeck as a result of a careful investigation of the behavior
of atoms of various types in magnetic fields. They were led to
the unmistakable conclusion that an electron has associated
with it a magnetic field arising from a spin about an axis passing
through its center. They found that the magnitude of the spin
corresponded to an angular momentum $h/4\pi$—half the least
value for orbital motion. Since any moving charge generates a
magnetic field, it follows that the electron is surrounded by a
magnetic field because of this spin. In fact, the electron behaves

like a tiny magnet and can be considered as such in the interests of simplicity. As we remarked earlier, this magnetic field is of great importance in understanding ferromagnetism.

65. The Pauli Principle.—Pauli's great discovery was made as a result of an attempt to discuss the types of orbits occupied by the electrons in various elements in the periodic chart. He first noted that all electrons cannot be in the lowest Bohr orbit; for in this event all the atoms would have chemical properties similar to those of hydrogen, and there would be no periodicity among the elements. He concluded that in hydrogen and helium the electrons occupy this level and that in lithium and beryllium the additional electrons enter orbits of higher energy. Similarly, in passing from boron to neon the additional electrons occupy a set of orbits of still higher energy. If we examine the orbits of hydrogen, which must be qualitatively the same as the orbits in any other atom, since the electrons move in a field that is centered about the nucleus in all cases, we find that there is one type of orbit of lowest energy, namely, a circle for which $l = 1$. Associated with $n = 2$ there is one orbit for which $l = 1$, and there are three orbits for which $l = 2$. As a result of extensive analysis, Pauli concluded that only two electrons are allowed in any one orbit and that these two electrons must have spins pointing in opposite directions. Since the groups of levels associated with a given value of n are comparatively widely separated from other groups, it follows that the completion of such a group is accompanied by comparatively great chemical stability, such as is actually observed in the rare gases.

Pauli's principle may be summarized by saying that no two electrons in a system moving in the same kind of orbit have the same spin.

66. Summary.—We may now summarize the state of affairs in atomic physics in 1925, when the new and final developments occurred:

a. It was known that the electron is a small particle having a definite charge, mass, and spin.

b. The atom possesses a small nucleus in which all the positive charge and most of the mass reside.

c. Light possesses the properties both of waves and of corpuscles.

d. One may conclude that the electrons revolve about the nucleus more or less in planetary fashion but must also conclude that this motion corresponds not to simple classical laws but to some modification of these, since the energy levels are discrete.

e. The electrons in atoms and in atomic systems are aware of each other's motions and restrict their motions so that no two are in the same state with the same spin. Electrons in the same orbit have opposite spin.

67. The Wave Theory of Matter.—The first stage in clearing the difficulties that beset the theories of matter and radiation was the development of the wave theory of matter. This development began as a purely speculative venture but was soon backed by excellent experimental work. Briefly, de Broglie and Schroedinger postulated that an electron, which had previously been regarded merely as a particle, should exhibit some of the properties of waves. In making this postulate they were guided entirely by an analogy with light. They argued that, since light, which had first been shown to be a wave phenomenon by Young and Fresnel, could possess corpuscular characteristics, it seemed only reasonable to expect that electrons, which had been regarded as corpuscles, should also possess wave characteristics. Their theory provided a relation between the wave length to be associated with an electron beam and the velocity of the particles in the beam, namely,

$$mv = \frac{h}{\lambda} \tag{1}$$

Here m is the mass of the electron, h is Planck's constant, v is the velocity of the electrons, and λ is their associated wave length. For convenience it is frequently desirable to replace λ by its reciprocal k, which is called the *wave number* since it represents the number of wave lengths in a unit length. The equation then becomes

$$mv = hk. \tag{2}$$

Using these equations, one finds that the wave length associated with an electron having 1 volt of kinetic energy is $12.3 \cdot 10^{-8}$ cm. These mathematical relations have been amply checked by experiments in which electrons of known velocity are diffracted by crystal lattices in much the way that X rays are diffracted.

This remarkable discovery obviously did not eliminate the difficulty of imagining how a beam of particles can behave like a train of waves. The difficulty was removed only when several radical changes in the meaning of physical theory were introduced. Before discussing these, however, it is more convenient to discuss the meaning actually given to the electron waves.

It is now believed that electrons and light quanta actually are particles. However, the motion of these particles cannot be described in the precise terms in which we are accustomed to describe the motion of bodies met with in everyday experience. Instead, it is necessary to restrict the description to probability language and discuss the *likelihood* that these particles will have particular attributes such as a given velocity or position. Thus the basic method of describing the behavior of the particles is to introduce a mathematical function which gives the probability that the particles will be found with certain values of position, velocity, and so forth, when it has other preassigned properties, such as a fixed value of energy. This *probability distribution function* satisfies an equation which is formally the same as that for a vibrating medium and hence is often called a *wave function*. In fact, the probability functions for a particle moving in free space are almost identical in form with those for a sound wave. Thus the wave properties of the particles arise because their probability distribution functions have wavelike form. This is true both for electrons and for light quanta and explains the origin of the dilemma.

It turns out that there are definite restrictions placed upon the functions which can be used to describe the behavior of particles. Thus, if a particle is enclosed within a box but is otherwise free, not all wave lengths are permitted, but only certain values for which the wave length bears a simple relation to the linear dimensions of the box. These relations are such as to explain the discreteness of the energy spectrum of any electron that is confined to a finite region, such as an electron that is attached to an atom. There is a close similarity between the origin of the discrete energy levels of an electron and the discrete frequencies of vibration of a violin string. In both cases, only fixed wave patterns are permitted. In the case of the violin string, this is a result of the finite length of the string and the fact that it is fastened at both ends.

We shall have cause to review these principles and their ramifications as we proceed with a discussion of the modern theory of metals, since they are used extensively in it.

The radical changes in the meaning of physical theory that were required to remove the wave-particle dilemma are connected with the introduction of probability concepts into physics. Before this point statistical concepts had been introduced only for convenience and not because of necessity. When we use probability theory to decide what faces will appear when a pair of dice are thrown, we do so only because it would be too difficult to tell with use of mechanics exactly how the dice would land. Actually, it would be possible to describe the motion of the dice exactly if we knew exactly how they were thrown. On the other hand, it is believed at the present time that probability techniques are introduced into atomic dynamics because it is inherently impossible to tell "exactly" how the fundamental particles, namely, electrons or light quanta, will behave.

Thus it is believed that all that atomic theory can be expected to tell us is the probability or likelihood that experimental measurements will have a certain result—the perfect theory does not necessarily present a picture of the detailed manner in which processes occur but rather tells us the probability that a given measurement will yield a given result. According to this viewpoint, it is not possible to rationalize the concepts of waves and particles on the basis of the Newtonian scheme of things, in which one knows what is happening at each instant of time, for this is asking too much of the theory.

Not all physical properties of an atomic system can be measured with arbitrary accuracy in a single experiment; hence, identical experiments will not generally yield the same results for all measured quantities. In fact, the values may be expected to show a spread that arises as a result of the indeterminate interaction between the measured system and the measuring apparatus. This uncertainty is inherent in the laws of nature and cannot be removed merely by refining the apparatus. In the formulation of this principle, which is accepted at the present time, it is believed that an experiment can be designed to measure any single attribute of an atomic system, such as its energy, to an arbitrary degree of accuracy, but in general it is not then possible in the same experiment to measure other randomly chosen attributes, such as the positions of the constituent parts, to an arbitrary degree of accuracy. For example, if the apparatus is first adjusted for measurement of energy and is then altered so that the positions of the constituent parts are accurately measured, the changes in the equipment ensure that the energy cannot be measured arbitrarily accurately. The limits of accuracy expressed by these principles are so fine that they do not influence ordinary engineering measurements in an appreciable way. They are usually important only when measurements are made on atomic systems. For this reason, it is natural that they should have been discovered only during the development of atomic theory.

As an illustration of these principles, let us suppose that an attempt is being made to measure both the position and the velocity of an electron. It can be shown from the theory that the natural uncertainties Δx and Δv in the measurement of these quantities satisfy the relation

$$\Delta v \Delta x \gtreqless \frac{h}{m} \tag{3}$$

in which m is the electron mass and h is Planck's constant. This limitation is important for an electron because m is small; however, the limitation is unimportant for a 1-g mass. It may be seen from Eq. (3) that, if the measurement is designed so that the uncertainty in the measurement in position is zero, the equation can be satisfied only if the uncertainty in velocity is infinitely large, and vice versa. Thus, as was mentioned above, the accurate measurement of one physical quantity associated with a system may preclude the accurate measurement of another.

CHAPTER XVI

THE DEVELOPMENT OF THE ELECTRON THEORY OF METALS[1]

68. The Solid Types.—Although we are primarily interested in the properties of metals, it is interesting to consider briefly the types of solid that are found in nature, for the types of binding found in other solids occur to a certain measure in both metals and alloys. It must be emphasized, of course, that any classification of the forms of solids is somewhat arbitrary; however, the following classification has much to be said for it:

> Metals
> Ionic crystals (salts)
> Valence crystals (abrasives)
> Semi-conductors
> Molecular crystals

Metals, of course, are readily distinguished from the rest by the fact that they have high electrical and thermal conductivities, generally possess "metallic luster," and usually are ductile. Ionic crystals, such as sodium chloride and calcium carbonate, are marked by the fact that they usually may be formed by precipitation from ionic solutions, and may be regarded as a carefully balanced aggregate of positive and negative ions. When in massive crystalline form, they generally exhibit good cleavage and, when pure, are transparent. Valence crystals, such as diamond and carborundum, are usually very hard. Their crystal lattices have the characteristic that each atom is surrounded by a number of neighboring atoms equal to its chemical valence. Semi-conductors, such as cuprous oxide and selenium, are distinguished by the fact that they possess a small, but measurable, electronic conductivity, which increases with

---

[1] A more detailed account of the contents of this chapter may be found in F. SEITZ, *The Modern Theory of Solids* (McGraw-Hill Book Company, Inc., New York, 1940).

increasing temperature, in contrast with the conductivity occurring in metals, which decreases with increasing temperature. Molecular crystals, such as dry ice, iodine, and paraffin, are loosely bound aggregates of stable molecules having low boiling and melting points. Most crystalline organic solids fall into this group.

A part of the purpose of the following chapters is to trace the origin of the differences between these types of solid.

It should be emphasized that many solids possess properties which allow them to be classified in more than one of these groups. Such substances represent transitions between the solid types that should be classified between two groups. The existence of such substances merely shows that any classification of solids is to some extent arbitrary.

69. The Drude-Lorentz Theory of Metals.—The discovery and development of the basic laws of atomic physics have had a far-reaching effect on all phases of the theory of matter. The knowledge of metals has not been unaffected by this research, for the better understanding of the internal constitution of metals followed the other advances closely.

As early as 1900, Drude suggested that the high electrical conductivity of metals could be explained on the assumption that their valence electrons are free and move about within the solid in much the same way as the atoms of a gas. This idea was developed further by Lorentz, and the resulting theory has come to be known as the Drude-Lorentz theory of metals. As we shall see later, the basic suggestion of Drude has been retained in all subsequent modifications of the theory, so that it can still be regarded as correct, at least in a qualitative way.

In a discussion of the Drude-Lorentz theory, it is convenient to keep in mind the following model: Since the electrons ordinarily do not leave a metal, even though they are free to roam within it, we may assume that there are appropriate forces near the surface which act to retain them. Thus, from the standpoint of energy, we may say that the electrons inside a metal have a lower potential energy than those outside. If the potential outside the metal is arbitrarily taken as zero, the potential inside may be designated by $-W$, where W is a positive quantity that we shall call the *work function* (see also Sec. 62). This state of affairs may be represented schematically in the manner shown in Fig. 138. The curve represents the variation of potential through the surface. It is now known that the actual variation, though not entirely abrupt as in the figure, takes place in a few atom distances, so that it may be regarded as abrupt for most practical purposes. Near the absolute zero of temperature, at which the free electrons possess no kinetic energy of motion according to the Drude-Lorentz theory, the energy of the electrons is equal to $-W$. As the temperature rises, however, the electrons obtain kinetic energy of motion. The average value of this energy is, according to the kinetic theory of gases, $3kT/2$.

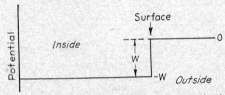

Fig. 138.—The variation of the potential of an electron in the vicinity of the surface of a metal. The zero of potential is arbitrarily chosen as zero outside the metal. The electron gains energy on entering the metal, the gain in potential being W. As an approximation, the potential may be regarded as constant inside the metal.

Since not all electrons have the same thermal energy, because of thermal fluctuations, it follows that at any finite temperature there is a finite chance that a given electron will obtain sufficient kinetic energy to pass over the barrier at the surface of the metal and evaporate. Naturally, the probability of this occurrence, which evidently corresponds to thermionic emission, increases with increasing temperature, so that the effect should be observed most commonly at high temperatures.

Let us consider the nature of the electron gas proposed by Drude on the assumption that its properties are much the same as those of a perfect gas, which obeys the following relation between pressure, volume, and temperature:

$$PV = nRT. \tag{1}$$

Here P is the pressure, V is the volume, R is the gas constant, T is the absolute temperature, and n is the number of moles of gas in the volume. In a metal such as copper, which contains one valence electron per atom, the volume associated with a mole of electrons is about 7.1 cm³. Since the volume occupied by a perfect gas at room temperature and 1 atmosphere of pressure is 22,400 cm³ it follows from Eq. (1) that the corresponding pressure of the electron gas would be of the order of 3,000 atmospheres. We evidently must postulate that the attractive forces between the electrons and the positive ions in the metal balance this pressure and produce the barrier shown in Fig. 138.

Carrying the analogy with the perfect gas further, we may assume, in accordance with Maxwell's theory, that the electrons are at rest at the absolute zero of temperature and have a kinetic energy of $3kT/2$ at absolute temperature T, where k is Boltzmann's constant. In addition, we shall assume that the electrons do not move indefinitely in a straight line but make collisions both with one another and with the atoms of the solid. The effect of such collisions is to alter the direction of motion. Drude and Lorentz assumed that the average distance the electrons move before colliding is of the order of magnitude of the interatomic spacing, that is, of the order of 10^{-8} cm. This assumption appeared entirely plausible at the time, since the atoms occupy the majority of the space in the lattice.

By the use of these assumptions, Lorentz derived the following equation for the resistivity of a metal:

$$R = \frac{3\pi m v}{8ne^2 l}. \tag{2}$$

Here m is the electronic mass, v is the mean velocity, which depends upon temperature, n is the number of free electrons per unit volume, and l is the mean free path. If v is computed from the equation

$$\frac{m}{2}v^2 = \frac{3}{2}kT$$

in accordance with Maxwell's theory, Eq. (2) becomes

$$R = \frac{3\pi}{8}\frac{\sqrt{3mkT}}{ne^2 l}. \tag{3}$$

If l then is taken equal to the atomic spacing, it is found in the case of copper that the resistivity computed by means of this equation agrees closely with the observed value at *room temperature*.

Unfortunately, the theory possesses the following two weaknesses:

1. As may be seen from Eq. (3), the resistivity predicted by the theory varies as $\sqrt{T}$. Actually, it is well known that the resistance of pure metals usually varies linearly with temperature. Thus the agreement between theory and experiment in the comparison of resistance at room temperature is only a superficial one, for the same agreement could not be found at either higher or lower temperatures.

2. If the electrons in a metal behave as though they are a perfect gas, we should expect them to contribute a term $3R/2$ to the gram-atomic heat of the metal. Actually, the specific heat of most simple metals such as copper, silver, and aluminum can be explained readily on the basis of the energy required to stimulate atomic vibrations. Thus it must be admitted that the electrons do not appear to contribute to the specific heat as they should if perfectly free. It is true that this difficulty could be avoided by arbitrarily assuming that only a fraction of the valence electrons are free; such an assumption, however, would spoil even the superficial agreement found between observed and calculated resistivity, for then the estimate of n in Eq. (3) would be incorrect.

In view of these difficulties, it follows that the Drude-Lorentz theory possesses only qualitative interest and cannot be relied upon to answer detailed questions concerning the properties of metals.

70. Early Theories of the Other Types of Solid.—During the period of time in which the Drude-Lorentz theory was being developed, similar treatments of the other solid types were under way. For example, Born and others developed a theory of ionic crystals which was based on the assumption that they are composed of rigid spherical ions which attract and repel one another with electrostatic forces like those between ordinary charged bodies. Using this theory, the investigators were able to explain many of the properties of the simpler salts such as cohesive energies, elastic properties, and optical properties in the infrared region of the spectrum.

Similarly, Baedeker developed an excellent theory of semi-conductors at about the same time. According to this theory, semi-conductors differ from metals in having their valence electrons loosely bound at very low temperatures. However, these electrons possess a finite "vapor pressure" at ordinary temperatures. The electrons that become free thermally are responsible for the conductivity. Since the density of free electrons should increase with increasing temperature, according to this picture, the theory provides a ready explanation of the observed increase in conductivity.

It is a characteristic of the theories developed during this period that they treat each type of solid on the basis of a different model. No attempt was made to provide a unified picture that could be used to explain simultaneously the properties of the different solid types.

71. The Sommerfeld Theory of Metals.—The theory of metals remained in a somewhat immobile form until Sommerfeld redeveloped it by the use of the principles of quantum theory. The essential assumptions of his theory are the following:

a. The valence electrons in a metal are free, as Drude and Lorentz assumed.

b. The energies of the valence electrons are discrete and are determined by quantum theory.

c. The levels in the entire solid are occupied by electrons in accordance with the Pauli principle.

In order to appreciate the changes which assumptions *b* and *c* produce in the Drude-Lorentz theory, let us consider the potential well shown in Fig. 138. As we remarked in the previous chapter, an electron has associated with it a wavelike function, the amplitude of which determines the probability that the electron will be found at any point in space. It turns out that in the present case, in which the electrons are within a potential well and do not possess sufficient kinetic energy to leave it, these waves may be chosen to be of simple sinusoidal type within the well. They must, however, have a node at the boundaries of the well (see Fig. 139). In this respect, the problem of finding the wave functions associated with the electron in the metal is analogous to that of finding the possible standing waves in a violin string or in an organ pipe. In the first case, for example, only those waves are allowed for which the amplitude is zero at the points where the string is held. The boundary conditions are somewhat different in the case of the organ pipe, but in both cases these conditions have the effect of limiting the frequencies with which the system may vibrate by limiting the permissible wave lengths. We find in the same way that the boundary conditions on the electron waves in a metal limit the allowed wave lengths which the electrons may possess and, as a result, the allowed velocities and energies. In other words, the energy spectrum becomes

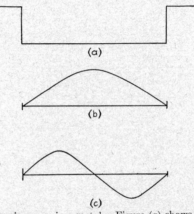

FIG. 139.—Electronic waves in a metal. Figure (a) shows the potential of an electron in a metal, the abrupt changes being at the surfaces. Figure (b) shows the electron wave of lowest energy. This has nodes only at the boundaries of the metal. Figure (c) shows an electronic wave of slightly higher energy. This possesses one node. Waves of higher energy possess more nodes.

discrete. An examination of the spacing between levels for a specimen of ordinary size shows that it is so small that it cannot be measured by direct means, as is possible, for example, for an atom or a molecule (see the discussion of the preceding chapter, page 238). Indeed, if it were not for the Pauli principle, the fact that the levels are discrete rather than continuous would be of little consequence. We shall call spectra of this type, which are discrete, but not observably so, *quasi-continuous*.

Actually, however, we must recall that the Pauli principle places a restriction upon the electrons which may populate any given state in a given system. Consider, for example, the wave function that possesses the longest wave length and hence is associated with the electron of lowest velocity. This is shown in Fig. 139*b*. According to the Pauli principle, only two electrons may occupy this state, and they must have opposite spins. When this state has been filled, additional electrons must occupy states of higher energy. Since there are of the order of 10^{23} valence electrons in a specimen of metal of ordinary size, it follows that the same order of magnitude of states must be occupied by the electrons in the normal condition of the specimen. This means that a negligible number of the electrons have energy

Fig. 140.—The relation between the height of the barrier at the edge of a metal and the width of the occupied region of levels. The shaded region shows the occupied region.

$-W$, at the absolute zero of temperature, as was assumed in the Drude-Lorentz theory. In fact, the situation must be somewhat like that represented in Fig. 140. Here, the levels extending over a finite range of the spectrum from $-W$ upward are densely occupied with electrons. Table XXII shows the width of this *occupied region* for a number of metals, as determined from the theory.

TABLE XXII.—WIDTHS OF THE OCCUPIED BAND AND VALUES OF W FOR SEVERAL METALS
(In electron volts)

Metal	Valence	Width	W
Li	1	4.72	6.9
Na	1	3.12	5.0
K	1	2.14	3.9
Cu	1	7.04	11.1
Ag	1	5.51	10.2
Au	1	5.54	10.3
Be	2	14.3	
Ca	2	4.26	7.5
Al	3	11.7	14.7

It follows as a consequence of these facts that most of the electrons in a metal are moving about at a high rate of speed even at the absolute zero of temperature. In fact, the velocity of the uppermost electrons in the filled region is of the order of magnitude of 10^7 cm per sec. This corresponds to a wave length of the order of several atomic distances.

When the metal is above absolute zero, the electrons are thermally excited in addition. Now the thermal excitation energy is always of the order of magnitude of kT per electron.

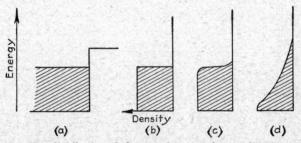

Fig. 141.—The distribution of electrons in a metal at various temperatures. Figure (a) is analogous to Fig. 140. Figure (b) shows the relation between the density of electrons (on a relative scale) and energy at the absolute zero of temperature. Figures (c) and (d) show the changes that take place in the density as the temperature is raised. The temperature required to attain the situation shown in Fig. (d) is above the practical range.

At room temperature, this is only about 1 percent of the width of the filled region in most metals. Since an electron on being excited can jump only to one of the vacant levels above the occupied region, because of the restrictions of the Pauli principle, it follows that only the relatively small fraction of electrons contained in a thin band whose width is of the order of kT and which is at the upper end of the filled region are capable of being thermally excited. Hence, only a small fraction of the valence electrons can receive thermal energy. This evidently explains the fact that the free electrons in metals ordinarily do not contribute appreciably to the specific heat.

The distributions in energy of the electron gas at absolute zero, at room temperature, and at a very high temperature where kT is comparable with the width of the filled region are shown schematically in Fig. 141. In a metal such as copper, the temperature at which the last of these distributions would be obtained is of the order of 50,000°C.

The equation for the resistivity obtained from Sommerfeld's theory is practically the same as Eq. (3) of Sec. 69, namely,

$$R = \frac{mv_o}{ne^2l} \tag{1}$$

in which v_o is now the velocity of the uppermost electron in the filled band and the other quantities are the same as in the previous equation. Since all the quantities except l are constants, it follows that the explanation of the temperature dependence of R rests entirely upon l in Sommerfeld's theory. Moreover, since v_o is about a hundred times larger than the mean velocity of the electrons determined from the Drude-Lorentz theory, it follows that l should be of the order of magnitude of 100 atomic distances at room temperature. At first sight, this seems to offer serious obstacles to the theory; for, from the viewpoint adopted by Drude and Lorentz, l should be a constant of the order of magnitude of the interatomic spacing. This paradox may be explained readily on the basis of wave mechanics. When the crystal lattice is entirely at rest, the conduction electrons may move through the lattice without being scattered. This may be seen from the fact that waves having a wave length longer than the grating spacing of a lattice are not diffracted (Sec. 2). As a result, the mean free path of the electrons is very large at the absolute zero of temperature. At finite temperatures, the atoms of the lattice are not at rest but are undergoing thermal oscillations. These oscillations produce imperfections in the lattice which cause the electrons to be scattered. It may be shown that the mean free path of the electrons varies inversely as the square of the amplitude of the atomic oscillations and hence inversely as the first power of the temperature in the vicinity of room temperature. As a result, the theory predicts that the resistivity should be proportional to the temperature, in agreement with observation. Thus the Sommerfeld theory removes another of the obstacles met by the Drude-Lorentz theory.

In the period following Sommerfeld's formation of the modified free-electron theory of metals, extensive calculations of the actual resistance of several simple metals such as the alkali metals were carried out. These computations show not only that the theory is qualitatively correct but that it also is capable of yielding quantitative values of the resistance.

It is interesting to note that the electrons at the very top of the occupied band are alone responsible for the electrical conductivity of metals, just as they are responsible for the specific heat. In the absence of an electrical field, the electrons are moving pairwise in opposite directions, so that there is no net current, even though each moving electron represents a small current. When the field is present, the electrons tend to be accelerated, that is, to change their state of motion. Those at the bottom of the occupied region cannot change their state of motion, however; for to do so they would have to jump to states that are already occupied, and the Pauli exclusion principle prevents this. On the other hand, those at the top of the occupied region may change their state because there are near-by vacant levels to which they may jump. As a result of such jumps, the statistical balance of motion that prevails when there is no field is upset, and a preponderance of electrons move in the direction of the force exerted by the field.

CHAPTER XVII

THE BAND THEORY OF SOLIDS

72. Introduction.[1]—As we remarked in the previous chapter, the theories of the different types of solid discussed there suffer from the defect that each is based on a specific model which is intended to be valid only for the particular type of solid under immediate consideration. For example, in the discussion of metals, it is assumed that all the valence electrons are free, whereas, in the discussion of ionic crystals, it is assumed that the electrons are rigidly bound to the ions, which resemble rigid spheres. We have a right to ask why a particular model is appropriate in a given case. Moreover, we may expect wave mechanics to yield us a straightforward answer to this question if it represents the atomic world accurately. At best, we may expect that wave mechanics will present us with a general framework for discussing all types of solid and that the particular models used in the last chapter will represent special cases of this general scheme which are valid for particular materials under well-defined conditions.

Let us examine carefully the Sommerfeld theory of metals, which seems to go a long way toward explaining the electrical and thermal properties of the electrons in metals, and see what revisions are required if we consider the internal structure of metals. In the first place, we have treated metals as if the potential inside were the same everywhere when determining the energy states of the valence electrons by use of the principles of wave mechanics. It is evident that this can be only an

---

[1] More extensive surveys of this topic may be found in the following books and review articles: F. SEITZ and R. P. JOHNSON, *J. Applied Phys.*, **8**, 84, 186, 246 (1937); J. C. SLATER, *Rev. Modern Phys.*, **6**, 209 (1934); W. SHOCKLEY, *Bell System Tech. J.*, **18**, 645 (1939); F. SEITZ, *The Modern Theory of Solids* (McGraw-Hill Book Company, Inc., New York, 1940); N. F. MOTT and H. JONES, *The Theory of Metals and Alloys* (Oxford University Press, New York, 1936); N. F. MOTT and R. W. GURNEY, *Electronic Processes in Ionic Crystals* (Oxford University Press, New York, 1940).

approximate procedure, for it does not take into account the fluctuations in the electric field from one atom to the next. Since each atom contains at its center a small nucleus, in which all the positive charge resides, it follows that the electric field in which the electrons move is stronger near the center of the atoms than at the point midway between atoms. In fact, we can expect the potential of the electrons to vary from atom to atom in the crystal in the manner shown in Fig. 142. Since the electron is attracted to the positively charged nucleus, the potential is lower near the center of the atom than near the periphery.

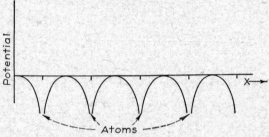

Fig. 142.—Schematic representation of the variation of potential energy of an electron from atom to atom in a solid. The pronounced minima occur at the positions where atoms reside.

It is evident that the free-electron theory of metals is based on the assumption that the variations in potential across the atom are negligible. We should expect this condition to be satisfied most closely when the atoms are monovalent, that is, when they have only one valence electron. For, in this case, the net positive charge on the tightly bound core obtained by taking the valence electron from the atom is one electronic unit, the smallest possible value, so that the field in which the electrons move should be smallest. Figure 143 compares the potential to be expected in a solid in which the atoms are monovalent with that to be expected when they have a higher valence. Now let us consider the pure solid phases of the elements in a given row of the periodic chart. We should expect the free-electron model to be more nearly valid for the solids composed of the atoms near the left-hand side of the chart than for those near the right-hand side. We find, in fact, that the monovalent and divalent metals invariably form metals (for example, the alkali metals,

the alkaline-earth metals, copper, silver, and gold), whereas
the solids formed of the atoms at the opposite side of the chart
are not always metallic (for example, the halogens, oxygen,
sulphur, selenium, nitrogen, phosphorus, carbon). We may
apparently conclude that solids in which the potential of the
electrons varies by a comparatively small amount from one
point of the lattice to another are invariably metals, whereas
those in which the field varies comparatively strongly are
frequently not metals. We must now pursue this lead further.

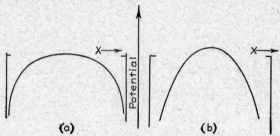

Fig. 143.—The variation of potential from atom to atom in (*a*) a solid in
which the atoms are univalent and in (*b*) a solid in which the atoms have higher
valence (see Fig. 142).

73. The Forbidden Regions of Energy.

—The kinetic energy
of a *perfectly free electron* is given by the equation

$$\epsilon = \frac{mv^2}{2}. \tag{1}$$

Since the velocity is related to the wave number k of the electron,
which is defined as the reciprocal of the wave length (see Sec. 67),
by means of the equation

$$mv = hk \tag{2}$$

in which m is the electronic mass and h is Planck's constant, the
energy of a perfectly free electron is given by the equation

$$\epsilon = \frac{h^2}{2m} k^2. \tag{3}$$

This equation is obtained by substituting Eq. (2) in (1).

If the free electron is in a box, as is assumed at least in principle
in the free-electron theory of metals, not all values of the wave

length and hence of the wave number are allowed. As we saw in Sec. 67, in this case only those waves which have zero amplitude at the boundaries of the box correspond to physically permissible states of motion of the electrons. It was this fact, it may be recalled, which made the energy states employed in Sommerfeld's theory discrete and hence which permitted the Pauli exclusion principle to influence so strongly the distribution of electrons.

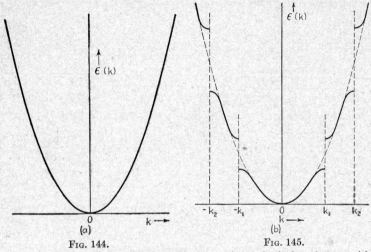

Fig. 144.   Fig. 145.

Fig. 144.—The variation of the total energy of a perfectly free electron with wave number.

Fig. 145.—The variation of the total energy of an electron that occurs when the electron is in a periodically varying field, such as that shown in Fig. 142. This diagram is valid for an electron traveling in a preassigned direction. It may be observed that breaks occur in the energy curve for certain values of the wave number. These values correspond to those at which the electrons are diffracted.

When the field in which the confined electrons move is no longer constant but varies from one point to another, as in an actual solid, we may expect that Eq. (3) relating the energy and wave number of the electrons is no longer valid. The exact solutions of the equations of wave mechanics for this situation show that this is the case. Let us consider the energies of electrons of various wave lengths, all of which are *moving in the same direction.* If the potential is constant, the relation between energy and wave number is given by the parabolic curve shown in Fig. 144, which corresponds to Eq. (3). On the other hand, when the potential is not constant but varies periodically, as in Fig. 142, the curve of energy versus wave number is like that shown in Fig. 145; that is, there are gaps in the allowed range of energy. The magnitude of these gaps depends upon the variations in the potential field. The gaps are zero when the potential does not vary (Fig. 144) and increase as the variations in potential increase. Thus they are small for solids composed of atoms lying on the left-hand side of the periodic chart and are large for solids composed of atoms on the right-hand side of the chart. It should be emphasized that the energy levels in the allowed regions between the gaps are not perfectly continuous but are, as in the free-electron case, quasi-continuous. In other words, they are so finely spaced that their discreteness cannot be detected by direct means; yet they are finite in number so that a region of finite width is occupied when the Pauli exclusion principle is taken into account, just as in the free-electron case

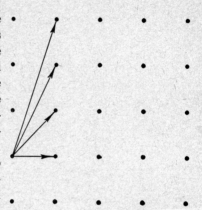

Fig. 146.—Two-dimensional example of a lattice that shows the manner in which the periodicity varies in different directions. The arrows show the distance by which the lattice must be displaced in order to coincide with itself if displaced in various directions.

considered in the Sommerfeld theory.

The values of the wave number at which the gaps occur obey well-defined rules. They correspond to the wave lengths for which the electrons are diffracted by the lattice in just the way that X rays are diffracted. In other words, the existence of the gaps is intimately tied up with the wave properties of electrons. Since the lattice possesses a different periodicity in different crystallographic directions, as is illustrated by the simple example shown in Fig. 146, it follows that the values of k at which the gaps occur are different for different crystallographic directions. There are two interesting cases to consider. Suppose first of all that the gaps are small, as actually occurs in the alkali metals. Then it can happen that, although a particular region of energy is forbidden for electrons traveling in one direction, this region is allowed for electrons traveling in another. This case is illustrated in Fig. 147a. The three curves represent ϵ versus k for electrons traveling in three prominent crystallographic directions. It may be seen that the gaps are small and occur for different values of k in each of the three cases and that the forbidden regions do not overlap. As a result, even though a particular

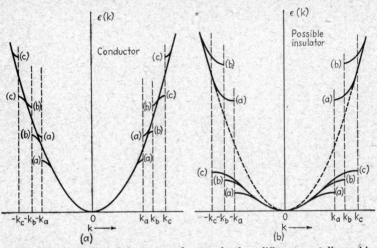

Fig. 147.—Variation of the ϵ-versus-k curves for three different crystallographic directions in two types of solid. In each case the three directions, which are assumed to be prominent crystallographic directions, are designated by a, b, and c. In (a) the atoms are of low valence and the gaps that occur in the ϵ-versus-k curves are sufficiently small not to overlap; that is, an energy that is not allowed for an electron traveling in the a direction is allowed for one traveling in the b direction, and so forth. In (b) the variation in potential is so great that the gaps overlap; that is, there are values of energy which are forbidden for electrons traveling in all directions. It will be seen below that case (a) is always a metal, whereas case (b) may be an insulator.

range of energy is not allowed for electrons traveling in one direction in the lattice, it is allowed for electrons traveling in other directions. In this case, the spectrum is quasi-continuous for all values of energy above a certain minimum value, and the energy-level diagram has the appearance of Fig. 148a.

Suppose, on the other hand, that the gaps are very large, as in Fig. 147b, and do not overlap for all directions. Then there are ranges of energy that are not allowed for electrons traveling in any direction, and the energy-level diagram has the form shown in Fig. 148*b*. It consists of bands of quasi-continuous levels that are separated by forbidden regions. From what has been said previously, it follows that the width of the forbidden regions is dependent upon the variation of the atomic field within the solid. If, in a case in which the gaps are large, the variations in field could be decreased, the width of the forbidden regions would decrease and the case corresponding to Fig. 147*b* would go over into that shown in Fig. 147*a*. We shall refer to cases like that of Fig. 148*a* as those in which the *bands overlap* and to cases like that of Fig. 148*b* as those in which the *bands are separated*.

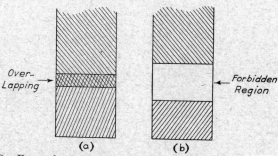

Over-Lapping

Forbidden Region

(a)   (b)

Fig. 148.—Energy-level diagrams for the cases shown in Fig. 147 (*a*) and (*b*). In the first case the bands of levels associated with values of the wave number lying between successive gaps overlap, whereas they are separate in the second case.

The existence of regions of energy for which no allowed states of motion occur is a common one in atomic systems, as we have seen earlier in the book. It will be found later that a particular kind of discrete level can occur in the forbidden regions in imperfect crystals.

Let us now consider the thermal and electrical properties of the solids possessing the two types of energy-level diagrams represented by Fig. 148*a* and *b* when the levels are occupied by electrons to various heights.

Let us suppose that the solid contains a sufficient number of electrons to occupy the lowest band of Fig. 148*a* to about half its height (see Fig. 149*a*). In this case the situation is very much the same as in the Sommerfeld model of a metal. The electrons occupying the lower levels of the filled region are not excited at ordinary temperatures because all the levels to which they could jump are completely filled. Only the electrons in the thin strip of width kT at the top of the occupied band can be excited thermally, since only they have vacant levels sufficiently near. Similarly, if the substance is placed in an electric field, the electrons near the bottom of the band cannot be accelerated because they are too tightly hemmed in by the electrons above them. Those near the top of the band can be accelerated, however, so that the substance is a metal, just as in the case considered by Sommerfeld. Evidently this is the only situation which can occur in the solid represented by the scheme of levels

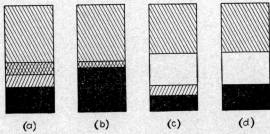

FIG. 149.—Various ways in which the levels of the bands shown in Fig. 148 (*a*) and (*b*) may be occupied. (*a*) and (*b*) of the present figure correspond to the situation shown in Fig. 148(*a*), whereas (*c*) and (*d*) of the present figure correspond to Fig. 148(*b*) (see text). The situations represented by (*a*), (*b*), and (*c*) correspond to metals, whereas (*d*) corresponds to an insulator.

shown in Fig. 148*a*, so that it will be metallic regardless of the extent to which the levels are filled.

Suppose, on the other hand, that the solid corresponding to the scheme of Fig. 148*b* contains just enough electrons to occupy completely the lowest band of levels. In this case, the electrons at the top of the filled band are hemmed in to the same extent as those at the bottom, for the vacant levels to which they may jump either as a result of thermal agitation or as the result of an electric field are separated from them by a wide band. It follows that this situation *corresponds to an insulator*. In other words, if the number of valence electrons in the solid is such that the occupied levels are immediately adjacent to unoccupied ones, the solid is a metal, whereas, if the occupied levels are separated from the unoccupied ones by a forbidden region, the solid is an insulator.

Mathematical analysis shows that with each band of levels are associated $2N$ different states of motion, where N is the number of basic cells in the lattice. The first conclusion that may be drawn from this is that the situation represented by Fig. 149d, in which there are just sufficient electrons to fill a band completely, can occur only in a solid containing an even number of electrons per basic cell. Thus any solid in which there is an odd number of electrons per basic cell should be a metal. We find that this condition is satisfied in all common cases in which it occurs. For example, there is one atom per basic cell in both the face-centered and the body-centered cubic lattices. In agreement, all monatomic solids that have this structure and are composed of atoms of odd valence are metals. In this category fall the alkali metals, copper, silver, gold, and aluminum, the last being trivalent.

We cannot conclude, as a converse principle, that all solids possessing an even number of electrons per unit cell should be insulators. It is possible that the spectrum may have the form of Fig. 148a, in which there are no forbidden regions. We may conclude, however, that, whenever a solid containing an even number of electrons per basic cell is a metal, its bands must overlap. This conclusion must be drawn, for example, for divalent metals such as the alkaline earths, tin, and lead and for all the metallic solids that are composed of elements of odd valence but are arranged in lattices that have an even number of atoms per unit cell. In the latter category are arsenic, antimony, and bismuth. Thus the case shown in Fig. 148a is amply represented among the known metals. Since the bands overlap commonly even among substances of high valence, it is reasonable to suppose that they overlap among the monovalent and trivalent metals for which such overlapping is not essential for metallic behavior.

74. The Monatomic Solids.—We are now in a position to understand what occurs as we go across one of the shorter rows of the periodic chart. Let us consider first the monovalent metals, of which sodium is typical. Sodium obviously must be metallic because it possesses an odd number of electrons per basic cell, like all the monovalent metals. Figure 150 shows the actual relation between ϵ and k for this metal for the (110) direction as determined by a direct solution of the basic wave equations for the system.   The fact that the bands overlap and that the electrons occupy the first band only part way is illustrated very strikingly by Fig. 151, which shows the behavior of the atomic levels of atomic sodium as the atoms are brought together to form the solid.   It is assumed that the union takes place in an ideal manner in which all the atoms are arranged in a body-centered cubic lattice and are brought together by decreas-

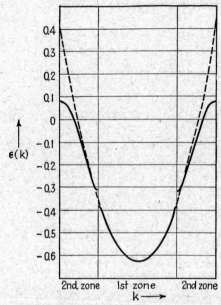

Fig. 150.—The ϵ-versus-k curve for the (110) direction in sodium.   (*After Slater.*)

ing the separation uniformly.   The right-hand end of the diagram represents the levels of atomic sodium and corresponds to infinite separation.   As the interatomic distance decreases, the atomic levels spread into quasi-continuous bands, which broaden continuously as the spacing decreases.   The spacing at which a given level begins to broaden into a band turns out to be the value at which the orbits that are on neighboring atoms and are associated with the level begin to overlap.   These bands correspond to the allowed regions that would occur if the lattice constant were much larger than the observed.   Eventually the bands overlap and are strongly intermixed at the observed interatomic spacing, which is represented by the vertical line.

It should be emphasized that the foregoing work shows that the valence electrons in an ideal metal are able to wander practically everywhere in the lattice, that is, within the atoms as well as within the interstitial spaces.

Beryllium occurs next in the first row and could be an insulator because it has an even number of electrons per basic cell. Actually, it is a metal. Computations analogous to those for lithium show that the bands do overlap in this case.

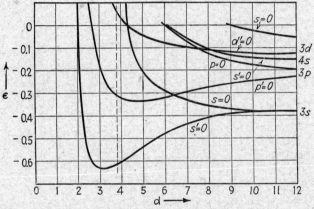

Fig. 151.—The behavior of the atomic levels of sodium as the atoms are brought together to form a solid. The horizontal axis represents the interatomic spacing in relative units, whereas the vertical scale represents the energy. The vertical dotted line shows the observed interatomic spacing. (*After Slater.*)

The crystal structure of boron is not known, but it is probably an insulator when pure. Theoretical calculations have not been made in this case; but presumably the bands are separate, and there are an even number of atoms in the basic cell.

Carbon possesses an even number of valence electrons per atom and forms two types of crystal, namely, graphite and diamond, both of which have two atoms per basic cell. The first is an insulator; in agreement with this, computations show that the occupied and unoccupied bands are well separated. Figure 152 shows the spreading of the atomic levels of the carbon atoms in diamond as they are brought together in a manner analogous to that of Fig. 151. The vertical line represents the actual interatomic spacing, as in Fig. 151. It is interesting to note that the atomic levels break into bands which overlap and then subsequently separate. This behavior may be regarded as a characteristic of the diamond lattice, for it does not occur in any of the simple lattices, such as the face-centered or body-centered cubic structures. It turns out that the number of electrons in diamond is just sufficient to fill completely the lowest band of levels at the observed separation, so that diamond is an insulator. If, however, the observed interatomic spacing corre-

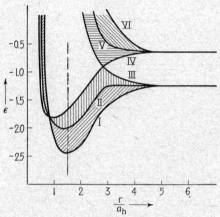

Fig. 152.—The behavior of the atomic levels of carbon as the atoms are brought together to form diamond. The vertical line shows the actual interatomic spacing. (*After Kimball.*)

sponded to the larger value for which the bands are more completely mixed, diamond would be a metal.

The corresponding scheme for graphite has not been computed, but it is not difficult to understand why it is metallic. There are two pronounced spacings in this solid, namely, the short spacing between atoms in the same plane (see Fig. 14, page 14) and the larger spacing between different planes. Evidently the average spacing corresponds more nearly to a point in Fig. 152 for which the bands overlap than to the observed spacing for diamond.

The remaining solids in the first row of the periodic chart, namely, nitrogen, oxygen, and fluorine, are molecular, that is, they evaporate in the form of diatomic molecules rather than as separate atoms. This implies that they are loosely bound aggregates of tightly bound pairs of atoms. Such solids may be understood best by starting with the diatomic molecules, which have discrete energy levels, just as atoms have. As the molecules are brought together in a manner analogous to that discussed in connection with Figs. 151 and 152, these discrete levels broaden into bands. It may readily be shown that in so-called *saturated* molecules, such as those considered in this case, the bands are either completely occupied or completely unoccupied *as soon as they split*. This is shown in Fig. 153.

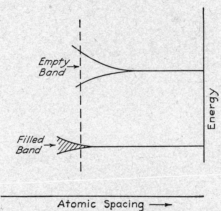

Fig. 153.—Schematic diagram showing the variation of molecular levels with interatomic spacing. The bands are comparatively narrow at the observed equilibrium distance.

As a prelude to a discussion of the elements in the longer periods with incomplete d shells, let us consider the case of copper, which possesses one valence electron outside a newly filled d shell composed of 10 electrons. As was pointed out in Chap. II, the electrons in d shells move in smaller orbits than do the electrons in the ordinary valence levels, which we there designated as s and p levels. As a result, the s and p levels begin to broaden much sooner than the d level as the atoms are brought together. Moreover, at the observed interatomic spacing, the d band is much narrower than the bands arising from the s and p levels. This is clearly shown in Fig. 154, in which the three types of level are distinguished. The d band shown actually contains five overlapping bands, which, individually, are able to accommodate two electrons per atom. As a result, at the observed interatomic spacing the d band, though narrow, can accommodate all ten d electrons per atom of copper. The additional valence electron per atom populates the levels arising from the s and p bands to a point well above the top of the d band. It follows that the uppermost electrons in the filled region of copper occupy levels which are much like those occurring in the alkali metals. The same situation undoubtedly occurs in gold and silver.

The nature of the valence-electron bands in copper at the observed lattice spacing is shown in Fig. 155, for further illustra-

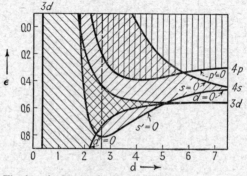

FIG. 154.—The broadening of the bands of atomic copper as the atoms are brought together to form a solid. The vertical dotted line represents the actual interatomic spacing. It may be seen that the band arising from the d level broadens less than the bands arising from the other levels. (*After Krutter.*)

tion of the points made above. Since ten times as many electrons crowd into the narrow d band as occupy the s-p band, it follows that the density of levels must be much higher in the former. The actual density is shown in Fig. 156, which completely confirms this conjecture.

Let us now consider nickel, which precedes copper in the periodic chart and has the same crystal structure. Since the nuclei of both nickel and copper have very nearly the same charge, we may suppose with reasonable assurance that the energy states for the individual electrons are very nearly the same in the two elements. As a result, we may use Figs. 155 and 156 as a basis for discussing the properties of nickel as well as those of copper when taking account of the difference in the number of valence electrons in the two cases. In effect, we must consider the changes that would occur in copper if one valence electron per atom were removed. It is clear from Fig. 155 that electrons would not be removed only from the *s-p* band; for in

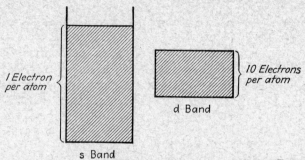

Fig. 155.—Relative form of the *d* band and the *s-p* band in copper. The *d* band is much the narrower even though it contains more levels.

this event the vacant lower levels in the *s-p* band would lie below occupied levels in the *d* electron band, and energy could be gained by transferring the electrons from the *d* band to the

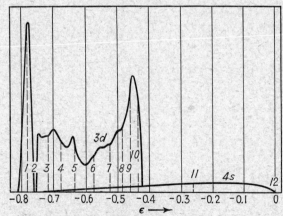

Fig. 156.—The relative densities of levels in the *d* band and the *s-p* bands of copper. The horizontal scale represents energy. The vertical dotted lines and the associated numbers show the number of electrons per atom required to fill the bands to the given energy. (*After Slater.*)

s-p band. The equilibrium situation is that shown in Fig. 157, in which both bands are filled to the same level. Evidently, less than one electron per atom has been removed from the *s-p* band, and the remainder has been removed from the d band. As we shall see in Chap. XX, there is reason for believing that the fraction removed from the s-p band is 0.4. It should be added that Fig. 157 requires modification, of a type we shall discuss later, in a range of temperature in which the metal is ferromagnetic. Thus Fig. 157 is valid for nickel above its Curie temperature (see Chap. XX).

Although this change in electronic structure in passing from copper to nickel seems slight at first glance, it must be recalled that it is accompanied by remarkable changes in the properties

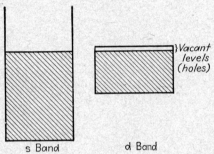

Fig. 157.—Relative filling of the d band and s-p band in a nonmagnetic transition metal in which the d band is not completely filled.

of the metals. The most important of these differences may be summarized in the following way:

   a. Copper is diamagnetic, whereas nickel is ferromagnetic. As we shall see in Chap. XX, The Magnetic Properties of Metals, this change is to be associated with the removal of electrons from the d band, rather than with the partial emptying of the s-p band.

   b. The electrical resistance of nickel is about fourteen times larger than that of copper. This effect can be shown (Chap. XXI) to be due to a decrease in mean free path of the valence electrons in nickel. The decrease results from the fact that the conduction electrons may make transitions from one band to another in nickel, but not in copper.

   c. The specific heat curve of copper obeys Dulong and Petit's law at high temperatures, whereas those of nickel and the other ferrous elements do not (see, for example, Fig. 40, page 61). Since the component of specific heat described by Dulong and

Petit's law is related to atomic vibrations and the residue is not, we must look toward the difference in electronic structure of copper and the nonferrous elements in order to explain the large residue. Now we have seen that the contribution to the specific heat from the valence electrons in simple metals such as the alkali metals is only about 1 percent of the value to be expected from Dulong and Petit's law. We may conclude that this is true for the electrons in copper. On the other hand, the density of electronic levels in the d band is far higher than that in the s-p band, so that we might expect a larger contribution from them under circumstances in which they may be excited by temperature. This evidently is possible in the ferrous elements; for their d bands are only partly filled, and there are near-by vacant levels to which the electrons at the top of the filled band may make transitions. Thus we may conclude that the excess of the specific heats of the transition metals over the Dulong and Petit value is related to the unfilled d bands and is, in fact, an excellent proof of the fact that these bands have a high density of levels and are unfilled.

The energy-level scheme for copper cannot be used to discuss the filling of levels in iron and cobalt with the same confidence as for nickel, for iron and cobalt do not normally possess the face-centered cubic lattice. Nevertheless, we may assume with certainty that these metals resemble nickel in having partly filled d and s-p bands in the manner shown in Fig. 157 and that their magnetic properties are associated with the fact that the d band is not completely filled.

The properties of solids such as zinc, gallium, and germanium that are formed of atoms having a higher atomic number than copper are not difficult to understand. Since the d shell is completely filled in copper, it follows that it is also filled in the solids further on in the same row of the periodic chart. As a result, they resemble closely the corresponding elements in the short rows of the periodic chart in the same sense that copper resembles lithium or sodium. Thus zinc resembles calcium and magnesium, gallium resembles aluminum, germanium resembles silicon, etc. The differences that actually occur between these corresponding solids are presumably to be explained by a comparatively small effect of the electrons in the newly filled group of *d* levels. This effect is more noticeable at the left-hand end of the chart, that is, for copper and zinc, than it is at the right-hand end, that is, for selenium and bromine.

Figure 156 shows the theoretically determined densities of levels in the *s-p* and *d* bands of copper. Curves of the same type have been obtained in several other metals, both by direct computation, as in the case of copper, and by a study of the emission and absorption of X rays by the solids. X rays are produced by bombardment of atoms with electrons of very high energy. It turns out that these electrons knock electrons out of the inner shells of atoms, thus leaving low-lying vacant levels in the atom. These levels are filled in a short time by electrons from higher levels in the atom, and X rays are produced during the transition in accordance with the equation

$$\Delta E = h\nu$$

in which ν is the frequency of the X ray emitted in a given jump and E is the change in energy of the electron that makes the jump. Now the levels of electrons in the inner shells are usually sharply defined, for these electrons move as though in an isolated atom, even when the atom is combined in a compound. The reason for this is that the orbits associated with these electrons are very small and those on neighboring atoms do not overlap, even in compounds. On the other hand, the valence levels are broadened in solid compounds, as we have seen above. As a result, when the vacant levels in the inner shells are filled by electrons from the valence-electron levels, the emitted spectrum covers a range of frequencies if the emitter is a solid (see Fig. 158). Moreover, the distribution of intensity with frequency in this band is simply related to the density of the *occupied* levels in the valence-electron band. From an analysis of this distribution it is possible to determine the density of the corresponding valence levels. When, conversely, the solid is irradiated with a continuous X-ray spectrum that contains frequencies in the neighborhood of those absorbed, the impinging radiation may excite electrons from the occupied inner shells to the vacant levels at the top of the occupied valence levels (Fig. 158*b*). In this case, the frequency distribution of the absorbed radiation is simply related to the density of *unoccupied* levels above the occupied region. Thus, by combining studies of the absorption and emission spectra of solids, it is possible to determine the density of levels both above and below the top of the filled region of the valence-electron spectrum.

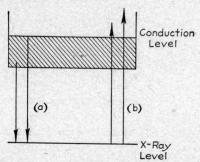

FIG. 158.—Schematic illustration of the manner in which X-ray spectra may be used to determine the distribution of electronic levels in the bands. When electrons jump from the occupied part of the band to the X-ray level [case (a)], the frequency distribution of the emission spectrum is determined by the density of levels in the *occupied* part of the band. Similarly, when electrons are raised from the X-ray level to the vacant levels of the band, the frequency distribution of the absorbed radiation is determined by the density of levels in the *vacant* part of the band.

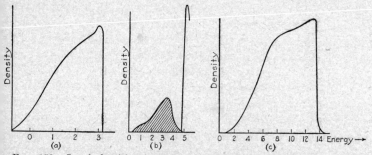

FIG. 159.—Level densities in three metals. The vertical axes represent the density of levels per unit energy, whereas the horizontal axis represents the energy in the same relative units. The first figure shows the density of the occupied levels in sodium; the second shows the density of both occupied and unoccupied levels in calcium; and the third shows the density of the occupied levels in aluminum.

Figure 159 shows the density of levels for a number of metals. The first curve is for sodium and was determined by means of the X-ray emission and absorption spectra as outlined above. Thus it illustrates the density of occupied levels. Actually, the density of levels continues to rise even above the top of the occupied region. This behavior is characteristic of a case in which the bands overlap extensively and may be said to be representative of an ideal metal. The second curve is for calcium, which was determined theoretically. The occupied region is indicated by the crosshatching. It is interesting to note that the density is very low at the top of the occupied region, which shows that the bands overlap only by a small amount. In other words, this metal is apparently almost an insulator. The third curve corresponds to aluminum, which is a trivalent metal. It is interesting to note that the density function is very much like that for sodium, even though there is more than one valence electron per atom. This indicates that aluminum is more nearly an ideal metal than are the alkaline-earth metals.

Completely satisfactory curves of the same type have not yet been obtained for the metals such as nickel and copper that contain partly or newly filled d bands, although Fig. 156 is undoubtedly qualitatively correct.

75. Ionic Solids.—We shall now consider the band structure of the simpler salts in order to confirm the supposition that they are not metallic because their valence-electron bands are either completely filled or completely empty.

Let us first consider lithium fluoride. Lithium possesses one valence electron outside a closed shell, and fluorine possesses seven. Since one atom of each type occupies the unit cell of the rock-salt type of lattice, it follows that there are eight valence electrons $(7 + 1)$ per unit cell. As a result, we may expect lithium fluoride to be an insulator if the bands do not overlap. Figure 160 shows the actual form of the valence-electron bands in the salt, as determined from the fundamental equations of the theory. The lowest band contains room for two electrons per unit cell and corresponds to the $2s$ orbits of the fluorine atom. It is a very narrow band because the $2s$ orbits on neighboring atoms do not overlap appreciably. The next band corresponds to the $2p$ levels of atomic fluorine and contains room for six electrons per unit cell. Actually, it is formed by the overlapping of three bands, which individually have room for two electrons per unit cell. The highest band corresponds to the valence-electron level of the lithium atom, which is a $2s$ orbit.

It follows that the lower pair of bands are completely occupied and that the upper band is completely empty. It is interesting to note that the band associated with the valence level of the alkali-metal atom is less stable in the solid than the band associated with the halogen atom, so that all the valence electrons prefer to be associated with the halogen atom. This confirms the chemist's supposition that the halogen atoms "borrow" electrons from the metal atoms in the course of combining with them. A careful analysis of the actual spatial distribution of the valence electrons in lithium fluoride shows that they are all

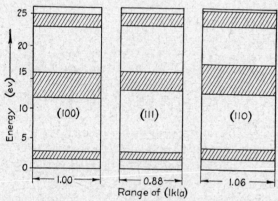

Fig. 160.—The allowed and forbidden regions of energy for electrons traveling in the (100), (111), and (110) directions in lithium fluoride. It may be seen that the forbidden regions overlap. The width of each diagram is proportional to the range of wave number between the gaps in the ϵ-versus-k curve.

to be found near the fluorine atom. Thus it is correct to regard the lattice as composed of negatively charged fluorine ions and positively charged lithium ions, as was done in the early theories of ionic crystals (see Sec. 70).

A similar analysis of the bands in other alkali-halide crystals shows that they are very much the same as those of lithium fluoride. As in lithium fluoride, it is found that all eight valence electrons in the unit cell are to be associated with the halogen atom, so that it is present in the lattice as a singly charged negative ion.

76. Semi-conductors.—We have seen in the previous sections that the properties of the various types of solid may be explained from a unified viewpoint by the use of the band theory. Semi-conductors were intentionally excluded from this discussion because they form a rather special group that may be discussed separately with more convenience.

It will be recalled that these solids possess the distinctive property that they are electronic conductors in which the conductivity increases with increasing temperature. Typical examples of the materials are cuprous oxide, silicon carbide, and selenium, all of which are extensively used for electrical purposes.

Practically any semi-conductor can be classed as one of the other four types of solid. For example, copper oxide can be regarded as an ionic crystal, selenium can be regarded as a cross between a valence crystal and a molecular crystal, whereas silicon carbide can be viewed as an example of a valence crystal. This suggests that semi-conductors possess some slight modification of the type of energy band found in the insulating type of solid. In fact, the properties of semi-conductors may be correlated very well by assuming that the highest occupied band is separated from the lowest empty one by a forbidden region, as in Fig. 148b, and that there are a few additional discrete levels in this forbidden region. Mathematical analysis shows that levels of this type could not occur in an ideally perfect crystal; however, they are to be expected in any crystal in which there are lattice imperfections or impurity atoms. Thus we may classify semi-conductors as materials that possess an inherent tendency to occur in an impure or an imperfect state and that possess additional energy levels in the forbidden region because of impurities or defects.

An electron occupying any one of the levels in a quasi-continuous band is able to wander about the lattice. However, an electron occupying one of the discrete levels in the forbidden range is closely localized about an impurity or imperfection, for it may be shown that the probability distribution function associated with these levels has a pronounced peak at the position of an imperfection or impurity atom. As a result of this fact, the energy-level diagram of a semi-conductor may be conveniently represented schematically in the manner shown in Fig. 161, in which the vertical scale is energy and the horizontal one is position. The ordinary bands of levels are continuous in such a diagram, since the electrons occupying these levels may wander about the lattice, whereas the discrete levels in the forbidden region are represented by lines of finite length located at the position of the impurity or imperfection with which the level is associated.

There are two interesting types of semi-conductor that are commonly observed. The first possesses the diagram shown

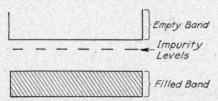

Fig. 161.—The position of the impurity levels in semi-conductors. Localized electronic states are associated with each of these levels (see text).

in Fig. 162a, in which there are *occupied* impurity levels lying very close to the vacant levels of the unoccupied band. The electrons in the occupied levels may be thermally excited into the conduction levels at a far lower temperature than those in the filled band. This situation commonly occurs in zinc oxide that has been calcined in the neighborhood of 1000°C. During calcination, a fraction of the oxygen atoms evaporate from the

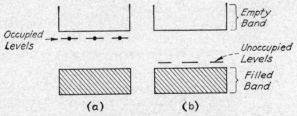

Fig. 162.—The two types of impurity semi-conductors. In case (a) the impurity levels lie close to the unoccupied band and are occupied, whereas in case (b) they are vacant and lie close to the occupied band.

solid as neutral atoms and leave behind an equal number of neutral zinc atoms, which diffuse into the lattice. The valence electrons on these atoms occupy levels which are like those shown in Fig. 162a and which are so close to the empty band that the crystal is conducting at room temperature.

The second type of semi-conductor possesses the diagram shown in Fig. 162b. In this case, there are *vacant* discrete levels near the top of the *occupied* band. When this material is warmed, electrons may jump from the occupied levels of the filled band to the impurity levels, thus introducing holes into the filled band and upsetting the statistical balance that prevents the electrons in this band from conducting a current. Copper oxide is a semi-conductor of this type. When it is heated in the presence of oxygen, the material absorbs a stoichiometric excess of oxygen, and vacant levels of the type shown in Fig. 162b are produced.

The semi-conductors of the two types can be distinguished on the basis of experiments that will not be discussed here.

It may be added that any insulator should become conducting at sufficiently high temperatures, for electrons will be excited from the filled to the empty band if sufficient thermal energy is supplied. This type of conductivity is known as *intrinsic*. It is not observed at an easily attainable temperature in any of the more ideal insulators, such as diamond, the alkali halides, or paraffin. It is a remarkable fact, however, that many of the semi-conductors which are conducting at room temperature by virtue of the presence of impurities or imperfections are intrinsic conductors at temperatures not very far above room temperature. This fact indicates that the insulating materials which show a marked predisposition toward the addition of impurities or imperfections are those in which the separation between the filled and empty bands is relatively small and hence which show an intrinsic semi-conductivity at a relatively low temperature.

CHAPTER XVIII

THE COHESION OF SOLIDS

77. Survey.—Before considering some of the detailed properties of metals and semi-conductors, it is interesting to summarize briefly the sources of the cohesive energies of solids.

Prior to the development of wave mechanics, the ionic theory of salts was the only theory in which an attempt was made to explain the cohesion of a type of solid. According to this theory, salts are held together by the mutual attraction of the positive and negative ions. The theory was able to give a very satisfactory account of the magnitudes of the cohesive energies of various salts, that is, of the energies gained by forming the crystalline salts from the free elements. This interpretation of the cohesion of salts is as valid today as it was twenty years ago; for the band theory of solids shows that, at least in the case of the simpler salts, such as the alkali halides, it is safe to say that the salts are composed of ions.

The nature of the cohesive forces in metals and in valence crystals was, on the other hand, a source of mystery until the development of wave mechanics. It is interesting to note that the source of cohesion is much the same in these two types of materials, even though there are striking differences in their properties.

Let us examine Figs. 151 and 152 (page 267), which show the variation in energy of the valence electrons, respectively, in an ideal metal and in an ideal valence crystal as the lattice is formed in the schematic manner discussed in Chap. XVII. It is evident that, as the atomic levels broaden into bands, the lower levels in the bands become depressed relative to the energies of the levels in the free atom, whereas the upper levels become raised (that is, *promoted*). It follows that the solid is more stable than the corresponding system of free atoms if the average energy of all the electrons is decreased as the solid is formed (see Fig. 163). Moreover, the equilibrium spacing of the lattice is determined by the interatomic distance at which the average energy is a minimum. Since all the valence electrons in diamond occupy the band that is greatly depressed during combination (Fig. 152), it follows that this substance should be very stable, in agreement with observation. Part of the occupied levels in sodium is depressed, but another part is promoted, as may be seen by noting the dotted curve in Fig. 151. As a result, we may expect this metal to be much less stable than diamond, also in agreement with observation.

It will be recalled (Sec. 74) that the bands arising from the levels of the molecules in molecular crystals are either completely

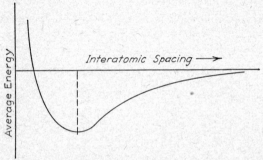

Fig. 163.—Schematic diagram showing the manner in which the average energy of the electronic system varies with interatomic spacing. The equilibrium spacing corresponds to the point at which this curve has its minimum.

empty or completely occupied as soon as they spread. Since the bands spread in a fairly symmetrical manner, we see that in these substances about as many electrons have their energy raised as have their energy lowered, so that the net cohesive energy should be very small. It is not surprising that these substances have very low boiling points.

Next let us examine Fig. 155 (page 271) for copper. We may expect, as was emphasized in the preceding chapter, that a similar diagram is valid for all the metals possessing partly filled or newly filled d shells. We note that in copper the d band is completely occupied so that, like the bands in molecular solids, it makes only a very minor contribution to the cohesive energy of this metal. The same is true in silver and gold, which are very similar to copper. On the other hand, in the metals preceding copper, silver, and gold, in the periodic table, the d band is partly empty. This fact favors cohesion for two reasons.

(1) The highest occupied levels in the s-p bands, which are promoted in copper, silver, and gold, are vacant in the transition metals. (2) A larger fraction of the electrons of the d band are depressed than are promoted because this band is no longer completely full. As a result, we may expect the transition metals to have higher cohesive energies than copper, silver, and gold. The heat of sublimation evidently provides a measure of the cohesive energy of a substance since it is the work required to separate the substance into its component atoms or molecules and place these at infinite distance from one another. The heats of sublimation of a number of transition metals are compared with those of copper, silver, and gold in Table XXIII. It may be seen that there is a definite decrease in the cohesive energy as the d band becomes filled. In the same connection,

TABLE XXIII.—THE COHESIVE ENERGIES OF A NUMBER OF METALS
(In kg cal/mol)

Fe	94.0	Ru	120	Os	125
Co	85.0	Rh	115	Ir	120
Ni	85.0	Pd	110	Pt	127
Cu	81.2	Ag	68.0	Au	92.0
Zn	27.4	Cd	26.8	Hg	14.6

it is interesting to note that the divalent metals zinc, cadmium, and mercury are much less stable than the monovalent metals. This is easily explained by the fact that the additional valence electron per atom in the divalent metals occupies a promoted level of the s-p band and hence decreases cohesion.

One may reasonably ask *why* the electrons in the depressed levels of the solid are more stable than the electrons in the corresponding level of the free atom. A careful investigation of the problem shows that the explanation is comparatively simple. The electrons are able to approach the nuclei more closely in the solid than they are in the free atom; hence, they spend a larger part of their time in the attractive field of the nucleus. This fact is not evident from any of the remarks that have been made either in this section or in the sections of the preceding chapter. It can be demonstrated only by a closer investigation of the principles of wave mechanics than would be appropriate in this book.

CHAPTER XIX

ALLOYS

78. Introduction.[1]—We are now in a position to apply the principles of the band theory to various properties of metals. As a start in this direction, we shall examine the implications of the band theory for alloys. As we have seen in Chap. III, there are two principal types of alloy, namely, substitutional and interstitial. In both types the alloying elements lie close to one another in the electromotive series of elements. In the first case, however, the atoms of the alloying element occupy the same type of position in the lattice as the atoms of the solvent metal, whereas in the second the atoms of the alloying element fit into the interstitial positions of the lattice of the solvent metal. On the whole, the experimental material relating to substitutional alloys is much more comprehensive and has been correlated more thoroughly than that relating to interstitial alloys. It is not surprising, as a result, that the principles of wave mechanics have been applied to these alloys much more fully than to interstitial alloys.

79. Substitutional Alloys.—The atoms that enter substitutional alloys are invariably very much alike, for they possess nearly equal radii and lie close to one another in the electromotive series of elements. As a result, it seems reasonable to assume that the energy bands are not appreciably changed as the composition of these alloys is changed within any range in which the structure remains constant, that is, within the solubility limits of any given phase. According to this assumption, the changes in the properties of the alloys as the composition is varied within solubility limits should arise entirely from changes in the filling of levels. On the other hand, the differences

[1] A more extensive discussion of this subject may be found in F. Seitz, *The Modern Theory of Solids* (McGraw-Hill Book Company, Inc., New York, 1940), and N. F. Mott and H. Jones, *The Theory of the Properties of Metals and Alloys* (Oxford University Press, New York, 1936).

between one phase and another should be associated with changes in the distribution of levels in the bands as well as with changes in the manner in which the levels are filled.

a. The Hume-Rothery Rules.—If we accept these principles, it is easy to understand why the electron-atom ratio is effective in determining the properties of the ideal substitutional alloys, as Hume-Rothery has found to be the case (Chap. III). This ratio determines the extent to which the bands of the metal are occupied. The larger the electron-atom ratio, the higher the levels are filled.

The credit for pointing out this connection between the electron-atom ratio and the band theory of solids belongs to H. Jones,[1] who, in addition, was able to give very satisfactory explanations of the Hume-Rothery rules. We shall review these explanations briefly. Consider first the fact that the electron-atom ratio is the same for typical phases of substitutional alloys having the same crystallographic structure (see Table IV, page 36). Jones computed the density of levels in the bands of each of the characteristic phases and found that they invariably satisfy the conditions which are illustrated in Fig. 164 for the face-centered and body-centered structures. In this example, the observed electron-atom ratio is lower for the face-centered phase than for the body-centered phase. It may be observed that the density functions are practically the same for values of the energy near the bottom of the band and that each curve rises to a sharply defined peak and then drops abruptly. The curve for the face-centered lattice has a peak for lower energies than the curve for the body-centered lattice and then drops well below this. Thus, if the levels of both solids were being filled at the same rate, it would be found that the two phases are almost equally stable as long as the levels filled lie below the point a. Then, as the region from a to b was being filled, it would be found that the electrons have a lower mean energy in the face-centered structure and consequently that this structure is the more stable of the two. The situation would be reversed after the point b was reached because the area under the peak

[1] H. JONES, *Proc. Roy. Soc.* **144**, 225 (1934), **147**, 396 (1934); *Proc. Phys. Soc.*, **49**, 243 (1937). See also N. F. MOTT and H. JONES, *The Structure of Metals and Alloys* (Oxford University Press, New York, 1936).

of the curve for the body-centered structure is larger than that under the peak of the other curve. That is, the levels are filled more efficiently in the body-centered structure when the filled region extends above b.

Thus we may expect the face-centered structure to be stable for one range of filling of levels and the body-centered to be stable for another. Jones found that the values of the electron-

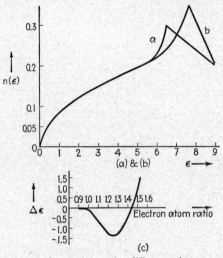

FIG. 164.—The upper figure shows the difference between the densities of electronic levels in face-centered and body-centered cubic lattices. The horizontal axis is the energy and the vertical axis is the density. Curve *a* corresponds to the face-centered lattice and curve *b* to the body-centered lattice. The lower figure shows the difference in the energy per electron for each of the lattices as a function of the electron-atom ratio. The face-centered lattice is more stable in the region where $\Delta\epsilon$ is negative, and conversely. [*After H. Jones, Proc. Phys. Soc.*, **49**, 243 (1937).]

atom ratio for the stable ranges derived from curves of the type shown in Fig. 164 agree closely with the observed values for all the common substitutional alloys.

We saw in Sec. 9 that substitutional alloys involving the transition metals can be fitted into Hume-Rothery's rule of electron-atom ratios if it is assumed that they have valence zero. This is readily explained by the band theory. It was pointed out in Chap. XVII that the transition metals actually possess vacancies in the d-shell band which must be filled before the height of the filled levels in the s-p band can be raised appreciably (see Fig. 157, page 272).

In addition to deriving Hume-Rothery's electron-atom ratios for the individual alloy phases on the basis of curves of the type of Fig. 164, Jones was able to determine the solubility-limit curves for the corresponding phases. It will be recalled that these limits are determined by the condition that the free energy of neighboring phases should be equal for compositions corresponding to the intersection of a horizontal, or isothermal, line

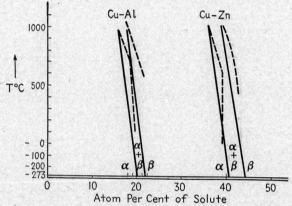

Fig. 165.—The boundaries between the α and β phases of the copper-zinc and copper-aluminum system as computed by Jones (full curves). The dashed curves represent the observed boundaries.

with the solubility-limit curves. It will also be recalled that the free energy is equal to $E - TS$ where E is the energy and S is the entropy. In the present case, E is determined entirely by the extent to which the levels are filled, whereas S, which measures the degree of randomness of the alloy, is determined by the number of ways in which the combining atoms may be arranged in the crystal lattice. Figure 165 shows the solubility-limit curves obtained by Jones for the α and β phases of the Cu-Al and Cu-Zn systems.

In addition to pointing out the correlation between the lattice structure and the electron-atom ratio, Hume-Rothery showed that the liquidus and solidus curves of the end phases of the substitutional alloys of copper and of silver can be made to coincide when they are plotted as functions of the electron-atom ratio. This fact also is readily explained by the band theory, for alloys that have the same structure and the same electron-atom ratio should have almost identical bands that are filled to the same level. As a result, their properties should be practically identical.

b. Properties of Homogeneous Alloys.—A number of properties of homogeneous phases of particular alloys have been clearly correlated on the basis of the band theory. Consider, for example, the colors of the α brasses. Pure copper is a reddish metal; however, the alloy becomes lighter and lighter as zinc is

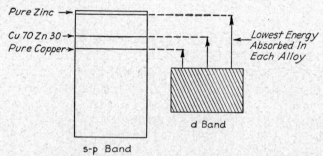

FIG. 166.—The wave lengths absorbed by the copper-zinc alloys. The heights to which the *s-p* band is filled in the various alloys are shown on the left, whereas the allowed transitions of lowest energy are shown by the arrows on the right. The longest wave lengths that may be absorbed shift toward the blue as zinc is added to copper.

added. This is not surprising, at first sight; for since zinc is practically colorless, one might naturally suppose that the effect of combining the two metals would be to lighten the color of copper. On the other hand, it is by no means clear why the color of the brasses should pass through the yellow stage characteristic of the 70-30, or cartridge, composition. The explanation of this was given by Mott[1] and is illustrated by means of Fig. 166.

Let us assume that the absorption of light which produces the reddish color of copper corresponds to transitions from the top of the filled *d* band to the unoccupied levels of the *s-p* band. The light quantum of longest wave length, or of lowest frequency, that may be absorbed is then given by the energy corresponding to the arrow shown in the figure. This presumably lies in the

[1] N. F. MOTT, *Proc. Phys. Soc.*, **49**, 354 (1937).

yellow part of the spectrum since red is obtained by removing both yellow and blue from the spectrum. If zinc is added to the copper, the top of the filled region is raised since zinc possesses one more valence electron per atom than copper. As a result, the longest wave length absorbed should shift farther and farther toward the blue and produce a color that contains more and more yellow. By the time the 70-30 composition is reached, only blue light is absorbed and the metal appears yellow instead of red.

Other properties of the homogeneous phases of substitutional alloys that can be correlated in a similar way will be discussed in the chapters that deal with magnetism and electrical conductivity.

c. The Substitutional Alloys of the Iron-group Elements.—The application of the principles of the band theory to the alloys of iron is still in the embryonic stage. There are, however, a few interesting facts concerning these alloys that have been correlated by the use of the theory.

Let us consider the relative stability of the α and γ phases of the alloys of iron. The fact that pure α iron transforms to γ iron at 930°C implies, of course, that the free energy of the former becomes larger than that of the latter at this temperature. As we have seen in Sec. 15, the origin of this change lies in the fact that the vibrational specific heat of the γ phase is larger than that of the α phase. Similarly, the reversion of the α phase to the body-centered phase at 1400°C is related to the fact that the electronic specific heat of the α phase is larger than that of the γ phase. It is evident that we cannot expect changes in composition of the order of a few percent to make an appreciable change in the lattice vibrational frequencies of alloys. On the other hand, it is conceivable that such changes in composition would alter the density of levels at the top of the filled band and thus influence the electronic heat in such a way that the transition temperatures for the phase changes are appreciably altered.

A basis for understanding the observed influence of the alloying elements on the transition temperatures for the γ range has been proposed by Smoluchowski[1] and is illustrated in Fig. 167.

[1] R. SMOLUCHOWSKI, *Phys. Rev.* (1942) (abstract), *Metal Progress,* **41,** 363 (1942).

Smoluchowski has suggested that the density of levels in γ iron increases with increasing energy at the top of the filled region, whereas this density decreases with increasing energy in the α phase. Thus, if an element that raises the height of the occupied region of the filled band is added to iron, it should increase the specific heat of the γ phase and decrease that of the α phase, thus increasing the range of stability of the γ phase. Conversely, if the alloying element decreases the height of the occupied region,

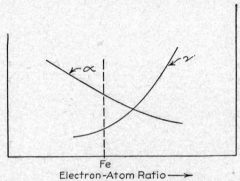

Fe

Electron-Atom Ratio ⟶

Fig. 167.—Schematic diagram showing the dependence of the density of the levels in the bands of α and γ iron on the electron-atom ratio for values of this parameter near that for iron. (*After Smoluchowski.*)

we should expect it to produce the reverse effect. Table XXIV contains a list of elements that when added to iron in small amounts have the effect of broadening the γ range and of closing it, respectively.

TABLE XXIV

Broadening Effect	Narrowing Effect
Co	Cr
Cu	Mo
Mn	V
Ni	W
Pt	
Zn	

With the exception of manganese, all the elements that open the γ range lie to the right of iron in the periodic chart and, as a result, have more valence electrons than iron. Similarly, those which close it have fewer. There are a number of elements, such as tin, titanium, and silicon, that close the γ range and yet have more s-p electrons than copper and zinc, which open it. It is questionable, however, whether these elements have bands sufficiently like those of the ferrous elements to be compared with the others.

80. *Interstitial Alloys.*—The principles of the quantum theory of solids have not yet been applied to the interstitial alloys. There is little doubt, however, that, when this field has been opened, it will provide some of the most interesting aspects of the subject.

CHAPTER XX

THE MAGNETIC PROPERTIES OF METALS

81. Introduction.[1]—Three types of magnetic materials are known, namely, paramagnetic, diamagnetic, and ferromagnetic substances. The first are feebly attracted to a magnet by a force that is proportional to the intensity of the magnetic field; the second are repelled by a force that varies in the same manner; and the third are the few ferrous metals of which permanent magnets may be made. The simpler metals that have one or two electrons outside the rare-gas structures, that is, the alkali metals, magnesium, calcium, aluminum, and so forth, belong in the paramagnetic group. Moreover, all the transition metals that are not ferromagnetic, such as manganese, chromium, tungsten, platinum, and palladium, also belong in it. All common insulators and all metals having newly filled d shells, such as zinc, copper, and gold, are diamagnetic. The largest known diamagnetism occurs in bismuth. Only four pure metals are ferromagnetic, namely, iron, cobalt, nickel, and gadolinium; however, it is possible to form a wide variety of ferromagnetic alloys by combining these with other metals. It is interesting to note that the ferromagnetic Heusler alloys contain none of the metals which are ferromagnetic in the pure state. Instead, they are composed of manganese, aluminum, and copper. There is little doubt that manganese represents the source of the ferromagnetism in this case, for it is strongly paramagnetic in the pure state.

[1] More detailed treatments of magnetism will be found in the following: F. BITTER, *Introduction to Ferromagnetism* (McGraw-Hill Book Company, Inc., New York, 1937); E. C. STONER, *Magnetism and Matter* (Methuen & Co., Ltd., London, 1934); R. BECKER and W. DÖRING, *Ferromagnetismus* (Julius Springer, Berlin, 1939); J. C. SLATER, *J. Applied Phys.*, **8**, 385 (1937); W. SHOCKLEY, *Bell System Tech. J.*, **18**, 645 (1939); W. F. BROWN, *J. Applied Phys.*, **11**, 16 (1940); F. SEITZ, *The Modern Theory of Solids* (McGraw-Hill Book Company, Inc., New York, 1940).

The magnetic strength of a substance is commonly measured in terms of its *susceptibility*, λ, which is defined by the equation

$$M = \lambda H. \tag{1}$$

Here H is the applied magnetic field strength, and M is the intensity of magnetization induced in the substance. λ is 10^{-6} for most diamagnetic substances, although it is as large as $200 \cdot 10^{-6}$ for bismuth. It is also small for most paramagnetic substances; however, it is of the order of 10^{-2} for some paramagnetic transition metals. Ferromagnetic substances obey

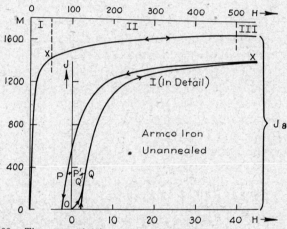

Fig. 168.—The magnetization curve for polycrystalline iron. The upper horizontal scale represents the applied magnetic field in oersted used to obtain the higher magnetization curve. The lower horizontal scale and figure show the portion of the upper curve near the origin in greater detail. The upper curve is divided into three sections I, II, and III, which are discussed in the text. (*After Brown.*)

Eq. (1) for weak fields, in which case values of λ as high as 2,000 are common. The magnetization M approaches a saturation value for sufficiently strong fields in these substances, as is shown for the case of pure iron in Fig. 168.

Diamagnetism is the most readily explained of the three magnetic effects. It is a well-known theorem of the theory of electrical circuits that the current induced in a circuit by a changing magnetic field is such as to keep the magnetic field within the circuit constant. It may readily be seen that this implies that the induced magnetization of the circuit is such that the circuit is repelled from regions where the magnetic field is strongest. Since the electrons moving in their orbits represent electrical circuits, it follows that a magnetic field changes the motion of the electrons in these orbits in such a way that the atoms are repelled by the field. Thus a diamagnetic tendency is a universal attribute of all atoms. Solids are paramagnetic only when a compensating tendency masks the diamagnetic one.

The origin of the tendency toward paramagnetism and ferromagnetism lies in the electron spin. As we remarked in Sec. 64, by virtue of its spin an electron behaves like a small magnet that may be aligned by a magnetic field as a permanent magnet is aligned. Whenever this alignment is allowed to occur without constraint, the energy of the electron is decreased by the field. Thus the electron is attracted to regions of stronger field. This conclusion has been reached as a result of detailed investigations, which we shall not attempt to discuss here.

There is, however, one direct type of experiment that merits mention. When a substance is placed in a magnetic field, there is, as mentioned above, a tendency for the orbital motion to change and for the spins to align themselves parallel to the field. When either or both of these changes occur, they are accompanied by changes in the angular momentum of the electrons and hence by changes in the angular momentum of the substance in which the electrons reside. As a result, a substance receives a rotary impulse when it is magnetized. The ratio of the induced magnetic moment to the induced rotary impulse is known as the *gyromagnetic ratio*. It may be shown that this ratio is different when the magnetism arises primarily from the alignment of electron spin and when it arises from the change in orbital magnetism. Careful experiments show, in fact, that the observed ratio in ferromagnetic and strongly paramagnetic substances is as would be expected from spin alignment.

82. Paramagnetism and Diamagnetism in Metals.—The manner in which the valence electrons in metals exert their paramagnetic effect is readily visualized in the band theory. It will be recalled that each occupied electronic level in a band is filled by a pair of electrons having opposite spin. The energy of one of these electrons is increased since it is oriented in the unstable position in the field, whereas the energy of the other,

which is oriented in the stable position, has its energy decreased. This effect may be represented conveniently by regarding the band of levels as composed of two bands that are individually associated with opposite spins, in the manner shown in Fig. 169. It follows that one of these bands is raised in the presence of the field and the other lowered. It also follows that electrons pour over from the raised band to the lowered band until the top of the filled region is the same in both. In this equilibrium state, it is clear that there is a larger number of electrons which have their energy lowered by the field than of those which have their energy raised. This corresponds to paramagnetism.

Evidently there is no paramagnetism if the filled region extends to the top of a set of bands, as in insulators, for then there is no room at the top of the band that has been lowered by the field to accommodate the electrons at the top of the band that is raised (Fig. 169).

It is clear from this picture that the metals having partly

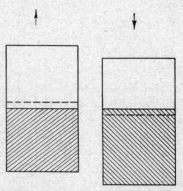

Fig. 169.—The origin of the diamagnetic tendency of free electrons. The bands associated with each type of spin are shown as they are displaced as the result of a magnetic field. The dotted lines show the extent to which the levels were filled before the field was applied.

filled d shells should be more strongly paramagnetic than those in which the d shells are entirely filled or entirely empty because the density of levels in the d band is so very large that a comparatively large number of electrons spill from the half of the d band associated with one spin to the other half when the two halves are displaced by a given amount.

Underlying this paramagnetic tendency of metals is, of course, the diamagnetic tendency associated with the change in orbital motion. Both the free electrons and those in the closed shells contribute to this, but their net contribution is smaller than the paramagnetic one in all metals except those containing newly filled d shells. It turns out that the diamagnetic contribution from a closed shell varies directly as the first power of the number of electrons in it and directly as the square of the radius of the electronic orbits. The effect is large for a newly filled d shell both because there is a large number of these electrons in it and because the radii of the orbits are very large compared with those of a newly filled shell of the rare-gas type. It is also true that the diamagnetic effect is comparatively large in the metals having partly filled d shells, but the paramagnetic effect is so much greater in these cases, for the reasons given in the preceding paragraph, that the diamagnetic effect may be neglected.

83. Ferromagnetism in Pure Metals.—Since ferromagnetism is the most interesting topic in the field of metallic magnetism,

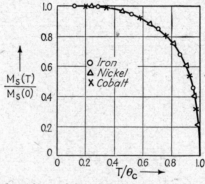

FIG. 170.—The dependence of the saturation magnetization upon temperature. The vertical scale shows the ratio of the magnetization at temperature T to that at the absolute zero. The horizontal scale shows the ratio of the absolute temperature to the Curie temperature.

we shall devote most of the remainder of this chapter to it. It was pointed out in Sec. 81 that at the present time there is conclusive evidence that this phenomenon is associated with the electron spin and, in the ferrous metals, arises from the d electrons.

The fact that the magnetization curve (see Fig. 168 for iron) reaches a saturation value for sufficiently strong magnetic fields indicates that there is a sharply defined upper limit to the amount of spin alignment which may be achieved in the specimen with practically attainable fields. This saturation value is markedly dependent upon temperature and invariably decreases with decreasing temperature. Figure 170 shows, for example, the dependence of the saturation value for iron and nickel on temperature. The temperature at which the saturation magnetization vanishes is known as the *Curie temperature*. Above this temperature the material is merely paramagnetic and cannot be used to make a magnet.

The manner in which the magnetization curve approaches saturation depends upon a large number of factors which have been explained to an appreciable extent as the result of careful

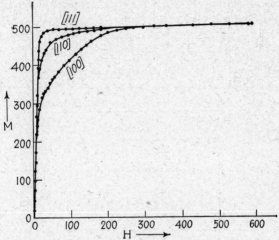

Fig. 171.—The magnetization curves of a single crystal of nickel for three crystallographic directions.

studies of the magnetic properties of single crystals. The important factors are as follows:

a. In single crystals, the magnetization depends upon the orientation of the crystal relative to the direction of the magnetic field. This is shown very strikingly in Figs. 171 and 172 for nickel and cobalt. In the first case, the saturation curves are shown for the three prominent crystallographic directions, namely, (100), (110), and (111). It may be seen that the saturation is reached for the smallest field in the (111) direction. Similarly, in cobalt, the magnetization curves are given for a direction parallel to the hexagonal axis and in a direction normal to this. The crystallographically equivalent directions in which saturation is attained with the lowest field are known as the *easy directions* of magnetization. They are the (111) directions in nickel, the axial direction in cobalt, and the (110) directions in iron.

Table XXV contains the values of the Curie temperature and the saturation magnetization M_s for the ferromagnetic metals. In addition, values of the ratio R of the saturation magnetic

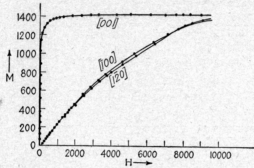

FIG. 172.—The magnetization curve of cobalt for three crystallographic directions.

moment per atom and the spin magnetic moment per electron are given.

TABLE XXV

	Fe	Co	Ni	Gd
θ, °C	780	1075	365	16
M_s, cgs units	1752	1446	512	1560
R	2.22	1.71	0.606	

b. The approach to saturation is not a completely continuous process as the smooth curves of Figs. 168, 171, and 172 would indicate. If the approach is studied with sufficiently great magnification, it is found that the increase in magnetization occurs in jumps, which are known as *Barkhausen jumps* in honor of their discoverer.

The existence of easy and hard directions of magnetization and the existence of the Barkhausen jumps can be neatly explained on the basis of the domain theory of ferromagnetism, which, in recent years, has been proved beyond all reasonable doubt. In the ferromagnetic state, according to this theory, the material contains regions, or *domains*, in which the electron spins are aligned along the easy directions of magnetization. In the unmagnetized state of the medium, that is, when the average magnetization is zero, these domains are arranged randomly in all the easy directions. They take up more preferred directions of alignment when the magnetic field is applied and thus give the specimen a resultant magnetic moment. The initial stages of this alignment are the easiest, for then the directions of the domains change from one easy direction to that easy direction most nearly parallel to the field. This change takes place discontinuously and gives rise to the Barkhausen jumps. This range of the applied field corresponds to that near the origin in which the magnetization curve rises nearly vertically (region I, Fig. 168). As the field becomes stronger, the directions of magnetization of the domains bend away from the easy directions to the direction of the applied field. This range corresponds to that extending from the end of the nearly vertical portion of the magnetization curve to the point at which complete saturation is obtained (region II, Fig. 168). All the domains are aligned parallel to the field at this point, so that no further increase is possible for stronger fields (region III, Fig. 168). We see from this that the saturation magnetization represents the magnetization within each of the domains.

The magnetization curve is particularly simple when the direction of the field is that of one of the easy directions of magnetization, for in this case it is only necessary for all the domains to flip to this easy direction in order to produce complete magnetization. Thus, in this case the curve contains only regions I and III of Fig. 168, as may be seen in Figs. 171 and 172 for nickel and cobalt. In cobalt, which has only one direction of magnetization, the situation is equally simple when the field is applied in a direction normal to the axis of easy magnetization. Then the vertical portion (region I) is absent because the flipping process does not alter the magnetization. The magnetized state is attained only when the domains are bent toward the field. A gain in magnetization always results from flipping in the cubic crystals since the majority of the directions of easy magnetization always possess a nonvanishing component along the direction of the field, regardless of the direction in which they lie.

When the domain theory was first proposed, it was believed that the domains were fixed units within the crystal and possibly should be associated with the mosaic blocks. Subsequent experimental and theoretical investigation has shown, however, that this is not the case and that the domain pattern is very variable. In order to appreciate this, let us consider the forces that give rise to domains. Let us consider a region *A* (Fig. 173) of the crystal in which the electron spins are oriented in the same direction and the magnetization has the saturation value. Next,

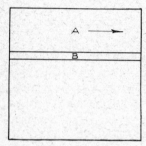

Fig. 173.—The region *A* has uniform magnetization. The region *B* is subject to two types of forces which individually would tend to make it have magnetization either parallel or antiparallel to that of *A*.

let us consider the equilibrium orientation in the region *B* below it. We may assume that the system gains some energy if the spins in *B* become parallel to those in *A*, for otherwise domains would not exist in the first place. There must, however, be a competing energy term that favors a different alignment of spins in region *B*, for otherwise the entire crystal would have the same magnetization throughout in the absence of an external field. The source of the competing term is not difficult to find. The region *A* may be regarded as a bar magnet having north and south poles at its ends. It follows from the normal behavior of magnets lying side by side that the region *B* would be most stably disposed, as far as the magnetic forces between it and *A* are concerned, if its magnetization were opposite to that in *A*. For then the north pole of *A* would be next to the south pole of *B*, and vice versa. It follows, then, that the region *B* is acted upon by two forces: the atoms at the boundary between *B* and *A* tend to have the same spin alignment, whereas the domain *B* as a whole tends to have opposite spin from that of *A*. Careful calculations show that, as long as the width of the domain *A* is only a few atomic distances, the first of these tendencies determines the orientation of the magnetization in *B*; however, as *A* becomes wider and wider, the second tendency becomes stronger and stronger and finally gains the upper hand. The critical thickness of A depends upon several factors but is frequently of the order of 1 micron.

Microscopic examination of specially prepared surfaces of the ferromagnetic metals on which colloidal suspensions of a magnetic material have been deposited show that this is indeed the thickness of domains in most materials. Similar experiments show that, when a field is applied to a specimen which favors the orientation of A rather than that of B, the latter domain may disappear both (1) by motion of the boundary of the domain A into that of B and (2) by spontaneous reversal of B from a point within the domain B. The Barkhausen jumps correspond to individual reversals of this type in which the magnetization of domains are altered by either one of these two mechanisms. The second process requires stronger fields than the first because it is equivalent to a crystallographic change that takes place by nucleation and hence can occur only when the field is sufficiently large to form the nuclei. It is evident that the first process corresponds to a crystallographic change in which the nuclei are already present and need only grow.

It is well known that there is a close correlation between the mechanical and the magnetic properties of materials. A mechanically hard steel is magnetically hard in the sense that strong fields are required to alter the magnetization of the specimen. For example, the materials used in permanent magnets are mechanically hard, whereas those used in transformers, in which little hysteresis loss is desired, are mechanically soft. This correlation finds its origin in the phenomenon of *magnetostriction*. When any magnetic material is placed in a magnetic field, it undergoes a slight change in linear dimensions; conversely, when the material is strained, the easy directions of magnetization are altered. The first of these complementary effects is, for example, responsible for the ordinary hum of a transformer; in this case, the variations in linear dimensions with varying magnetic field generate sound waves. As a result of magnetostriction, the residual strains introduced in a metal by cold-work or by any of the other methods of hardening alter the easy direction of magnetization from one point of a grain to another. It turns out that strong fields are required to force the domain boundaries past points where these variations occur. Thus the presence of residual strains makes it difficult to alter the magnetization. It should be added that the magnetostriction varies appreciably from one material to another and is small in many of the alloys employed commercially for transformers.

The phenomenon of magnetostriction provides an explanation of the fact that ferromagnetic materials usually possess a very high internal friction (see Chap. X). When a ferromagnetic body is stressed, the domains usually change their orientation slightly because of a change in the directions of easy magnetization. The shift in direction of local magnetization is, in turn, accompanied by the generation of eddy currents, which represent a dissipation of energy and hence a source of internal friction. This component of internal friction may be greatly decreased by placing the material in a strong magnetic field, which holds the domains firmly in a given orientation and thereby decreases the eddy currents.

It is clear from this explanation of the correlation between mechanical and magnetic properties that a polycrystalline medium should be magnetically harder than a single crystal, for the direction of easy magnetization varies at the grain boundaries. Thus we should expect these boundaries to inhibit the passage of domain boundaries. This is, in fact, the case. Use of this knowledge is made in the construction of transformers by employing steels in which a high degree of preferred orientation is attainable by rolling and annealing. These materials have properties very nearly like those of single crystals and hence, when properly oriented, are very soft magnetically.

From this discussion it follows that parts I and II of the magnetization curve of a given material (see Fig. 168) are dependent more upon the macrocrystalline state of the specimen than upon its detailed composition. The properties in this region may be varied by altering the crystalline texture or the hardness of the material. On the other hand, the saturation value of the magnetization, which is attained in region III, is related to the intrinsic atomic structure of the material and cannot be altered by the factors that alter the curve in regions I and II. Thus we may expect that the values of the saturation magnetization of different metals would be the easiest quantities to correlate on the basis of the band theory, which is primarily concerned with those properties which are immediately related to the intrinsic atomic structure.

Let us consider, first, the origin of ferromagnetism. We saw in the preceding section that paramagnetism can be explained by the fact that the two halves of a band associated with opposite spin are displaced relative to one another in the presence of a magnetic field. As a result of this displacement, the electrons near the top of the band that is raised pour into the vacant levels at the top of the other until the levels of the two are equal. It is possible to explain ferromagnetism if it can be shown that in the ferromagnetic metals the half band associated with one spin is automatically lowered when the vacant levels at its top are filled by levels from the top of the other half band. This would be true, for example, if the cohesive energy of the system were increased when as many electrons as possible have parallel spin. This topic has been investigated extensively. Although a quantitative treatment of the problem is not possible at the present time, the following qualitative principles have been well established:

a. The effect can occur only in *d* or *f* bands. The reason for this is as follows: If an electron from the top of one half band is placed in a vacant level of the other, its kinetic energy is increased because it now lies in a level having shorter wave length. There is a net decrease in energy only if there is a decrease in potential energy that more than compensates for this. Since the quasi-continuous levels are more widely spaced in the *s-p* bands than in the narrower *d* and *f* bands, it follows that the gain in kinetic energy is much larger in the former. In fact, detailed investigation shows that in *s-p* bands the gain is always much larger than the corresponding decrease in potential energy, so that ferromagnetism is impossible in metals in which only the *s-p* band is partly filled.

b. The change in potential energy associated with the transfer of electrons from one half band to the other is commonly known as the *exchange energy*. The source of this change in potential energy is intimately associated with quantum mechanics. Consequently, no attempt will be made to discuss the origin here other than to say that it is ultimately connected with the *electro-*

static forces between atoms rather than with the magnetic forces. It is known that the exchange energy may have either sign; evidently, only that case in which it favors binding can result in ferromagnetism. We shall adopt the convention that the exchange energy is regarded as positive when it favors ferromagnetism and negative when it does not.

c. Figure 174 shows the manner in which it is believed that the sum of the kinetic and potential energies varies with the interatomic spacing. This sum is negative for small interatomic dis-

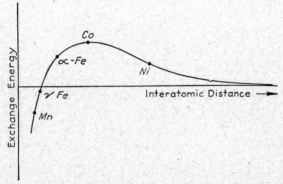

Fig. 174.—The exchange energy of a pair of transition metal atoms as a function of their interatomic distance. Ferromagnetism is favored when this energy is positive.

tances and opposes ferromagnetism in this range. It is positive for larger distances. The curve given is representative of the elements in the iron group. It shows schematically the interatomic distances corresponding to γ iron, α iron, cobalt, and nickel. It may be seen that the energy favors magnetism in the last three cases, but not in the first. It may also be seen that in the ferromagnetic cases the energy is highest for cobalt and lowest for nickel. The theory based on these curves shows that the Curie temperature is proportional to these energies, so that we should expect this temperature to decrease for the three ferromagnetic metals in the sequence cobalt, iron, and nickel. Table XXV shows that this is the case.

It is interesting to note that the absence of ferromagnetism in γ iron can be explained, at least qualitatively, on the basis of the smaller interatomic spacing occurring in this lattice. It may be added that chromium and manganese, which are not ferromagnetic, also have smaller interatomic distances than the ferromagnetic metals. Although the interatomic distances in the transition metals of the other long periods are larger than those of iron, cobalt, and nickel, an entirely different curve of the type shown in Fig. 174 is valid for them, since they possess *d* electrons of a different type. We may conclude that they are not ferromagnetic because their interatomic spacing is smaller than the critical value required for ferromagnetism in the case appropriate for them.

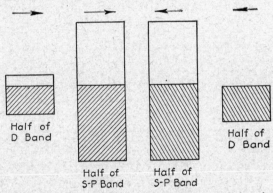

FIG. 175.—The filling of levels of the *s-p* and the *d* bands in a ferromagnetic metal. The arrows at the top indicate the direction in which the spins of the electrons in the bands are aligned.

Returning to the energy-level diagram for the ferromagnetic metals, we may say that the situation is described in the manner shown in Fig. 175. One half of the *d* band is completely filled and is suppressed below the top of the occupied region in the other half of the band and in the *s-p* band. The energy gained as a result of ferromagnetism evidently is proportional to the extent to which half of the *d* band has been depressed. This in turn is proportional to the ordinate of the curve shown in Fig. 174 for the corresponding element.

The manner in which ferromagnetism disappears with increasing temperature is illustrated by means of Fig. 176. As the temperature is raised, electrons in the filled half of the *d* band are thermally excited to the vacant levels in the other pair of bands. Such excitation decreases the net stability of the

depressed levels.   As a result, when the temperature is raised
still higher, the remaining electrons evaporate more easily.   Thus
the depressed band rises with temperature at an ever-increasing
rate until it reaches the same height as the other half of the d
band.   When this temperature is attained, the metal is no
longer ferromagnetic, but paramagnetic.

According to Fig. 175, we should expect the saturation magnetization to increase as the number of vacancies in the d band
increases, for then the difference between the numbers of electrons
having each kind of orientation increases.   To be more exact,

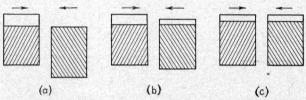

(a)   (b)   (c)

FIG. 176.—The variation in the relative position of the halves of the d band
associated with each spin as the temperature is raised (a) shows the situation
at low temperature; (b) shows the situation at a high temperature in which
part of the magnetization has disappeared; (c) shows the situation above the
Curie temperature in which both halves of the d-band are filled to the same
height.

the filled half of the d band has room for 5 electrons per atom,
so that 5 of the n valence electrons per atom will occupy it.
The remaining $n - 5$ will occupy the s-p band and the other half
of the d band.   Let us designate the number in the other half of
the d band by m.   Then the difference between the number
of electrons per atom in the d band having opposite spin is
$5 - m$.   This should be equal to the quantity R given in Table
XXV (page 298).   We note, for example, that in the case of
nickel this is 0.6, so that m must be 4.4.   Thus the total number
of electrons in the d band of nickel is 9.4.   Since there are 10
valence electrons per atom in nickel, it follows that there must
be 0.6 electron in the s-p band.   Now it is reasonable to suppose
that the number of s-p electrons is about the same in nickel,
cobalt, and iron, for the height of the filled part of the d band
should not be appreciably different in these three metals.   Since
these elements have 10, 9, and 8 electrons per atom, respectively,
we should expect the value of $5 - m$ to be 0.6, 1.6, and 2.6, respec-

tively, if one half of the d band remains completely filled. It may be seen from Table XXV that the actual values of R, which should be equal to $5 - m$, are 1.7 and 2.2, respectively, in the last two cases. Thus our expectation is closely fulfilled in the case of cobalt, but not in that of iron. The source of this low value of R for iron will be discussed again in connection with alloys.

84. Ferromagnetism of Alloys.—The ferromagnetic properties in all three of the regions shown in Fig. 168 may be altered

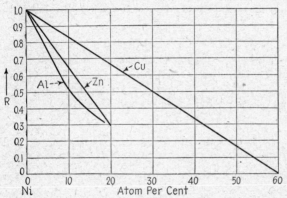

Fig. 177.—Variation of the relative magnetization of nickel alloys as the content of the alloying element is varied. The elements chosen lie to the right of nickel in the periodic chart and hence fill the vacant levels at the top of the d-band.

by the use of alloying agents. Alloying elements affect regions I and II by changing the directions of easy magnetization, the magnitude of the magnetostrictive effect, and the degree of preferred orientation obtainable after cold-work and annealing. As we saw in the preceding section, these properties determine the manner in which the magnetization curve approaches saturation. Similarly, the alloying agents affect the saturation magnetization by changing the Curie temperature and by varying the extent to which the d band is filled. The present section will be entirely devoted to the influence of alloys on the saturation magnetization.

One of the simplest effects that may be predicted on the basis of the band theory is the disappearance of ferromagnetism with the addition of an alloying agent that fills the d band. For example, we know that the d band of nickel should be filled as copper is added to it. Since nickel possesses 0.6 vacancy per atom, we should expect the ferromagnetism to vanish when 0.6 of the nickel atoms have been replaced by copper. Figure 177 shows that this is the case. In fact, this figure also shows that the magnetization decreases linearly with the addition of copper, exactly as we might expect on the basis of the band theory. Figure 177 shows a similar decrease of the saturation magnetization of copper as other metals containing one or more

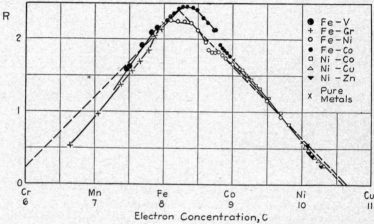

Fig. 178.—The magnetization per atom, R, of a number of ferromagnetic alloys as a function of the number of valence electrons per atom. It may be observed that the curves lie close to the curve formed by the two dotted lines. The peak magnetization occurs for an electron-atom ratio slightly larger than that observed in iron. (*After Shockley.*)

available valence electrons per atom are added. The curves fall closely upon one another when the electron-atom ratio instead of the atomic percentage is used as abscissa. This shows that the magnetization is determined entirely by the extent to which the bands are filled.

Figure 178 shows the saturation magnetization as a function of electron-atom ratio for a large number of ferromagnetic substitutional alloys containing all the ferrous elements. It may be seen that the various curves define quite closely a single symmetrical function which is represented by the dotted curve. This curve cuts the axis on the right-hand side for the electron-atom ratio corresponding to the 40Ni60Cu alloy already discussed, rises to a peak at a point corresponding to an electron-atom ratio between that of pure iron and cobalt, and then crosses the axis again at a point between manganese and vanadium.

The line passing through the points for nickel and cobalt is that which would be obtained if it were assumed that the number of electrons in the *s-p* band is unaltered as the electron-atom ratio is decreased and that the electrons are removed entirely from one half of the *d* band, the other half remaining completely

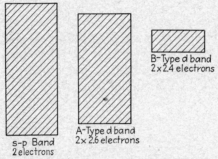

B-Type d band
2 x 2.4 electrons

A-Type d band
2 x 2.6 electrons

s-p Band
2 electrons

FIG. 179.—Proposed division of the *d*-band into two subbands which have room for 5.2 and 4.8 electrons per atom, respectively.

filled. The fact that this line does not pass through the point for iron is in accordance with the result found in the preceding paragraph that the value of R for iron is 2.2 (see Table XXV) instead of 2.6, as we should expect from the simple band picture. It follows that we cannot remove as many as 5 electrons from one half of the *d* band without at the same time removing some from the other half. In fact, the maximum difference attainable occurs when only about 2.4 electrons have been removed. The cause of the restriction of this limit to the value of 2.4 is not yet determined. It has been suggested by Pauling, for example, that the *d* band has two parts, as is shown in Fig. 179, and that only the upper part, which has room for about 4.8 electrons, plays a role in ferromagnetism. Although this explanation fits the observed facts concerning ferromagnetism, it has not yet had the additional substantiating support necessary for its acceptance.

85. Influence of Magnetization on the Expansion Coefficient.—

The expansion coefficient of most simple metals varies linearly with temperature above the characteristic temperature. The ferromagnetic metals, however, are usually exceptions to this rule, particularly for temperatures in the vicinity of the Curie

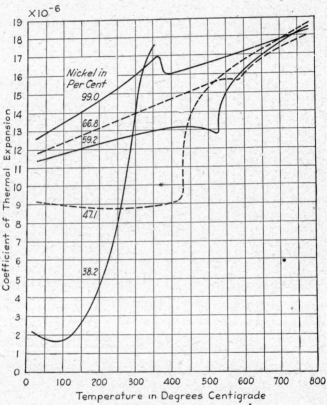

Fig. 180.—The expansion coefficients of iron-nickel alloys as a function of the temperature.

temperature. This property of the ferromagnetic metals is employed in a number of useful ways. For example, certain of the alloys have variations in expansion sufficiently like those of glasses so that they may be used in making metal-to-glass seals; others, such as Invar steel, have nearly vanishing expansion coefficients in useful temperature ranges.

The source of the correlation between magnetization and the expansion coefficient of glasses is easy to find. Let us examine Fig. 174 and consider the particular case of nickel as an example. We note that the energy of magnetization of nickel would be increased if the lattice constant were contracted. This means that there exist forces, associated with the magnetization, which tend to compress the lattice. Evidently other forces, associated with the normal cohesive energy, neutralize these forces at the observed interatomic spacing. When the metal is heated in the vicinity of the Curie temperature, the forces arising from magnetization disappear because of the transition to the nonmagnetic state. As a result, the opposing forces of nonmagnetic origin are no longer completely compensated and may be expected to cause a lattice expansion in the vicinity of the Curie temperature. The curve of Fig. 180, corresponding to nearly pure nickel, shows that this is the case. Conversely, we should expect iron to exhibit a contraction in the vicinity of the Curie temperature, for in this case the forces of magnetization evidently tend to expand the lattice and are counterbalanced by forces of nonmagnetic origin that tend to contract it. Figure 180 shows the manner in which the expansion coefficient varies in the iron-nickel series of alloys. It may be seen that there is a pronounced change in sign, as predicted by these simple considerations.

CHAPTER XXI

THE ELECTRICAL CONDUCTIVITY OF METALS

86. Introduction.[1]—In the presentation of Sommerfeld's theory of metals, it was pointed out that the ordinary conduction electrons of metals should be able to pass through an ideal undistorted lattice without being scattered. That is, a crystal lattice should be "transparent" for the propagation of electronic waves as long as the wave length of the waves is larger than the interatomic distance and as long as the atoms are not distorted from their ideal positions. These conditions are very similar to those which must be met for the undistorted transmission of optical waves through transparent media. Since the mean free path is infinite when the electron waves are not scattered and since the electrical resistivity is given by the equation

$$\rho = \frac{1}{\sigma} = \frac{mv}{ne^2l}$$

[see Eq. (1), Sec. 71], it follows that the electrical resistance should be zero under ideal conditions. The factors that may bring about a finite electrical resistance are as follows:

a. The lattice may be in thermal oscillation, as is always the case above absolute zero of temperature.

b. There may be impurity or alloying elements present in the lattice that produce temperature-independent distortion.

c. The specimen may contain residual strains as a result of cold-working or precipitation hardening. The variations in lattice spacing near the strained regions should scatter the electron waves.

d. Some of the conduction electrons may have wave lengths that satisfy the conditions for diffraction. This is invariably the case if the top of the filled region extends into two bands.

[1] For a more extensive treatment of this topic see F. Seitz, *The Modern Theory of Solids* (McGraw-Hill Book Company, Inc., New York, 1940).

We shall now summarize the way in which each of these effects influences the resistance of metals in practice.

87. The Thermal Dependence of Resistance.—The observed variation of the resistance of silver with temperature is shown in Fig. 181. It may be seen that the curve is linear at high temperatures and drops rapidly to zero below the characteristic temperature. The corresponding variation of the mean free path is shown in Fig. 182. It is interesting to note that the mean free path becomes of the order of magnitude of 1 cm at temperatures in the vicinity of 1°K. This type of variation in the

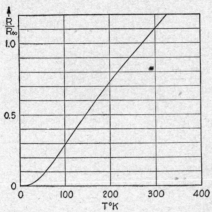

Fig. 181.—The variation of the resistivity of silver with temperature. The vertical scale is the ratio of the resistivity at the given temperature to that at 0°C. The horizontal scale is the absolute temperature. It is to be noted that the resistivity approaches zero more rapidly than the first power of temperature near absolute zero.

mean free path can be explained entirely in terms of the scattering of electron waves by the thermal vibrations of atoms.

There are many ways of looking at the effect of lattice vibrations; the following is probably the most illuminating: The thermal oscillations of the atoms in a lattice can be resolved into a system of waves that pass back and forth through the medium. With each of these waves may be associated a new periodicity in the lattice that is derived by compounding the periodicity of the wave with the natural periodicity of the lattice. The presence of these new periodicities permits a much greater range of electron waves to be diffracted and hence allows the ordinary conduction electrons to be scattered.

The scattering increases with temperature for two reasons.

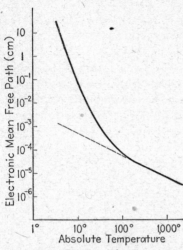

(1) The amplitude of the vibrational waves, and hence the magnitude of the scattering they produce, increases with temperature. (2) The number of different vibrational waves increases with increasing temperature. The second of these factors plays an important role in the range between absolute zero of temperature and the characteristic temperature. All possible vibrational waves are stimulated to some degree in the range above the characteristic temperature, so that only the first factor influences the resistivity there. This is the range characterized

Fig. 182.—The dependence on temperature of the mean free path of the conduction electrons of silver. Note that both scales are logarithmic.

by the linear portion of the curve of Fig. 181.

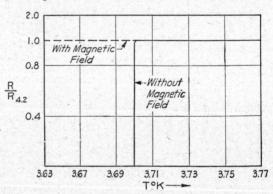

Fig. 183.—The conductivity of metallic tin as a function of temperature and magnetic-field strength in the vicinity of 3.70°K. In the absence of a magnetic field the metal becomes superconducting in the manner shown. In the presence of a field of sufficient strength the transition to the superconducting state does not occur.

It should be emphasized that the disappearance of resistance which occurs in Fig. 181 near absolute zero of temperature is *not* the much discussed phenomenon of superconductivity. In fact, silver, like the other monovalent metals, does not become superconducting. In metals in which superconductivity does occur, it sets in abruptly at a well-defined temperature in the manner shown in Fig. 183 for tin and is associated with a complete disappearance of resistance for a finite range of temperature. Although the explanation of superconductivity is not clear at present, it seems very likely that it is not to be associated with a sudden increase in the mean free path. Instead, it seems more probable that the metal is transformed to an entirely new phase in which the electronic motion has changed and in which the relation between current and voltage is no longer expressed by means of Ohm's law. This change of phase may be prevented by placing the specimen in a magnetic field of sufficient intensity. It is found that the normal phase possesses normal electrical properties below the transition temperature (see Fig. 183), so that the onset of superconductivity cannot be regarded as a mere change in mean free path.

It was mentioned in Sec. 71 that quantitative calculations of the absolute value of the mean free path have been made on the basis of quantum mechanics without recourse to additional empirical information. These computations have led to results that are in good agreement with experimentally determined values for several of the simpler metals. The agreement obtained substantiates the foregoing picture of the origin of the temperature-dependent part of the normal resistance of simple metals.

88. The Influence of Impurities and Alloying Agents on the Resistance.—Impurities and alloying agents may have two effects on the electrical resistance. (1) They may introduce centers of distortion that scatter the electrons. (2) They may alter the density of free electrons by raising or lowering the height of the filled region. The first effect is present alone in alloys such as that of silver and gold in which the elements have the same valence and combine in all proportions. Figure 184 shows the room-temperature resistivity of this alloy system. Only the portion of the curve above the dotted line vanishes when the alloys are cooled to very low temperatures. This shows that the mean free path does not become infinite at the absolute zero of temperature in the alloys as it does in the pure metals.

The resistance remaining at absolute zero of temperature is commonly called the *residual resistance*. We see that this resistance passes through a peak at the 50-50 composition and approaches zero at each end of the phase diagram. Thus its maximum value occurs at the composition for which the lattice presumably has maximum distortion. It may be seen that the residual resistance actually is several times larger than the resistance of the pure metals at room temperatures, which shows that the alloying agents appreciably shorten the mean free path of the electrons. The fact that the resistivity of an ideal alloy

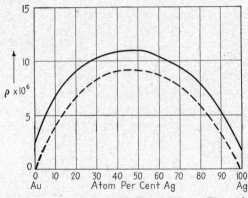

F<small>IG</small>. 184.—The resistivity of the gold-silver system. These elements form a system of perfect solid solutions. The dashed curve represents the residual resistance at absolute zero of temperature.

system can be expressed as the sum of the residual resistance and a term which varies with temperature in a manner resembling closely the resistivity of a pure metal is commonly known as *Matthiessen's rule*.

The wave-mechanical theory of the scattering produced by alloying agents correlates all these facts very simply and shows that the parabolic type of resistance curve of Fig. 184 is valid only as long as the alloying atoms are distributed at random throughout the lattice. It is not valid if the alloying atoms become arranged into an ordered structure, as occurs in many alloy systems. Figure 185 shows, for example, the resistance versus composition curve for copper-gold alloys that have been quenched from an elevated temperature and for alloys that have been carefully annealed. The arrangement of atoms among the various sites of the face-centered cubic lattice is completely random in the quenched alloys. As a result, the resistance versus composition curve has the same general form as for the gold-silver alloys. On the other hand, the annealed alloys of composition Cu₃Au and CuAu are ordered (see Sec. 3). That is, the copper atoms assume definite positions relative to the gold atoms so that the arrangement is more nearly like that occurring in an ionic crystal, in which the electropositive and electro-

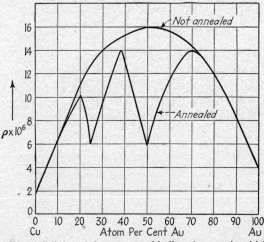

Fig. 185.—The resistivity of the copper-gold alloys in cases in which they have and have not been annealed. In the second case the elements form ideal solid solutions and the resistivity curve resembles that shown in Fig. 184. In the first case, however, the alloys of composition Cu₃Au and CuAu become ordered, and the resistivity curve shows pronounced minima.

negative atoms are precisely ordered relative to one another. As a result of the higher degree of order, the mean free path is much longer in the vicinity of these compositions and the curve showing resistance versus composition exhibits minima.

Figure 186 shows the manner in which the resistance of ordered and disordered specimens of β brass varies with temperature as the temperature is raised to the value at which the ordered phase becomes disordered. It may be seen that the resistance of the ordered phase is lower than that of the disordered phase at low temperatures and that the two approach one another as the temperature is raised to 750° K, which is the transition between the ordered and disordered phases.

The amount by which the addition of a given alloying atom raises the resistance of a metal depends very much upon the relative position of the solvent and solute in the periodic chart.

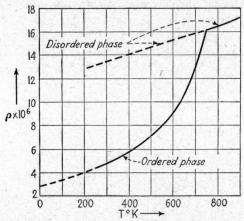

Fig. 186.—Variation of the resistance of ordered and disordered specimens of β brass with temperature. The dashed lines are hypothetical.

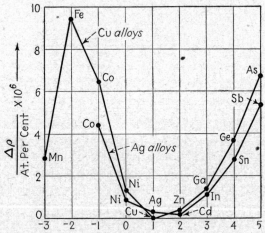

Fig. 187.—The incremental increase in resistivity of a sequence of copper and silver alloys per atomic percent of additional agent. The horizontal axis is the valence of the added metal.

Figure 187 shows, for example, the amount by which the resistances of copper and silver vary with the addition of 1 atomic percent of various elements. The residual resistance varies approximately quadratically with the difference in the valence of the solute and solvent. This result illustrates the fact that the distortion in the electric field of the lattice determines the effect produced on the mean free path by the solute atoms.

The variation in resistivity produced by changes in the height of the filled region as the composition of an alloy changes is usually small compared with the variation produced by distortion of the lattice. There are, however, a few notable exceptions to this rule, particularly in cases in which the alloying agents open or close a d shell. This effect will be discussed further below.

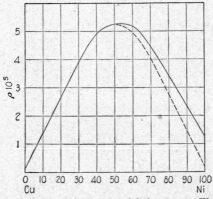

Fig. 188.—The resistivity of the copper-nickel system. The full curve represents the measured values, whereas the dashed curve on the right-hand side represents the mirror image of the left-hand part. It may be seen that the resistivities of the nickel-rich alloys are comparatively high.

89. The Resistance of the Transition Metals.—A comparison of the resistivities of the metals in which the d shell is either completely filled or completely empty with those of the transition metals shows that the latter invariably are much higher. For example, the resistivity of nickel is about eight times larger than that of copper, and the resistivity of palladium is about seven times larger than that of silver. This effect has a simple explanation on the basis of the band theory. The mechanism by which an electron is deflected under the action of a distortion in the lattice is such that the electron jumps from one state to another. The likelihood of such a transition depends not only upon the magnitude of the lattice distortion, but also upon the

density and kind of states that are available for the electron to jump into. In the event that the *d* band is either filled or empty, the available states are only those in the ordinary valence band at the top of the filled region. On the other hand, when the *d* band is only partly filled, the electrons in the *s-p* band may also jump into the relatively dense levels of the *d* band. As a result, the likelihood of the electron being deflected increases and the mean free path decreases. This effect is shown very clearly in Fig. 188, which represents the resistivity versus composition curve for the copper-nickel alloys. It may be seen that there

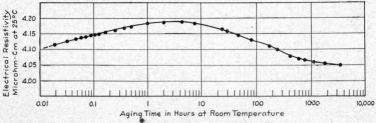

Fig. 189.—The variation with time of the resistivity of a quenched aluminum-copper alloy at room temperature. The copper content of the alloy is 4 percent. (*After Fink.*)

is a pronounced decrease in resistance at the point at which the *d* band of nickel becomes filled, that is, at the composition 60Cu40Ni.

90. The Influence of Cold-work on Electrical Resistance.— As we remarked in the introductory section of this chapter, we may expect any of the factors that introduce lattice distortion to increase the residual resistance of a metal or alloy. This includes factors such as the residual stresses introduced during any of the hardening processes. These effects are on the whole small compared with those observed as a result of alloying, for the following reason: We saw in Sec. 22 that the density of dislocated atoms produced during extensive cold-work is of the order of $\frac{1}{10}$ percent. Thus, at maximum, we might expect the change in resistance produced by extensive hardening to be no more than that produced by the addition of $\frac{1}{10}$ percent of alloy. This is actually the magnitude of the effect observed during cold-work.

Figure 189 shows[1] the change of resistivity of Duraluminum that takes place during the precipitation of copper. It may be seen that the resistance passes through a maximum during the precipitation process and then drops to a value lower than the value for the case in which the copper is dissolved in the lattice. The origin of the rise in resistivity during precipitation is probably twofold. In the first place, the residual stresses increase during the early stages of precipitation. As Mott[2] first pointed out, however, this cannot be the only factor influencing the rise, for the peaks for hardness and resistivity do not occur at the same time, as we should expect them to if they originated in the same effect. Mott proposed that the peak value of the resistivity occurs when the precipitated particles attain the size for which the scattering of electrons is a maximum. It is a general rule for the scattering of waves by particles that this maximum value should occur when the wave length and the particle dimensions are about the same. For example, this rule governs the scattering of light by the pigment particles in paints. Since the wave length of the conduction electrons is usually of the order of two or three atomic distances, it follows that the precipitate should contain between 10 and 100 atoms at the point of maximum resistance.

[1] See the survey article by W. L. Fink, D. W. Smith, and L. A. Willey, *Age Hardening of Alloys* (American Society for Metals, Cleveland, Ohio 1940), as well as those cited in connection with the discussion of precipitation hardening in Sec. 31.

[2] N. F. MOTT, *Proc. Phys. Soc.*, **52,** 86 (1940).

NAME INDEX

SUBJECT INDEX